MAGNETIC THIN FILMS

HARPER'S

PHYSICS SERIES

Frederick Seitz, EDITOR

MAGNETIC THIN FILMS

Ronald F. Soohoo

ASSOCIATE PROFESSOR

DIVISION OF ENGINEERING

AND APPLIED SCIENCE

THE CALIFORNIA INSTITUTE

OF TECHNOLOGY

HARPER & ROW

PUBLISHERS

NEW YORK, EVANSTON, AND LONDON

Library of Congress Catalog Card Number: 65–10123

To my wife, Rosie

CONTENTS

PREFACE

The purpose of this book is to introduce the reader to the study of the fundamental properties of magnetic thin films. It is based, in part, upon several years of teaching, research, and industrial consultation by the author in this field. The treatment emphasizes the basic physics underlying the behavior of magnetic thin films, although applications are also discussed to illustrate their technological import.

Since the first reported preparation and investigation of magnetic thin films by Blois in 1955, extensive studies on numerous aspects of their behavior have ensued. As a result of this intense effort, the basic mechanisms and underlying physics of magnetic film behavior are now reasonably well understood, although certain detailed aspects of the subject still await complete resolution.

The material has been presented in a self-contained manner so that the book can be used both as a text for students and for self-study by physicists and other research workers in this field. To this end, I have given as comprehensive a treatment as possible consistent with the scope and level of presentation of the book. A rather extensive bibliography is included for ready reference.

The topics in this book have been selected to cover the important aspects of magnetic thin-film behavior, while their treatment emphasizes the close correlation between theory and experiment. The degree of mathematical complexity varies from chapter to chapter, depending upon the nature of the subjects involved. For example, Chapters 6, 10, and 11, dealing respectively with thin-film magnetization, ferromagnetic resonance, and spin-wave resonance, are highly mathematical, while Chapters 2 and 12, dealing with preparation and application respectively, are predominantly descriptive. The subjects of domains, domain walls, and imperfections in thin film are treated in Chapters 3 through 5, with relatively simple calculations that can be correlated with experiment. The origin of the anisotropy and coercive force and related topics are discussed in Chapters 7 and 8. Finally, the magnetization reversal processes are treated in Chapter 9.

In a comprehensive treatment of the kind undertaken in this book, the author is indebted to numerous other workers in the field for their original calculations and experiments. He is also indebted to his wife for encouragement, understanding, and perseverance during the course of this work.

R. F. SOOHOO

Pasadena, California

CHAPTER 1

INTRODUCTION

In this introductory chapter we shall briefly discuss the historical development of the science and technology of thin films in general and of magnetic thin films in particular. We shall also elaborate on the physical and chemical properties of magnetic thin films and their technological import.

1·1 HISTORICAL DEVELOPMENT

Although the optical properties of thin films have been studied for many years, the study of their magnetic properties is of comparatively recent origin. The earliest recorded investigation of the optical behavior of thin films was apparently made in the seventeenth century.[1] However, it was not until the turn of the present century that thin reflecting films were used in optical interferometry. Within the last decade, conducting, semiconducting, and dielectric films have found extensive optical applications as reflecting surfaces in interferometers, filters and polarizers, and protective coatings. The recent interest in the optical properties of thin films may be attributed, in part, to the improvement in the methods of preparation using vacuum deposition and to investigation by means of electron diffraction and microscopy.[2]

The preparation and magnetic properties of thin films (~ 1000 Å thick) of vacuum deposited 80-20 Permalloy were first reported by Blois in 1955.[3] Partly because of their important potential application as computer elements and partly because of their interesting magnetic state, magnetic thin films have been extensively investigated in the last seven or eight years. Consequently, whereas some aspects of the behavior of magnetic thin films have yet to be resolved, the basic mechanisms and the underlying physics are now reasonably well understood, as we shall enumerate in what follows.

1·2 PHYSICAL AND CHEMICAL PROPERTIES

The behavior of magnetic thin films may be different from that of bulk materials for two essential reasons. First, in contrast to the interior electron spins, the surface spins are usually in an environment of lower symmetry due to the fact that there are neighbors only on the film side. Second, the arrangement of the atoms of the first few layers on the substrate side of a thin film is influenced by the nature of the substrate and its temperature during deposition. Substrate materials for polycrystalline films are

[1] I. Newton, *Opticks*, Samual Smith and B. Walford, London, 1704; Dover Publications, Inc., New York, 1959.

[2] O. S. Heavens, *Optical Properties of Thin Solid Films*, Academic Press Inc., London, 1955.

[3] M. S. Blois, Jr., *J. Appl. Phys.*, **26**: 975 (1955).

usually of the amorphous type such as glass or quartz so that they can not influence the crystal structure of the film per se. Nevertheless, imperfection and imperfect flatness of these substrates are unavoidable and these defects will to some extent determine the equilibrium positions of at least the first few layers of the atoms during deposition. Furthermore, on the nonsubstrate side, the film is exposed to the imperfect vacuum during deposition and to the air afterwards. Thus, oxidation of the surface layers may occur, which further complicates the behavior of thin films. From the above discussion, it is easy to surmise that if the surface spins are a significant fraction of the total number of spins in the material, as is the case with many thin films, the behavior of the material may differ from that in bulk. Indeed, under certain circumstances, thin films may be considered as another state of matter. It is because of this intrinsic difference between the thin film and bulk states, as well as the great technological import of magnetic thin-film elements to be discussed below, that the behavior of thin films is of basic interest in physics.

Inasmuch as the volume and surface inhomogeneities of a thin film may play an important role in its magnetic behavior, as enumerated above, the study of the thin films can be expected to be more complicated than that of bulk matter. For example, from electron microscopic evidence, thin film is seen to be in a somewhat disordered state. The low states of order due to substrate and other imperfections and granular structure may account for many observed anomalies in thin films. Antiferromagnetic layers on the surfaces of a film may effectively "pin" the surface spins in a ferromagnetic resonance experiment.[4] Furthermore, the pinning of these surface spins gives rise to surface modes whose rf magnetization decreases rapidly from the surface toward the interior, and this may influence the process of magnetization reversal. Since spin-wave resonance techniques can yield a great deal of information on the fundamental parameters of ferromagnetism in thin films, we shall discuss this subject at length in Chaps. 10 and 11.

The magnetization of the thin-film state is also of considerable theoretical interest. Again, if the film is sufficiently thin, say less than 100 Å thick, its magnetization departs noticeably from the bulk value, according to the theories of Klein and Smith,[5] and Valenta.[6] The experimental results on the magnetization of thin films, on the other hand, is nowhere as consistent. Whereas some experiments indicate that no noticeable decrease in the magnetization occurs for film of thickness down to 10 Å, others found that the magnetization decreases quite noticeably for thicknesses less than about 500 Å. The difference in these experimental results has been attributed to the varying degrees of vacuum during deposition giving rise to different amounts of film oxidation. Since the problem of thin-film magnetization involves the basic question of whether or not a two-dimensional lattice is ferromagnetic, we shall discuss in detail both the theoretical and the experimental results in this regard in some detail in Chap. 6.

Thin films of interest for computer applications are made of nickel-iron alloy (Permalloy) with chemical composition in the neighborhood of 80% nickel and 20% iron (80–20 Permalloy). In the neighborhood of this composition, the magnetostriction is very small and makes a negligible contribution to the uniaxial anisotropy of Permalloy films which is to be minimized to reduce the energy required for magnetization reversal. Due to fractionalization of the melt and the slight difference in the sticking

---

[4] C. Kittel, *Phys. Rev.*, **110**: 1295 (1958).

[5] M. J. Klein and R. S. Smith, *Phys. Rev.*, **81**: 378 (1951); S. J. Glass and M. J. Klein, *Phys. Rev.*, **109**: 288 (1958).

[6] L. Valenta, *Czech. J. Phys.*, **7**: 127 (1957).

probabilities of nickel and iron, the final film composition may deviate slightly from the starting value in the vapor deposition process. The chemical process of metallic vaporization and solid-state diffusion and nucleation will be taken up in Chap. 2 along with several other methods of film deposition to facilitate our understanding of the chemical properties of thin films.

Although the subjects of preparation and investigation of insulating ferrite and garnet films are still in their infancy, the study of thin-film ferromagnetism, without complications from the eddy currents in metallic films, may be facilitated by their recent availability. Therefore, the methods of preparation of ferrite and garnet films, mostly chemical in nature, are also studied in Chap. 2.

In bulk material, ferromagnetic domains are usually of the 180° variety accompanied by 90° closure domains at the surfaces of the material. The walls separating these domains are of the Bloch type, within which the spins rotate from the orientation in one domain to that in the neighboring domain about an axis perpendicular to the plane of the wall. If the thickness of a film is sufficiently small compared to its other linear dimensions, the film is usually in a predominantly single central domain state oriented along the easy axis of magnetization surrounded by small reversed edge domains. The existence of these edge domains is attributed to the demagnetizing field near the edge of the film and to edge imperfections. Of considerable interest is the fact that the walls separating the central and edge domains may not be of the Bloch type but of the Néel type. Within the Néel wall, the spins rotate in the plane of the film or about an axis in the plane of the wall. This situation arises entirely from energy considerations since the demagnetizing field perpendicular to the film plane is relatively large to prevent the spins from pointing away from the film plane. The subject of domains, domain walls, and imperfections in thin films, will be treated in Chaps. 3 through 5.

The magnetic anisotropy, coercive force, and rectangularity of the easy-axis loop are parameters of both basic and applied significance. The origin of the uniaxial anisotropy in Permalloy films deposited in the presence of a magnetic field is not completely clear. However, experimental evidence indicates that the two major sources of contribution to the anisotropy are probably directed iron-pair formation in a nickel lattice[7,8] and imperfections due to the presence of nonmagnetic atoms, vacancies, dislocations, etc. The subject of anisotropy in thin films will be discussed in Chap. 7. The origin of the coercive force due to the presence of unavoidable porosity and imperfections and hysteresis will be discussed in Chap. 8.

The magnetization reversal process in thin films is of special interest. It affords a unique opportunity for the study of various modes of magnetization reversal with minimum complications. Depending upon the value of the drive field, magnetization reversal in the easy direction may occur via domain wall motion, incoherent rotation, or rotation in unison as discussed in Chap. 9.

1·3　APPLICATIONS

The main application of thin films at present is their use as computer memory and logic elements. In addition, they are being used as variable inductance coupling elements in parametric circuits in the megacycle frequency range and in millimeter

---

[7] L. Néel, *Compt. Rend.*, **237**: 1468, 1613 (1953); *J. Phys. Rad.*, **15**: 255 (1954).

[8] S. Taniguchi, *Sci. Rept. Res. Inst.*, Tohoku Univ., A7: 269 (1955).

wave isolators. These applications will be treated in some detail in Chap. 12. Here we shall indicate some salient features of these applications only.

When a Permalloy film is deposited on a substrate with a static magnetic field applied in a given direction during deposition, an easy axis develops in this direction. The film remains anisotropic even after the static field is removed subsequent to the deposition process. This induced uniaxial anisotropy may be represented by $K_1 \sin^2 \theta$, where K_1 is the first-order anisotropy constant and θ is the angle between the magnetization and the easy axis. Thus, two directions of minimum energy ($\theta = 0, \pi$) exist; these bistable states may be used to represent the "0" and "1" states in a binary system. Thus, if a film is already in a state "0", application of a field to align the magnetization in the zero-state direction will not alter the state of the system. On the other hand, if the film was originally in state "1", its magnetization will be reversed in this process giving an output signal. Because of its small physical size and easiness of flux reversal, a memory using thin films has great promise in high-speed computer circuitry. Since the hysteresis loops of thin films are highly rectangular, no film reversal occurs for reversing fields less than the coercive force H_c. Thus, a small H_c is required to minimize the film drive. In addition to their use as memories, films can also function as logic elements.

As a variable reactance element in a parametron, a film could be used to generate the first subharmonic frequency ($f/2$). Recently, ferrite films have also found microwave applications in unilateral isolators.

For completeness, it may be mentioned that other kinds of films such as superconducting films could also be used as computer memory elements by distinguishing between the resistance of the superconducting and normal states.

CHAPTER 2

PREPARATION
OF THIN FILMS

In this chapter, we shall discuss the various methods of preparation of thin magnetic films, both insulating and metallic. The nature of the substrate material, mechanism of film formation, film chemical composition, and methods of thickness measurement are also examined. The discussion is essentially self-contained, but pertinent references are also given for those who are interested in certain specific aspects involved in film deposition.

2·1 METHODS OF PREPARATION

Thin films may be prepared by four different methods: (1) vapor deposition, (2) electrodeposition, (3) cathode sputtering, and (4) chemical deposition. The vapor deposition method is the one most widely used for film preparation. In this method, the materials are evaporated in vacuum and the resulting vapor stream is allowed to impinge upon a substrate usually made of glass or quartz. In the electrodeposition method, the films are formed by the method of electrolysis. In the cathode sputtering method, the glass or quartz is sputtered with Permalloy in a low-pressure glow discharge. Several chemical methods of deposition may be employed. In the coprecipitation process used for the deposition of insulating ferrite films, hot suspensions of hydroxides are directed onto a heated substrate. Ferrite films could also be deposited by pyrolytic hydrolysis of metal inorganic salts. In this method, the films are prepared by atomizing a mixed solution of the metal chlorides into a reaction tube heated to 800°C. In another chemical deposition method, alcoholic solutions of ferrite nitrate and other metal nitrates were combined in necessary proportions to yield stoichiometric ratios of the desired ferrite, which were then deposited on substrates. Firing the coated substrates between 900–1100°C in a controlled atmosphere resulted in spinel or garnet structure formation. We shall discuss each of these processes in turn and also examine their relative advantages and disadvantages.

(a) Vapor Deposition Method[1]

Briefly stated, the vapor deposition method involves the melting of the metals to be deposited in a vacuum and allowing the resulting vapor beam to strike a substrate thus

---

[1] A rather extensive treatise on the vapor deposition of thin films may be found in L. Holland, *Vacuum Deposition of Thin Films*, John Wiley & Sons, Inc., New York, 1958. Much of the recent work on this subject can be found in the *1958–1962 Vacuum Symposium Transactions*, Pergamon Press, New York.

forming a film. If the source to target distance is sufficiently small compared to the mean free path of the vapor molecules in the atmosphere of the deposition system, then a large fraction of the molecules of the metals will reach the target without suffering collision with molecules of the residual gas in the system. Indeed, according to the results of the kinetic theory of gases, the fraction N/N_o of the emitted molecules which travels a distance z without experiencing collisions with gas molecules is given by

$$\frac{N}{N_o} = e^{-z/L} \tag{2.1}$$

where N_o is the number of emitted atoms and L their mean free path in the residual gas. The mean free path of the molecules in air is about 45 cm at 25°C and at a pressure of about 10^{-4} mm of Hg; and the mean free path of water vapor, the predominant component of residual gas in a kinetic system, at the same temperature and pressure is 34 cm. For a silver atom at various pressures of residual oxygen, the mean free path is 4.5 cm and 4.5×10^4 cm at 10^{-3} and 10^{-7} mm of Hg, respectively, with L inversely proportional to pressure within this pressure range.[2] The mean free paths of other vapor molecules of metals, halides, and sulphides, etc., in gases at low pressures are generally unknown, but they are not likely to differ greatly from the mean free paths of the atoms and molecules quoted above if their radii do not differ greatly from each other. Therefore, for a typical laboratory system with the dimensions of orders of tens of centimeters, the mean free path would be much larger than the source-target distance at a pressure of 10^{-5} mm Hg. This order of reduced pressure could easily be obtained in an ordinary laboratory-size vacuum system. However, there is an additional and more stringent condition to be fulfilled by an evaporator if the influence of the residual gas on the film structure is to be reduced to negligible proportions. This has to do with the rate at which residual gas atoms strike the surface of the target during the deposition of the film. This source of contamination has often been ignored in the investigation of vacuum-deposited films. From the kinetic theory of gases, we know that the number of gas molecules at pressure p and absolute temperature T striking unit area of a plane surface per unit time is given by

$$N = \frac{p}{\sqrt{2\pi mkT}} \tag{2.2}$$

where m is the mass of the molecule and k is Boltzmann's constant. For oxygen at 10^{-5} mm Hg and at a typical substrate temperature of 250°C, N is equal to about 4×10^{15} atoms/cm²/sec. Taking the area occupied by an absorbed oxygen atom on the surface to be 1.4 Å², we find that the residual oxygen atom would form a monomolecular layer on the substrate in about 1 sec. For a typical evaporation rate of 1000 Å of film thickness per minute, we would have 17 Å of film or about six layers of metallic atoms forming on the substrate per second. If the sticking probabilities of the oxygen and metallic atoms are similar, the absorption of residual gas and metal atoms by the substrate would therefore be roughly competitive processes if the substrate were exposed to them for an equal length of time. But since the substrate is usually exposed to the residual gas for a time (minutes or hours) very long compared to the evaporation time

---

[2] O. S. Heavens, *Optical Properties of Thin Solid Films*, Academic Press Inc., London, 1955.

(time of exposure of substrate to metallic atoms) of the order of a minute, oxygen layers may be formed and in turn cause a formation of metallic oxides (e.g., NiO) for the first few evaporated layers. The existence of such antiferromagnetic layers may influence certain aspects of the magnetic behavior of thin films, e.g., excitation of spin waves. However, if the substrate is at a sufficiently high temperature (e.g., at 250°C), the outgassing action at these elevated temperatures would permit the formation of only a few layers of gas molecules as the residual atmosphere is usually mainly composed of water vapor, oxygen, and nitrogen gas. This would probably be the case if the substrate is metallic since the sticking probability of gas atoms on a clean metallic surface is high. However, if the substrate is made of an amorphous substance such as glass which is composed of mainly oxygen and silicon, the residual oxygen atoms and the oxygen in the substrate may interact to form a very complicated surface. As soon as the first layer of metallic atoms is formed on the substrate, the residual gas atoms will now tend to be deposited due to the high sticking probability of oxygen on metal. According to our calculation above, we would have an oxygen metal atom ratio of roughly 1 to 6 at an evaporation pressure of 10^{-5} mm Hg, if the residual atmosphere is all oxygen. However, for the ordinary kinetic pumping system, most of the residual atmosphere is water vapor so that our calculation of the oxygen contamination is probably too pessimistic. However, if the substrate remains at a high temperature following deposition for any length of time, oxidized layers of metals may be formed on the nonsubstrate side if the vacuum is not sufficiently good; cooling the substrate down quickly immediately after deposition will of course minimize this source of oxidation. Nevertheless, it appears that pressures much lower than 10^{-5} mm Hg (e.g., 10^{-7} mm Hg) may be desirable during deposition for consistent and repeatable results in the investigation of thin films.[3] It may be mentioned in this connection that the vacuum usually drops (pressure rises) during evaporation by as much as an order of magnitude dependent upon the rate of evaporation. This pressure rise is presumably, in part at least, due to the outgassing of the system at the high temperatures required for the evaporation of the source. Since there may be gases in the system whose partial pressures are lower than that of the vacuum system as a whole, it is not clear that a vacuum gauge, usually located away from the substrate, would accurately represent the rise in pressure near the substrate.

The vacuum system and lead-in arrangements used in the deposition of thin magnetic films are usually of conventional design[4] with pressures ranging from about 2×10^{-5} down to 5×10^{-6} mm Hg before evaporation. Because of the tendency of molten iron, nickel, and cobalt to alloy with tantalum, molybdenum, and other refractory metals commonly used for crucibles, it is necessary to use alundum crucibles and high frequency induction heating. With a commercial heating unit having a nominal power output of 2 KW, a sample of iron or iron alloy of 10–15 grams could be melted quite conveniently.

Since the mean free path of the evaporating atoms is large compared with the dimensions of the system, and therefore with the size of the aperture of the oven, conditions of molecular streaming occur. On a plane surface at a distance y from the oven, the intensity I or the number of atoms arriving per unit area of the surface per unit time in a direction θ measured from the source surface normal is given by

---

[3] K. H. Behrndt, *1961 Vacuum Symposium Transactions*, p. 912; C. A. Neugebauer, *1961 Vacuum Symposium Transactions*, p. 924.

[4] See, e.g., J. Strong, *Procedures in Experimental Physics*, Prentice-Hall, Inc., Englewood Cliffs, N.J., 1945.

$$I = \frac{N_o}{(2\pi M_o RT)^{1/2}} \frac{pA}{\pi y^2} \cos^4 \theta \tag{2.3}$$

where A is the area of the orifice, N_o Avogadro's number, R the gas constant and M_o the molecular weight of the evaporating substance. Eq. (2.3) may be easily derived from Eq. (2.2) by considering the geometry of the source substrate system. Varying the rate of evaporation causes both the intensity of the condensing beam and the mean velocity of arrival of the atoms to vary. However, it has been experimentally found that the variations in film structure on varying the rate of evaporation result mainly from the variation of beam intensity and not from thermal velocity variations. It may be noted here that the melting points of iron and nickel are 1535°C and 1455°C so that the source heating element must be able to produce a temperature of about 1600°C. This high temperature may be measured by a platinum-rhodium thermocouple placed near the source.

It has been observed that during evaporation using a crucible, a slug is formed on the surface melt. This slug is composed of crucible material as well as metallic oxides. To avoid this contamination, a ring source[5] or melting of the alloy by electron bombardment may be used instead.[6] Film thickness variations may be minimized alternatively by rotating a shutter between source and substrate[7] instead of by using a ring source close to the substrate. It may be noted here that according to Eq. (2.3), the beam intensity and therefore the thickness of the film decreases radically from the center of the source when a crucible is used.

We now turn to a more detailed discussion of the vacuum system.[8] Figure 2.1 is a schematic diagram of a conventional vacuum system. It consists of a large bell-jar system employing an oil-diffusion pump, liquid-nitrogen baffle, and organic vacuum seals. Such systems are readily available from most equipment manufacturers. The liquid-nitrogen trap is a simple thimble design which requires a minimum of one collision with a cold surface in order for an oil molecule to pass the trap. The liquid-nitrogen trap in the roughing line serves to minimize diffusion of forepump oil into the bell-jar chamber during roughing operations and also to maintain the fore-pressure of the diffusion pump at approximately 10^{-4} mm Hg. The high vacuum portion of the system is constructed of either hard glass or welded stainless steel sections. Readings of pressures are usually made by a thermal couple and an ionization gauge located in the pump line. Since evaporators are dynamic systems, these readings during depositions may differ by a factor of 5 from readings obtained on an ionization gauge located in the bell jar close to the substrate.

The substrates may be baked by a radiant tungsten heater or by an external infrared source prior to deposition and holding them at elevated temperatures during deposition. Graphite rods radiating up to 1 kW of power may be used to give the vacuum chamber a mild bake. A liquid-nitrogen trap in a bell jar or a Meissner trap may be constructed from copper tubing through which liquid nitrogen is circulated continuously.[9] This trap increases the possible vacuum available significantly. Titanium for oxygen-getting purposes may also be evaporated at the top of a bell jar from

---

[5] K. H. Behrndt and R. A. Jones, *1958 Vacuum Symposium Transactions*, p. 217.

[6] D. M. Hart, *1958 Vacuum Symposium Transactions*, p. 230.

[7] K. H. Behrndt, *1962 Vacuum Symposium Transactions*, p. 111.

[8] For details of mechanical arrangements of the vacuum system used for vapor deposition of thin films, see Ref. 5 and F. S. Maddocks and K. H. Behrndt, *1958 Vacuum Symposium Transactions*, p. 225.

[9] C. R. Meissner, *Rev. Sci. Instr.*, **26**: 305 (1955).

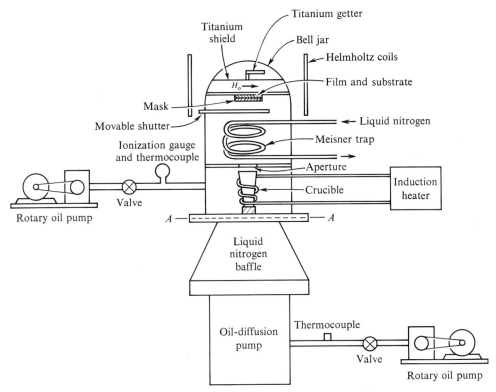

FIG. 2.1.   Schematic diagram of thin-film vacuum deposition system.

a tungsten wire around which had been wrapped a titanium wire. The titanium evaporation should be shielded from the Ni-Fe evaporation enabling both to be performed simultaneously. With the above modifications of a commercially available conventional vacuum evaporator, pressures in the order of 10^{-7} mm Hg may be achieved.[10] A very careful analysis of the residual gases in typical evaporators has been done by Caswell and we shall summarize some of his pertinent results in what follows.

Since the main constituent of a kinetic vacuum system is water vapor, the ionization gauge reading would be indicative of the partial pressure of water vapor but not necessarily of other residual gases such as nitrogen, oxygen, or hydrogen. Using a mass spectrometer, Caswell found that the major residual atmosphere constituent is indeed water vapor but that the amount varies from day to day by as much as one order of magnitude depending upon humidity, the length of time the system remains at atmospheric pressure, and the length of time the system has been under vacuum. To minimize contamination from water vapor, it is therefore important to let the system down to atmospheric pressure with a dry gas such as nitrogen. Furthermore, he found that for rapidly changing conditions, such as that existing during evaporation, specific mass peaks appear continuously or at frequent intervals. It appears that a mild bake of the vacuum chamber is very effective in reducing the nitrogen and oxygen content.

Fourteen mass peaks were found using the mass spectrometer. By measuring the mass to charge ratios corresponding to these peaks, it was found that the residual atmosphere in a conventional vacuum system is composed of predominantly water

---

[10] H. L. Caswell, *IBM J. Res. Develop.*, **6**: 130 (1960).

vapor and various amounts of nitrogen, oxygen, hydrogen, argon, carbon, carbon monoxide, carbon dioxide, and the hydro-carbons. Since the complexity of the apparatus and the time required for deposition increase with decreasing pressure, it is pertinent therefore to determine what gases are detrimental to the physical characteristics of interest and to pump these gases preferentially rather than to attempt to reduce the total pressure. Examples of preferential pumps are a liquid-nitrogen-cooled surface (i.e., liquid-nitrogen or Meissner trap) for water vapor, carbon dioxide, and to some degree hydrocarbons; a titanium film for oxygen; and a nickel-iron film for hydrogen. Since oxygen and hydrogen both probably affect the characteristics of a thin magnetic film, it seems appropriate to subject the vacuum chamber to a mild bake before deposition and to use a titanium getter to reduce the film oxygen content and to use also dummy nickel-iron films for the getting of hydrogen before deposition. The latter is particularly important if evaporation is made with Permalloy on tungsten wire since undegassed tungsten wire contains a large amount of hydrogen as indicated by the outgassing data on Permalloy films.[11] These results emphasize the importance of using thoroughly outgassed source materials.[8] Since stock refractory metals contain tremendous quantities of gas, vacuum-melted or degassed materials must be used. In either case, a source should be thoroughly outgassed at a temperature well above its normal operating point prior to its use in evaporating films.

With two rotary oil pumps, it is possible to keep the pump on the roughing line leading to the oil-diffusion pump operating at all times. If the vacuum chamber is to be open to insert source and substrate materials, the chamber could be shut off at plane A–A shown in Fig. 2.1 thus exposing only the portion above A–A to atmospheric pressure. This would allow the diffusion pump which could operate only at reduced pressure (less than about a micron) and the liquid-nitrogen baffle to stay in operation at all times. In contrast to this, if only one pump (the one leading to the diffusion pump) is used, the whole chamber must be lowered to atmospheric pressure and therefore requires a great deal of time to pump down again before the next evaporation commences. Thus if two pumps are used, the pump leading to the vacuum chamber could be turned on again after insertion of the source and substrate. When the pressure in this chamber is roughly a micron, the separator at plane A–A can be opened. We may then proceed with the evaporation after the pump leading to the vacuum chamber has been shut off. Consequently, although two pumps are not necessary, it is expedient to use them to reduce deposition time required.

Hydrocarbons present a problem in vacuum systems as they enter the evaporation chamber through back-streaming of diffusion pump oil, handling of evaporation components, and outgassing of organic gaskets. Well-designed liquid-nitrogen baffles or substitution of a mercury for an oil-diffusion pump can reduce diffusion of hydrocarbons from the pump, and improved handling techniques could reduce contamination. It has been found,[10] using the mass spectrometer, that Viton, Kel-F, and Teflon contain less gas than conventional neoprene or Buna-N gasket seals. Viton was found to contain only water vapor; Kel-F, somewhat more water vapor and a trace of methane; Teflon has still more water vapor and detectable propane, butane, and pentane peaks. Neoprene and Buna-N has 6 and 30 times respectively as much butane and pentane as Teflon and appreciably more water vapor. Therefore, it appears that a suitable choice of gasket material may significantly reduce the hydrocarbon content in a vacuum system. "Vac Ion" pump may be used in place of the oil-diffusion pump to

---

[11] F. R. Gleason, J. H. Greiner, and L. R. Yetter, *1959 Vacuum Symposium Transactions*, p. 222.

obtain high vacuum, but the composition of the gases remains essentially the same except their partial pressures are much smaller.

To obtain a uniaxial anisotropy in a Permalloy film in a given direction, a magnetic field H_o of about 200 Oe is applied to the substrate during deposition by a pair of Helmholtz coils or by a permanent magnet as shown in Fig. 2.1.

(b) Electrodeposition Method

In the electrodeposition process, metals are deposited upon the substrate by electrolysis. As a typical example of electrolysis, let us consider a chemical cell containing a solution of nickel sulfate and ammonium chloride, a nickel anode connected to the positive terminal of a battery, and a copper cathode connected to the negative terminal of the battery. A schematic diagram of such a deposition system is shown in Fig. 2.2; a magnetic field of some 200 Oe is usually provided for orienting the uniaxial

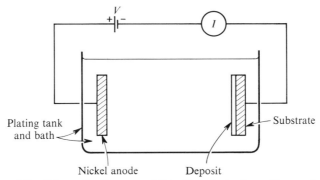

FIG. 2.2. Schematic diagram of thin-film electrodeposition system.

anisotropy axis during deposition of Permalloy films. Under the action of the electric field between the electrodes, the cations Ni^{++} and NH_4^+ travel to the cathode, while anions SO_4^{--} and Cl^- move in the opposite direction. If the chemical cell is examined after the current has been flowing in the circuit for some definite time, it will be found that a mass M of metallic nickel Ni has been deposited on the cathode and an equivalent mass M of metallic nickel has been removed from the anode, leaving the concentration of the solution unchanged. The nickel ions are transferred through the external metallic portions of the circuit. According to Faraday's law, the mass M of any substance liberated from the solution depends only upon the total charge passing through the circuit, or

$$M = \frac{1}{F} \frac{A}{v} Q \tag{2.4}$$

where the Faraday constant $F = 9.65 \times 10^4$ coulombs/gram—at. wt, and A and v are respectively the atomic weight and the valence of the element. Here M is given in grams and $Q \ (= It)$ in coulombs so that the current I is in amperes and the time t in seconds.

It may be noted from the discussion above that when current passes, all the Ni^{++} and NH_4^+ ions move toward the cathode, but only Ni^{++} ions are discharged from the solution and deposited on the cathode. The accumulation of the nonreducible NH_4^+

ions at the cathode alters the environment from which the Ni^{++} ions are being discharged. This accounts for the familiar fact that salts which are added to a plating bath to improve its conductivity may have an influence on the form of the metal that plates out.

If a metal is placed in a solution containing its own ions, e.g., if a piece of nickel is inserted in a solution of nickel salt, a potential difference is set up between the metal and the solution. When in contact with the solution there is a definite tendency for all atoms of the metal to lose one or more electrons and to pass into solution in the form of ions. At the same time there will be a tendency for the nickel ions already in the solution, which are produced by the ionization of the nickel salt that is present, to undergo the reverse (discharge) reaction. After some elapse of time, the ionization and discharge reactions will take place at exactly the same rate so that the system of metal and solution will be at equilibrium. The equilibrium potential E evidently depends upon, among other things, the ion concentration C, usually expressed in gram-ions per liter. From thermodynamic arguments, it can be shown that

$$E = E_o + \frac{RT}{vF} \ln C \tag{2.5}$$

where R is the gas constant and T is the absolute temperature. E_o is a constant for the given metal assumed to be in a pure state, and is called the standard potential. A table of the standard potential[12] arranged in the order of increasing E_o is sometimes called the "electromotive series"; metals higher in the series will, in general, displace from solution those below them. Since hydrogen occupies a definite position in the electromotive series, it should behave like metal with respect to displacement from solution. Metals above hydrogen in the table, for example, nickel and iron, should thus be able to liberate this gas from solution.

Any departure of an electrode from equilibrium conditions is termed polarization. The particular type of polarization associated with the discharge of ions is called overvoltage[13] denoted by V, and it is defined as the numerical difference between the actual deposition potential and the value to be expected for a reversible electrode in the same solution. Thus, the right-hand side of Eq. (2.5) must be augmented by $-V$. The magnitude of the overvoltage depends on the current density expended in the discharge of hydrogen ions, but for the purpose of the present discussion it would be sufficient to consider the overvoltage corresponding to the point at which visible formation of hydrogen gas commences. Under so-called "bubble overvoltage" conditions, the plating out of metals such as nickel, iron, or cobalt will thus be accompanied by the evolution of some hydrogen, and the current efficiency for metal deposition, defined as the ratio of the rate of metal reduced divided by the theoretical rate if every electron was captured by a metal ion, will be less than 100%. This efficiency can be kept high by increasing the pH and the current density to avoid hydrogen bubble formation. Raising the temperature has a similar effect, for it decreases the overvoltage for nickel deposition more than it does that for hydrogen evolution. The Ni–Fe–Co system used for magnetic thin films is a remarkably advantageous system for electrodeposition because the standard potentials of the three metals are close together ($-0.25V$, $-0.44V$,

---

[12] See, e.g., S. Glasstone, *The Fundamentals of Electrochemistry and Electrodeposition*, Franklin Publishing Co., Inc., Palisade, N.J., 1960, p. 50.
[13] For a table of overvoltage for various elements, see *ibid.*, p. 63.

and $-0.277V$ for Ni, Fe, and Co respectively) and all three metals deposit with a high polarization (overvoltages $0.21V$, $0.18V$, and $0.16V$ for Ni, Fe, and Co, respectively). In what follows, we shall discuss the bath and plating conditions for the electro-deposition of magnetic thin films.[14,15]

An electroplating aqueous solution contains cations of the metal to be plated, anions for the most advantageous deposition conditions, and additive for special purposes. The cations, which generally occur in relatively high concentrations, may exist in the plating bath as solvated ions or as complexes. At sufficiently high cathode current density, a cation depletion region exists in the cathode vicinity which is re-plenished by ion diffusion from the main body of the solution at a rate dependent upon the difference in concentration between the two regions; cobalt and ferrous ions are more readily reduced than nickel. Therefore, the ion ratios of Co or Fe to Ni is kept small relative to the desired ratios on the plate. In order to avoid composition gradients across the thickness of the film, proper agitation of the bath and low plating current density or pulse plating current may be employed to increase the concentration of the more readily reducible ion in the cathode depletion region.[16]

The most important anions used for magnetic material plating solution are sulfate, chloride, fluoborates, sulfamate, hypophosphite, and cyanide. The selection of the anion to be used depends upon the specific properties desired for the bath. The most commonly used plating solution for the deposition of Permalloy films is the sul-fate chloride bath proposed by Wolf and McConnel.[17] However, a sulfamate bath has been shown to give results almost the same for Permalloy films as those obtained from the sulfate-chloride bath through range of plate compositions 82–100% nickel.[15] A sulfamate bath allows plating with high current efficiency for nickel, iron, and cobalt and thus reduced hydrogen formation. The chloride ion improves the anode dissolution problem which sometimes occurs with high nickel content anodes. Although differences may be found in some cases when different anions are incorporated in the bath if these anions affect physical or metallurgical properties of the deposit such as internal stress grain size, or orientation, most of these effects can be neutralized by additives. There-fore, the choice of anions is not usually critical since many different properly developed baths can yield deposits with very similar properties. However, if the anion enters into the reaction at the cathode, the situation is quite different. For example, the presence of hypophosphite results in the inclusion of phosphorous in the deposit. This results in a decrease of H_c and anisotropy field H_k in Permalloy films.

Many additives may be added to the plating bath for special purposes. They may be classified into three main types: nonreducible cations, inorganic, and organic compounds. Among the nonreducible cations, calcium and potassium increase the solution conductivity. In addition, potassium also reduces stress in the deposit. Since ammonium ion may act as a complexing agent, its role in the plating process may be a rather complicated one. Its presence affects the nickel-iron ratio in the plate com-position of Permalloy.

[14] Much of the work in the electrodeposition of thin films is reported in the 1960 and 1961 *Electrodeposition Symposia of the Electrochemical Society.*

[15] A good review of work in this area has been given by I. W. Wolf, *J. Appl. Phys.*, **33**: 1152 (1962) and our summary here is similar in part to that given by him.

[16] G. H. Cockett and E. S. Spenser-Timms, *J. Electrochem. Soc.*, **108**: 906 (1961); P. Kuttner and D. Clemson, *Electrodeposition Symposia of the Electrochemical Society*, 1961.

[17] I. W. Wolf and V. P. McConnel, *Proc. Am. Electroplaters Soc.*, **43**: 215 (1956); I. W. Wolf, *J. Electrochem. Soc.*, **108**: 959 (1961).

The inorganic compounds give rise to buffering or pH control action. The buffering action takes place at the cathode, thus allowing a greater range of permissible pH. An organic compound such as hydrogen peroxide could also be used as an oxidizing agent, added to reduce hydrogen bubble formation and thus pitting at the cathode. Organic compounds are used as wetting agents for better cathode and anode behavior, leveling, brightening, complexing and stress reduction. Wetting agents, such as sodium lauryl sulfate, are beneficial in reducing cathode pitting by removing hydrogen bubbles; similar action at the anode, especially if oxygen is formed, is beneficial. It should be mentioned here that stress-reducing materials usually also change crystal size and orientation, brighten and sometimes level the deposits. However, a wide variety of types of organic compounds, the sulfon groups on resonant structures, act as stress reducers almost exclusively.

Plating conditions such as solution temperature, plating current density, substrate, and acidity may influence the character of the deposition. The magnetic characteristics of thin Permalloy films deposited using a sulfate-chloride bath at low current densities do not vary appreciably for bath temperatures in the 10 to 60°C range. Current densities from 0.25 to 500 mA/cm² have been successfully used. However, the optimum temperature and current density required could not be easily generalized.

The upper limit of hydrogen ion concentration in the acid bath is determined by its tendency to compete for the electrons at the cathode. For Permalloy deposition from a sulfate-chloride bath, the corresponding minimum pH is 2.5. The upper limit of pH is more difficult to define. However, within the allowable range of pH for iron deposition, magnetic characteristics of Permalloy have not been found to have a large pH dependence.

The subject of substrates will be discussed in detail in a later section of this chapter. However, it may be stated that for almost all low coercivity thin-film applications, substrates should have minimum roughness and maximum randomness of orientation of crystals. In the Permalloy deposition process, the substrate could be either of circular or plane geometry. In the former case Long[18] used a 5 mil smooth OFHC copper wire as the cathode of the electrodeposition cell while the best anode material found is rolled, depolarized nickel. The electrolyte used is a mixture of nickel and ferrous sulfamate in acid solution since commercial nickel sulfamate bath gives high quality, low-stress deposits. In this case, the plated material is derived from the electrolyte rather than from the anode material. Simple iron content titrations with subsequent additions of ferrous sulfamate are adequate for holding the bath concentration (5% ferrous ions) within good working limits. The composition of Permalloy deposited is affected primarily by the current density, the electrolyte temperature, the percentage of ferrous ions in the bath, and the degree of stirring. The nickel content of the film increases with increased current density, decreased temperature, decreased iron concentration, and less agitation. It is found that about 40 amp/cm², 150°F, a pH of 4, and a high degree of circulation is required to produce 81 (nickel)-19 (iron) Permalloy. A sodium lauryl sulfate especially free of inorganic salts is a good wetting agent which does not react with the bath constituents to form side reactions.

In the actual plating process used by Long, current passes down the wire, past the plating chamber, to the common ground and thus supplies the circumferential field during deposition which induces the magnetic anisotropy. The plating chamber is made

18 T. R. Long, *J. Appl. Phys.*, **31**: 123S (1960).

of Pyrex tubing. The anode is a cylindrical cage concentric with the wire. A thermocouple is located adjacent to the wire to hold the temperature to $\pm0.3°F$. Electrolyte is recirculated through this chamber from a separate reservoir at rates as high as 3 liters/min.

For the planar geometry, glass slides may be used as substrates to receive conducting films of either vacuum evaporated chromium-gold films or fired gold films.[19] The chromium is present only to improve the adhesion of gold to glass. The fired gold films were made by dipping the slides in a liquid bright gold solution, heating slowly to 600°C, and then furnace cooling. Sulfate chloride solution was used as plating bath[17] for the electrodeposition of Permalloy films; graphite was used as the anode. Serious depletion of the electrolyte was avoided by limiting the number of specimens for each bath. Sample iron titrations were also taken before and after each series of specimens to ensure control. Permanent magnets were used to provide 200 Oe of field in the plating cell as illustrated in Fig. 2.2.

(c) Cathode Sputtering Method

For certain metals, e.g. platinum and molybdenum, for which the thermal deposition method is difficult on account of their high melting points, the cathode sputtering method is a convenient one for producing thin films. Since the melting point of nickel and iron is sufficiently low so that vacuum evaporation is feasible, little work has been carried out on the sputtering of Permalloy films. The process involves maintaining a discharge in a gas, preferably inert, at a pressure of about 10^{-4} to 10^{-1} mm Hg, the cathode being made of the metal to be sputtered.[20] Positive ions in the glow discharge, being accelerated toward the cathode by the negative potential, bombard the cathode and transfer their energies to the cathode atoms and cause them to be emitted and sputtered on the anode or substrate. This is the case with physical sputtering where the accelerating voltage is above $300-400V$. Below this voltage, scattering may arise from the residual gas chemically combining with the cathode material to produce compounds which are volatile at normal temperatures. This form of sputtering is known as electrochemical sputtering. Since the applied voltage is some $3500V$ in a typical thin-film sputtering apparatus, only physical sputtering processes are of interest here.

A glow discharge, being quite different from a vacuum environment, provides a more complex surrounding for nucleation and growth of thin films. A number of theories, all of which are partially successful in explaining experimental results, have been proposed to explain the physical sputtering process. These theories, in order of their historical appearance, are: momentum-transfer theory, evaporation theory, age theory, statistical theory, and the energy-chain theory. The momentum-transfer model involves a two-step process in which a surface atom is depressed by an incoming ion so that a second ion scattered from it can back-scatter another atom from the surface layer. The evaporation theory assumes that a small area of the target surface is raised to a very high temperature when the energy from the incoming ion is dissipated into a small volume in a short time. This high local surface temperature thereby causes surface atoms to evaporate. The age theory relies on results obtained from neutron diffusion theory while the statistical theory is based upon radiation damage and diffusion

[19] M. Lauriente and J. Bagrowski, *J. Appl. Phys.*, **33**: 1109 (1962).

[20] Details of the typical experimental arrangement for the sputtering of thin films may be found in L. Holland, *op. cit.*, p. 437.

theories. In the energy chain concept, direct transmission of energy along close packed directions of the lattice is assumed. These theoretical models for the sputtering process have been reviewed recently by Harrison, who attempts to combine elements of the statistical and the energy-chain concepts in a semiquantitative manner in the theory of sputtering.[21]

As an example of this method of film deposition, Permalloy is sputtered onto a substrate in a commercial bell jar using a cathode shaped as 6 in. square plates.[22] The plates were made from either solid Permalloy, by sintering pressed metal powders, or from copper previously electroplated with Permalloy using the sulfate-chloride solution.[17] Corning glass substrates were used and were supported on a water-cooled aluminium plate anode of the same shape and surface area as the cathode. Before each run the bell jar was pumped down to 5×10^{-6} mm Hg. Then, argon was leaked through at a pressure of about 100 μ. The sputtering rate was 900 Å/min at a potential of $3500 V$ and a current of 150 mA.

The deposition rate and also the magnetic properties of the films deposited in the presence of a 20 Oe field applied parallel to the film surface, were found to depend critically upon the density of the cathode. Using 85 % density solid Permalloy cathodes, 1 hr was required to obtain a film of 1000 Å thick whose coercive force has an abnormally high value of 50–100 Oe. By using 92–95 % solid Permalloy cathodes or copper cathode electroplated with Permalloy, the deposition rate could be markedly increased. The resulting films have a low coercivity of 2 or 3 Oe. Porosity of the cathode, or the presence of local fissures or pinholes which might contain pockets of air, presumably modify the process to one of reactive sputtering.

The film thickness distribution depends upon electrode area and separation, and upon the applied voltage. In this experiment, the optimum electrode area and separation were 6 in. square and 1 in., respectively, and the optimum potential was 3500 volts. With these optimum operating conditions, the films were uniform in thickness to within 2 % over a square surface of 3 in. at the center of the anode.

In a glow discharge, a substrate is subjected not only to the impinging material sputtered from the cathode but also to electron bombardment, the intensity and directional component of which depend entirely on the specific location of the substrate within the glow discharge and the direction of the applied external field. At the high pressure end of a typical working range, 10^{-1} mm Hg, the transport mechanism of sputtered material to the substrate is diffusion controlled, whereas at the lower limit of the pressure range, 10^{-4} mm Hg, the transport is by molecular flow. To study these effects, one may perform an experiment similar to the one described above. Here the cathode of a two-electrode glow discharge apparatus was made of material to be transported, with substrates held at various positions within the apparatus.[23] Both electrodes were water cooled and the flow rate of inert gas through the system was regulated. An external magnetic field was applied to increase the path lengths of the electrons, and consequently the amount of ionization in order to maintain a glow discharge in the low-pressure range where the mean free path of electrons is large.

The mass ratio of incident ions to cathode atoms, as well as the chemical nature of both, determines the ejection. Deposition rate, temperature, substrate environment, and subsequent film characteristics depend largely upon the current-voltage-pressure and geometry characteristics as well as on the location of the substrate with respect to

[21] D. E. Harrison, Jr., *1961 Vacuum Symposium Transactions*, p. 259.
[22] M. H. Francombe and A. J. Noreika, *J. Appl. Phys.*, **32**: 97S (1961).
[23] E. Kay, *J. Appl. Phys.*, **32**: 99S (1961).

the various glow discharge zones. Body-centered cubic alpha-iron was deposited onto amorphous glass, carbon, freshly cleaved single-crystal NaCl, and mica substrates. By placing substrates in the various characteristic zones of the discharge or outside of a contained glow discharge, thin films exhibiting a variety of characteristics were obtained. All films were completely polycrystalline with no evidence of preferred crystal orientation. Surprisingly, the preferred magnetic orientation which occurs in evaporated Fe films was not observed on any of these films as observed on a hysteresis-graph, even though some were deposited in the presence of an external field of 200 Oe in the plane of the film. Also surprisingly, no inert gas was found to be physically trapped in occlusions; and other gases, mainly H_2 and CO, were found at levels comparable to films evaporated at 10^{-6} mm Hg.

(d) Chemical Deposition Methods

Chemical deposition methods are used mainly for the preparation of insulating magnetic thin films of ferrites and garnets. In this section we shall discuss several of these methods briefly. To begin with, it may be mentioned that ferrite films may be prepared also by a not exclusively chemical method. The method involves the controlling of oxidation parameters of metallic alloy films in the 10^3 Å range produced by the vacuum evaporation of mixtures of metals in specific ratios.[24] The vacuum deposition method for metallic alloys is adequately discussed in subsection (a) above. It may be pointed out here, however, that in contrast to the case of vacuum deposition of Permalloy films where substrate temperature of about 250°C is typically used, the substrate temperature for this form of ferrite film deposition should be much lower, 25–30° say, in order to speed up the oxidation procedure to follow. The reason for this is that a cold substrate leads to a poorly crystallized film replete with structural defects; such a surface is normally highly reactive, probably due to the fact that grain boundaries can act as highly conductive channels of atomic diffusion.

Subsequent oxidation times following alloy (e.g., 2 to 1 atomic ratio of Fe to Ni mixture for nickel ferrite) deposition ranged from 3 to 28 hr at temperatures of 900–1100°C while cool-down times averaged about 8 hr. Both pure oxygen and air atmosphere were utilized in fabricating these films. The resistivity values of the ferrites were highly dependent upon the atmosphere, whether oxidizing or reducing, utilized in the oxidation steps of the preparation. The major difference between the resulting film and bulk material appeared to be relatively poor crystallinity in the films.

Another method of preparing thin ferrite films, also partly via oxidation, has been described by Lemaire and Croft.[25] The technique involves spraying a suspension of the reactants, present as hydroxides, onto a heated substrate. The film is chemically deposited on the substrate surface essentially through oxidation and coprecipitation mechanisms. For example, nickel ferrite films were prepared by coprecipitating nickel and ferrous hydroxides in varying proportions and then oxidizing the suspension with air. Films so deposited are generally isotropic even in the presence of a magnetic field of up to 2000 Oe in the plane of the film during deposition. All films examined, regardless of composition, exhibited loops with a high degree of squareness (remanent magnetization/maximum magnetization > 0.95) with coercive force ranging from 50 to 400 Oe depending upon composition and thickness.

---

[24] E. Banks *et al.*, *1960 Vacuum Deposition Symposium Transactions*, p. 297; *J. Appl. Phys.*, **32**: 44S (1961).

[25] H. P. Lemaire and W. J. Croft, *J. Appl. Phys.*, **32**: 46S (1961).

Ferrite films can also be prepared by pyrohydrolytic deposition, i.e., deposited onto Vycor substrate by hydrolysis at elevated temperatures of an atomized solution of the desired metal chlorides.[26] The solution is atomized by a burst of argon at a pressure of 20 psi. The optimum spray time is 2.5 sec with 4.5 sec between successive sprays. In this chemical deposition process, oxides are first formed by hydrolysis reaction at the elevated temperature to form the oxides; the oxides in turn react to form the desired ferrite. These reactions, most probably, take place at the heated substrate surface, with the hydrolysis reaction immediately preceding the ferrite formation.

Film composition has been found to be dependent upon the concentration of the starting solution, substrate temperature (optimum value at about 800°C), temperature gradients along with the spray path, length of time at the desired temperature, and the nature of the carrier gas. The initial permeability of about 100 for these films is usable in certain integrated circuits.

There is another chemical method of preparing ferrite films. In this method, the substrate is coated with stoichiometric ratios of alcoholic solutions of metal nitrates and each coat is subjected to a preliminary firing at 400–700°C for approximately 1 min, with cooling at room temperature prior to recoating. Then, the coated substrate is fired in nitrogen, air, or oxygen atmospheres, depending upon the kind of ferrite or garnet involved.[27] Alumina and fused quartz, which can stand the required temperature of 1200°C, are used as substrates. Crystallographic studies have shown that the amount of the main phase generally ranges from approximately 90 to 100%. Results of microwave resonance measurement led to the construction of a millimeter resonance isolator at about 35 Gc/sec using these films.

Other methods of ferrite preparation have included sputtering in argon and oxygen atmospheres[28] and pyrolytic spraying of metal organic complexes.[29]

2·2   COMPARISON OF PREPARATION METHODS

In the foregoing section, we have discussed in some detail the various methods of preparation of thin magnetic films, both insulating and metallic. It would be pertinent to briefly compare their relative advantages and disadvantages here. The vapor deposition technique, as mentioned previously, is the most widely used technique for metallic film preparation. Although there are a number of possible film contaminants in the residual gas of the vacuum system, some of these can be preferentially pumped by various techniques. Alternatively, high-vacuum techniques may be used to reduce the partial pressures, although not so much their relative composition, of these residual gases. Furthermore, source contamination due to the crucible container may be essentially eliminated by a ring source or by melting the charges by electron bombardment. If the source is also carefully outgassed and the substrate appropriately clean, in principle at least, the properties of vacuum deposited magnetic thin films can be controlled and reproduced. However, it is well known that the properties of vapor-deposited films are in general not exactly reproducible; two films deposited under presumably identical conditions almost never have exactly the same characteristics.

[26] F. R. Gleason, Jr., and L. R. Watson, *J. Appl. Phys.*, **34**: 1217 (1963).

[27] W. Wade *et al.*, *J. Appl. Phys.*, **34**: 1219 (1963).

[28] R. W. Johnston and G. G. Palmer, *WADC* (Wright Air Development Center) *Tech. Rept.*, 56–274 (1955).

[29] F. V. Schossberger *et al.*, *WADC Tech. Rept.*, 59–363 (1959).

This situation may be attributed, at least in part, to the generally relatively poor vacuum ($\sim 10^{-5}$ mm Hg during deposition) used and to the absence or inadequate use of preferential pumping of undesirable gases. From the above discussion, it may be inferred that films deposited in a carefully controlled vacuum atmosphere should be reproducible to within tolerable limits for fundamental studies of their properties and for technological applications, although the best yields to date ($< 50\%$) for magnetic memory fabrication are not particularly impressive. On the other hand, films produced by electrodeposition or cathode sputtering are subjected to a much more complex environment, which makes their properties difficult to control; abnormal behavior of films so deposited can not be easily explained by rigorous theories.

Consider first the case of electrodeposition. Here, numerous plating baths could be developed for the process. The constituent and optimum composition of these baths can not be theoretically predicted but must be experimentally determined. Even when a given acceptable bath is developed, it is never certain whether a similar or entirely different bath would not yield better results. This is particularly true in the case of special purpose additives, the selection of which involves a great deal of alchemy. Furthermore, it has been shown that temperature, current density, substrate, acidity, time-varying currents and agitation all influence the nature of the electrodeposit. However, the effects involved are often complex and can not be easily generalized. In spite of these apparent complexities involved in the electroplating process, electro-plated films with acceptable properties for memory applications have been produced in several cases.[15] It may be concluded here that although it is probably more preferable to use vapor-deposited rather than electrodeposited films for the study of their fundamental properties, it is nevertheless possible to produce films of acceptable characteristics for technological applications economically and expediently using the electrodeposition process.

In the case of film deposition by the cathode sputtering method, the glow discharge environment is much more complicated even than that existing in a plating bath. Indeed, as we have discussed in Sec. 2.1(c), the sputtering mechanism itself is incompletely understood. Under these circumstances, coupled with the fact that metals of importance for magnetic thin films such as nickel and iron, can be readily melted at reasonable temperatures ($\sim 1600°C$), the vapor deposition method of film deposition is preferable to the sputtering method. The only obvious advantage of the sputtering method is that if sputtering occurs in gases of atomic weight comparable with that of the cathode material and at sufficiently high pressures ($\sim 10^{-1}$ mm Hg), deposition proceeds by diffusion and thus eliminates the oblique incidence effect (preferential elongation of crystallites) found in vapor-deposited films.

As discussed in Sec. 2.1(d), there are many methods of preparation for insulating ferrite or garnet films. These arts are still in their infancy, and it is not possible to realistically evaluate their relative merits because of the lack of substantial amount of data to date. It may be pointed out, however, that insulating films, because of their low conductivity, may be more suitable in some respects for the study of the basic properties of magnetic thin films.

2·3 SUBSTRATE MATERIAL

The nature of the substrate affects the properties of a magnetic thin film. For example, if the coefficients of expansion of substrate and deposited materials are not the same, stress may be set up in the film which may in turn influence certain magnetic properties of the film such as anisotropy via magnetostriction. The first few layers deposited above the substrates of a thin film would be expected to conform to the contours and imperfections of the substrate. Thus, the properties of an ultrathin film (about tens of angstroms thick, say) may be a very sensitive function of the presence of scratches and nucleation centers of the substrate. For polycrystalline films, it is therefore desirable to use smooth substrates with maximum randomness of orientation. For single-crystal films, we presumably should use substrates of the same crystal structure and similar lattice constant as the alloy to be deposited. Furthermore, substrates must be precleaned carefully to avoid accidental contaminations to the film. In this section, we shall discuss each of these aspects in some detail.

(a) Polycrystalline Films

The first requirement of a substrate is that it be smooth on a scale comparable to the film thickness. Thus, the substrate surface need not be optically flat in the optical sense, but while it may be undulatory in profile there should not be any small-scale scratches, pits, or bumps. Glasslike materials which may be fired polished would easily satisfy the aforementioned requirement. However, the substrates should also withstand fairly high annealing temperatures, up to say $1000°C$. Furthermore, it may be desirable to have the coefficient of expansion of the substrate to be nearly equal to that of the alloy, since the condensed film is formed at an elevated temperature, and stresses set up by the cooling of the structure to room temperature might result in undesirable magnetic properties.

Ordinary microscope slides, being glazed ceramic materials with a very high expansion coefficient, were found to serve well as substrates at moderate temperatures[30] and are thus widely used. Their expansion coefficient, which is probably in the range 8–$10 \times 10^{-6}/°C$, compares well with that of 50–50 Permalloy which is about $9.7 \times 10^{-6}/°C$ at comparable temperatures. The nature of the forces existing between the metal atoms at the interface is found to depend strongly upon the substrate and its state of cleanliness. The principal forces involved are usually considered to be of the Van der Waals type, but it seems likely that chemical bonds might form in some instances, giving a much greater stability. This may be attributed to chemical binding to the interstitial bound oxygen in the glass, or alternately, the result of diffusion of metal atoms into the glass providing a sort of atomic dovetailing.

Quartz may also be used as substrate material. Because of its hardness, it could be much thinner than that of a microscopic slide. Typical thickness may be about 0.005 in. Because of the availability of the microscope slides, they are most widely used for substrates of the vacuum deposited films, although quartz substrates are also used under certain circumstances.

Many substrate cleaning procedures, some more elaborate than others, may be used. In a normal procedure, substrates are first cleaned using a detergent and nitric acid, and then dried in successive rinses of alcohol, acetone, and ether. After the detergent cleaning, the substrates are subjected to about 45 min. of ultrasonic agitation in distilled water and dried as before. More elaborate cleaning procedures than the normal one discussed above seem to result in better magnetic characteristic of thin films.[31]

[30] M. S. Blois, Jr., *J. Appl. Phys.*, **26**: 975 (1955).

[31] K. H. Behrndt and F. S. Maddocks, *J. Appl. Phys.*, **30**: 276S (1959); J. S. Lemke, *J. Appl. Phys.*, **33**: 1097 (1962).

The size of the crystallites is influenced by the substrate temperature during film deposition, as the rates of diffusion and nucleation of the metallic atoms are functions of temperature. If the substrate temperature is low, large islands of metallic crystallites tend to form on the substrate as can be verified from electron micrograph studies. On the other hand, if the substrate temperature is high, the crystallites tend to be small and are separated by thin grain boundaries. Optimum substrate temperature for vapor deposition of thin films has been found to be about 250°C.

In the case of electroplating on circular substrates, particularly smooth OFHC Cu wire may be used. In order to obtain consistent results with uniform adherence, stress, and magnetic characteristics, it is necessary to plate on a meticulously clean substrate. The cleaning procedure utilized removes vegetable and mineral oils in a hot ultrasonically agitated detergent bath. A hot peroxide bath oxidizes the animal fats. Animal fat residue plus physical contaminants are then removed in an ultrasonically agitated deionized water bath. The remaining copper oxide is removed in a hydrogen furnace from which it passes directly under the surface of the electrolyte and is plated.

(b) Single Crystals

Single-crystal films of nickel, iron, and Permalloy may be prepared epitaxially by vacuum deposition onto the (001) cleavage surface of NaCl, CaF_2 and MgO.[32] Substrates were heated up to 500°C and then cooled down to the temperature at which deposition is carried out. Although single-crystal films are of little practical use, they afford a more precise investigation of magnetic properties, particularly of the induced magnetic anisotropy, of thin magnetic films.

2·4 FILM CHEMICAL COMPOSITION

The source composition and the film composition may be different due to fractionalization of the melt and possible difference in the sticking probabilities on the substrate of the metallic atoms involved. In this section we shall discuss the reasons for these differences along with the methods of film composition determination. Experimentally determined spatial variation of film composition by means of the microprobe is also examined.

(a) Starting and Final Composition

The raw material used in vacuum deposition of Permalloy films is usually of high purity (99.999%, say) nickel or iron rods or shots. If an alloy mixture is heated to a very high temperature and evaporated quickly, the equilibrium indicated by the phase diagram is never reached. Thus, the chemical composition of the vacuum-deposited film may be different from the percentage distribution in the starting material due to fractionalization and possible difference in the sticking probabilities on the substrate of metallic atoms involved. Using the vapor-pressure data for metals and applying the law of Raoult for the vapor pressure of solutions, one may determine the relative rates of vaporization for each constituent of a given alloy at any given temperature. For example, if the starting material was 83.4% Ni–16.6% Fe, we find the vapor

---

[32] S. Chikazumi, *J. Appl. Phys.*, **32**: 81S (1961); R. R. Verderber and B. M. Kostyk, *J. Appl. Phys.*, **32**: 696 (1961).

pressures for nickel and iron of 28.1 μ and 17.2 μ, respectively, at 1600°C. This should yield a film composition of 62% Ni–38% Fe. However, it was found that the mean composition for a series of films is 81.5% Ni–18.5% Fe which shows the expected tendency of iron enrichment but by a much smaller amount.[30] One would surmise from this that Raoult's law is not applicable to the case in point. Very extensive work on the comparison of the film and melt composition of Permalloy films has been carried out by various workers and it has been found that the initial and resulting compositions vary little from each other.

(b) Film Composition Determination

Whereas the melt composition can be determined simply by weighing the desired amounts of metal to be deposited in a sensitive balance, film composition must be determined by more elaborate methods. For example, thin-film composition may be determined by chemical analysis. For the nickel determination, the film is dissolved in nitric acid, oxidized to the higher valence state with bromine, and neutralized with ammonium hydroxide. This also removes the excess bromine color. Addition of dimethylglyoxime produces the red nickel complex, the optical density of which is measured in a spectrometer and compared with standard solutions. Dilutions are kept high enough to stay within the linear range. The amount of iron is then determined on a separate aliquote by a thiocyanate reaction in much the same way.

Another way of determining the composition is by measuring the magneto-elastic constant.[33] This is accomplished by measuring the dependence of H_k on small applied strain. It is found that typical data obtained in this way are given by the relation

$$H_k = H_{ko} + \frac{dH_k}{de} = H_{ko} + \frac{2B}{M} e \qquad (2.6)$$

where $B = dK/de$ is the isotropic magnetoelastic constant. Plotting B as a function of melt composition and comparing with the result of Schulze for bulk material provides a calibration of the actual film composition.[34]

Film chemical composition could also be measured by X-ray fluorescence techniques. When an element such as nickel or iron is irradiated by K_α radiation of suitable wavelength, part of the energy absorbed by the element subsequently appears in fluorescence, i.e., with emission in all directions. Since the emission lines, representing characteristic radiation of a particular element, are quite sharp, the alloy composition of a film can be determined in this way by measuring the relative intensities of the characteristic radiation of different elements involved by a Geiger counter spectrometer.

(c) Spatial Variation of Film Composition

Microprobe X-ray analysis, employing an instrument similar to that developed by Castaing[35] has been used to explore the chemical composition of thin films by Chu et al.[36] Small regions 10 μ in diameter at intervals 0.001 and 0.010 in. are analyzed. It

[33] J. B. Goodenough and D. O. Smith, *MIT Lincoln Lab. Tech. Dept. No. 197*, 5 (1959).
[34] A. Schulze, *Z. Phys.*, **50**: 448 (1928).
[35] *Natl. Bur. Std. Circ. No. 527*, March, 1954, Paper No. 34.
[36] W. W. L. Chu, I. E. Wolf, and B. C. Wagner, *J. Appl. Phys.*, **30**: 272S (1959).

is found that maximum variation in nickel content between neighboring regions may be as much as 3%.

2·5 FILM-THICKNESS MEASUREMENT

The thickness of thin films could be measured by several methods with varying degrees of accuracy. We shall discuss in this section several of the common methods used in film-thickness determination with particular reference to their relative merits and accuracies.

(a) During Evaporation

Thickness of thin films may be monitored during evaporation by measuring their instantaneous resistance and comparing the value so obtained with a known resistance vs film-thickness calibration. In practice, the resistance of a dummy film deposited at the same time as the actual film whose thickness is desired, instead of the actual film, is measured. In this way, wires may be soldered to silver contacts on the substrate of the dummy film instead of the actual film for resistance measurement purposes. The resistance vs film-thickness curve may be obtained by measuring the resistance of films of varying thicknesses, the thickness being measured by an apparatus such as the Tolansky interferometer to be described below. Alternatively, a quartz crystal monitor whose oscillating frequency is dependent upon the coated film thickness may be used.

(b) Multiple-Beam Interferometry

These methods, developed to a remarkable degree by Tolansky,[37] utilize the resulting interference effects when two silvered surfaces are brought close together and are subjected to optical radiation. As we shall describe below, these interference techniques, which are of great value in studying surface topology in general, may be applied simply and directly to film-thickness determination.

When a wedge of small angle is formed between unsilvered glass plates which are illuminated by monochromatic light, broad fringes are seen (Fizeau, 1862) arising from interference between the light beams reflected from the glass on the two sides of the air wedge. At points along the wedge where the path difference between those two beams (allowing for phase changes at the surfaces) is an integral number of wavelengths, bright fringes occur. Where the path difference is an odd number of half-wavelengths, dark fringes occur. If the glass surfaces of the plates are coated with highly reflecting layers, one of which is partially transparent, then the reflected fringe system consists of very fine dark lines against a bright background. A schematic diagram of the multiple-beam interferometer along with a typical pattern of Fizeau fringes from a film step is shown in Fig. 2.3. As shown in this figure, the film whose thickness is to be measured is overcoated with a silver layer to give a good reflecting surface and a half-silvered microscope slide is laid on top of the film whose thickness is to be determined. A wedge is formed by the two microscope slides, and light multiply reflected between the two silvered surfaces forms an interference pattern with a

---

[37] S. Tolansky, *Multiple Beam Interferometry of Surfaces and Films*, Clarendon Press, Oxford, 1948.

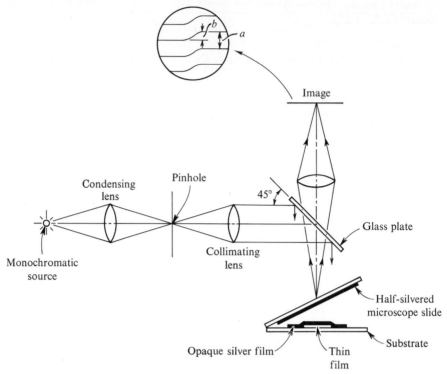

FIG. 2.3.   Multiple-beam interferometer for the measurement of the thickness of thin films.

discontinuity at the film edge as shown in Fig. 2.3. The thickness of the film d can then be determined by the relation

$$d = \frac{\lambda}{2} \frac{b}{a} \tag{2.7}$$

where λ is the wavelength and b/a is the fractional discontinuity identified in the figure. In general, the green line of mercury is used, for which $\lambda = 5460.7$ Å. In practice, several half-silvered slides of varying thickness and therefore of varying transmission are prepared, and one of these is selected for maximum resolution. A resolution of about 20 Å may be obtained in a careful measurement and about 100 Å in a routine procedure. Accurate determination of fringe spacings are difficult and time consuming; but a method of image comparison which considerably improves the ease and rapidity of measurement has recently been developed.[38] Other refinements of the Tolansky method which uses two mercury lines and obviates use of tables can also be found in the literature.[39] Alternatively, a simple film-thickness gauge utilizing Newton's rings may be developed, which involves no critical adjustment of wedges, etc., and which reduces error in film-thickness determination.[40]

In conclusion, we might mention that the Tolansky method of film-thickness measurement is the most widely used and in many respects also the most accurate and satisfactory one.

[38] T. M. Green and L. N. Hadley, *J. Opt. Soc. Am.*, **45**: 228 (1955).
[39] S. J. Lines, *1961 Vacuum Symposium Transactions*, p. 846.
[40] A. W. Winston, C. A. Baer, and L. R. Allen, *1959 Vacuum Symposium Transactions*, p. 249.

(c) Using a Hysteresisgraph

When the pickup coil of a hysteresisgraph is larger in size than the film, the height of the rectangular hysteresis loop in the easy direction is proportional to the volume of the film. If the area of the film is measured, the thickness can be determined. The form factor of the pickup coil is usually difficult to calculate with any precision so that a height of the rectangular hysteresis loop vs thickness calibration must be obtained by using, say, the Tolansky method described above. The details of a hysteresis loop tracer will be described in detail in Chap. 7 and will not be further elaborated here.

(d) Other Methods

Film thickness may also be measured by several other methods. For example, if the film is excited by K_α radiation of suitable wavelength, the resulting X-ray fluorescence radiation, which consists of sharp characteristic emission lines of the element in the film, may be measured by a Geiger counter and from this the thickness of the film may be inferred. Thus, this X-ray method yields numbers which are proportional to the number of atoms per unit area responsible for fluorescence. This method may be an advantageous one to use in the case of ultrathin film (tens of angstroms), whose structure is in all probability inhomogeneous. The presence of isolated islands in these films makes it difficult to attach any physical significance to a thickness defined on the basis of a continuous film. Again, the intensity of the fluorescence radiation vs thickness curve must be again obtained from a method such as the Tolansky method described above.

The stylus[41] and several other methods[42] may also be used to determine thin-film thickness with varying degrees of accuracy. However, it may be mentioned again here that, in general, the Tolansky method is the most preferable.

2·6 MECHANISM OF FILM FORMATION

In recent years, a great deal of interest has been developed in the mechanism of formation of thin films on amorphous or crystalline substrates. The phenomenon of oriented overgrowth of a material on single-crystal substrates in particular has attracted much attention. Although an appreciable number of facts has been accumulated experimentally, it has not yet been possible to formulate a comprehensive theory of epitaxy that would explain all the experimental observations. Pashley,[43] in a comprehensive review of the entire field, attributed this failure primarily to the lack of knowledge concerning the basic mechanism of nucleation and thin-film growth. Recently, Poppa has investigated *in situ* the early stages of the growth of thin metal films by transmission electron microscopy.[44] The apparatus consists basically of microevaporation source and ion gun used for cleaning and thinning the thin-film substrates. These growth experiments are conducted directly inside the electron microscope and have yielded some very interesting results. For example, in the case of growth of silver on mica by the vacuum evaporation method, electron micrographs indicate preferred nucleation along mica cleavage steps, growth behavior of individual nuclei, and collapse of several smaller nuclei into a larger one.

---

[41] N. Schwartz and R. Brown, *1961 Vacuum Symposium Transactions*, p. 836.
[42] O. S. Heavens, *op. cit.*, p. 96.
[43] D. W. Pashley, Advances in Physics, *Phil. Mag.*, **5**: 174 (1956).
[44] H. Poppa, *1962 Vacuum Symposium Transactions*, p. 21.

The theory of nucleation on solid surfaces has been reviewed recently by Rhodin and Walton.[45] There are essentially three steps necessary in the calculation of the nucleation rate, i.e. the rate at which small deposits appear. First, an expression is obtained for the concentration of critical nuclei, assuming that the system is in equilibrium, the system consisting of substrate, absorbed single molecules, and clusters. Then multiplying this expression by the rate of single molecules, the nucleation rate is obtained. Lastly, a correction is applied which takes into account the departure from equilibrium due to nucleation and the fact that some of the nuclei have transformed through the accretion of single nuclei. This treatment is concerned mainly with overgrowth on crystalline substrates. The growth of deposits on amorphous substrates is even more complicated. However, it may be concluded that in any case, the principle contribution of the initial surface to the effectiveness of condensation occurs when the condensed layer is not more than approximately a few atom layers in thickness. Subsequent condensation is then determined primarily by the state of the deposit itself.

---

[45] T. N. Rhodin and D. Walton, *1962 Vacuum Symposium Transactions*, p. 3.

CHAPTER 3

DOMAIN STRUCTURES

Domain and domain wall configurations in a ferromagnetic material are determined by the condition of minimum energy. The energy in a ferromagnet is made up of several components comprised of the exchange energy, the anisotropy energy, the magnetostatic or demagnetizing energy, magnetostrictive energy, domain wall energy, and if external magnetic fields are applied, Zeemann energies. For bulk matter, the energy minimization procedure yields a great number of domains within each of which the spins are all aligned by very strong exchange forces. These domains are separated by finite boundaries called Bloch walls, within which the spin orientation changes from the one in a given domain to that in a neighboring domain by rotating about an axis perpendicular to the plane of the wall. Using the Bitter magnetic powder technique, an accurate visual picture of the surface domains may be obtained, providing the surface of the specimen is carefully polished. However, since only the surface domain structure can be observed by the magnetic powder technique, the domain configuration within the bulk sample can only be inferred.

The domain situation in a thin film, on the other hand, is fortunately quite different. First, thin films naturally have a very smooth surface so that no previous polishing is required before the Bitter technique can be applied. Secondly, due to large shape anisotropy of a thin film the thickness of which may be smaller than that of a domain wall, walls with their planes parallel to the surfaces of the film in general will not occur, and the surface domain configuration as observed by the Bitter technique is representative of the domain configuration of the entire film. Domain walls in thin films can also be observed by utilizing the Kerr magneto-optic effect and by electron microscopy. These various methods of domain observation will be discussed in this chapter.

Of particular interest to the study of domain and domain wall configurations in thin films is the fact that the domain walls in thin films are in general not of the Bloch type. The simplest type of wall in a thin film is the Néel wall, within which the spins rotate continuously from the direction in a given domain to that in a neighboring domain about an axis in the plane of the wall. Most thin films consist of a large central domain oriented along the easy axis surrounded by reversed edge domains at the edge of the film, the walls between these domains being of the Néel or other types. Depending upon the evaporation conditions, the imperfections, strain, easy axis dispersion, etc., various types of domains such as the anular and the checkerboard type may exist. Correspondingly, cross-tie walls, spiral and concentric-circle walls, and probably even more complicated walls can exist. The presence of these types of domains and domain walls in thin films, in contrast to the case of bulk matter, can be easily verified by several well-developed techniques of observation discussed above. The subject of domains in thin films will be discussed at some length in this chapter while the relatively more complex problem of domain wall configurations will be extensively treated in Chap. 4.

3·1 GENERAL THEORETICAL CONSIDERATIONS

In this section, we shall determine the probable spin system configuration in a magnetic thin film by minimizing the sum of the pertinent energy components involved. For a perfect single crystal, the energy minimization calculations can be rigorously carried out. It is recognized, of course, that the presence of imperfections, strains, inhomogeneous internal fields, grain boundaries in a polycrystalline sample, etc., can drastically change the details of the domain configuration. These complicating factors and their probable influence upon the domain configuration are discussed in this section, while actual calculations of domain wall configuration about imperfections will be carried out in Chap. 5.

(a) Energy Minimization

For a very thin magnetic film, unless there is a magnetocrystalline easy axis perpendicular to the plane of the film, the magnetization will lie in the plane of the film due to the large shape anisotropy. Thus, a magnetic field of about 10,000 Oe is required to magnetize a thin 80–20 Permalloy film to saturation in the direction of the film normal. There is no preferred direction, however, in the plane of the film and all orientations of the magnetization within the plane are equally probable. On the other hand, as was discovered by Blois, a uniaxial anisotropy will develop within the plane of the film if it was deposited in the presence of a magnetic field in a given direction in the film plane.[1] In this case, a predominantly single domain configuration in the plane results.

For films whose thickness is less than 2000 Å (area ~ 1 cm^2), demagnetization in the plane of the film proper ($\sim .15$ Oe) can be neglected. However, for the minimum energy state, the edges of the film may still show demagnetization effects exemplified by the appearance of 90° domains of closure first proposed by Landau and Lifshitz.[2] The calculation of the dimensions of these domains is a rather formidable micromagnetics problem and is as yet unsolved. It may be pointed out here, however, that this problem is complicated by the fact that the demagnetizing field is inhomogeneous near the edge of the film due to the departure of the shape of the film from a true ellipsoid; it is well known that only true ellipsoids can have demagnetizing fields which are uniform in direction and magnitude within them.[3]

The closure domains at the edges of the film play an important role for film reversal by wall motion. When no domains occur at the edges and no wall is present in the film, a wall must first be nucleated before wall motion can take place. Nucleation normally starts at a higher field than that at which wall motion occurs. In actual films the closure domains play the role of the nuclei and the coercive force of the film is equal to the critical field for wall motion.

[1] M. S. Blois, Jr., *J. Appl. Phys.*, **26**: 975 (1955).
[2] L. Landau and E. Lifshitz, *Physik, Z. Sowjetunion,* **8**: 153 (1935).
[3] J. A. Osborn, *Phys. Rev.*, **67**: 351 (1945).

A further complication regarding the edge domains is that in the remanent state their configurations are not necessarily the ones corresponding to minimum energy, presumably due to the presence of imperfections at the edges of the film; after saturation in the easy direction, the edge domains are found to be 180° reversed domains and highly irregular in shape. However, if a small ac field is applied in the hard direction, the walls would start to creep and eventually the domain configuration with the minimum energy is assumed. Experimentally, it has been found that such resulting edge domains have configurations resembling those of 90° closure domains predicted by theory.[2] However, even this minimum energy configuration, as mentioned in the last paragraph, has not been able to be deduced from rigorous calculations. This difficulty stems, in part at least, from the inability to take into account easily the role of the magnetostatic energy in a nonsaturated state in determining the associated domain and domain wall configuration. However, if a sufficiently simple experimentally observed configuration is used as the starting point of a calculation, the dimensions of the edge domains can in principle be determined as a function of other pertinent parameters of the film. A good example of this situation is shown in Fig. 3.1 where we have shown the

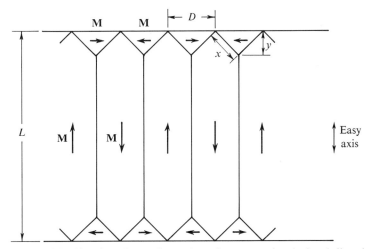

FIG. 3.1.   Thin-film domain configuration after saturation in hard direction.

domain configuration after saturation in the hard direction and with the subsequent reduction to zero field. The closure domains are clearly shown along with the longitudinal domains in the easy direction. Because of the flux closure, i.e. normal component of the flux being continuous across the domain boundary, the magnetostatic energy is zero. On the other hand, the closure domains, being magnetized in the hard direction, introduce anisotropy energy. It is seen from the figure that the domain configuration is sufficiently simple that a rigorous energy minimization may be carried out. In this way, although by a somewhat deviate route, we may learn something about the characteristics of edge domains without solving the complicated domain problem after saturation in the easy direction.

(b) Probable Spin Configuration

It is instructive to determine the width of the domains D as functions of σ_w, L, and K_1, where σ_w and K_1 are respectively the wall surface energy per unit area and the anisotropy energy density and L is the linear dimensions of the film. σ_w is a function of the crystallographic direction of the boundary plane and of the total change in spin direction across the boundary. Thus, the wall energy E_w is given by

$$E_w = \sigma_w S \tag{3.1}$$

where S is the total area of the domain boundaries within the body. The anisotropy energy arises from the existence of preferred axis of orientation for the magnetization in a ferromagnetic crystal. The anisotropy energy E_a is given by

$$E_a = K_1 V_a \tag{3.2}$$

where K_1 is the anisotropy energy density and V_a is the total volume of the domains in the specimen not oriented near the easy axis.

For the configuration of Fig. 3.1 we see that

$$E_w = \sigma_w [4xNT + N(L - 2y)T] \tag{3.3}$$

where N is the number of domains. From geometrical considerations we easily find that $x = D/\sqrt{2}$ and $y = D/2$. For a unit area of the film $NDL = 1$ so that Eq. (3.3) becomes

$$E_w = \sigma_w \left(2\sqrt{2} + \frac{L - D}{D} \right) \frac{T}{L} \tag{3.4}$$

On the other hand, the anisotropy energy is

$$E_a = K_1 (2N)(\tfrac{1}{2}) \left(\frac{D}{\sqrt{2}} \right)^2 T = K_1 \frac{D}{2} \frac{T}{L} \tag{3.5}$$

The domain width D corresponding to the minimum energy state could be obtained by setting $\delta E/\delta D = 0$, where $E = E_w + E_a$ is the total energy per unit area of the film. Carrying out this procedure, we find

$$D = \left(\frac{2\sigma_w L}{K_1} \right)^{1/2} \tag{3.6}$$

Unfortunately, neither the $L^{1/2}$ dependence of D nor the σ_w calculated from Eq. (3.6) using known values of D, K_1, and L agrees with experiment.[4] Presumably, this is due to factors which we have implicitly neglected in our simple calculation given above. This question will be reexamined in more detail in Sec. 3.4.

For Permalloy films with a magnetoelastic easy axis normal to the film due to internal isotropic strain in films having a negative magnetoelastic constant, multi-domains with the magnetization oriented perpendicular to the plane of the film may result above a certain critical thickness. Following the method used above for the case

---

[4] S. Middelhoek, *Ferromagnetic Domains in Thin Ni-Fe Films*, Drukkerij Wed. G. Van Soest, N.V., Amsterdam, 1961, pp. 37–38.

of domains parallel to the plane of the film, we easily find from Fig. 3.2 that for unit area of the film

$$D = \left(\frac{2\sigma_w T}{K_1}\right)^{1/2} \tag{3.7}$$

$$E_{min} = (2\sqrt{2} - 1)\sigma_w + (2\sigma_w T K_1)^{1/2} \tag{3.8}$$

In this calculation we have assumed that there are no easy directions in the plane of the film. For the case where the film is uniformly magnetized in its own plane, we find for a unit area of the films

$$E_a = K_1 T \tag{3.9}$$

Equating Eqs. (3.8) and (3.9), we easily find the transition thickness T below which the film is composed of a single domain parallel to the film as

$$T = 5\frac{\sigma_w}{K_1} \tag{3.10}$$

For a typical film $T \sim 10,000$ Å according to Eq. (3.10), but the experimentally observed value is about 1,200 Å. Thus, the configuration of minimum energy is probably somewhat more complicated than that shown in Fig. 3.2; that is, a configuration

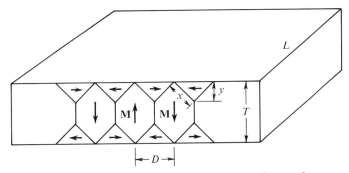

FIG. 3.2.   Domains oriented perpendicular to film surfaces.

in which the magnetization twists continuously in a spiral fashion may give better agreement between theory and experiment.[5] However, it is clear from the discussion above that domains not entirely oriented with their magnetization parallel to the film surface may exist for films with negative magnetostriction.

If the magnetostrictive constant is positive, the film could still be composed of multidomains, separated by domain walls, parallel to the surface of the film if the thickness to diameter ratio is sufficiently large. In this case, the breaking up of the single domain structure into a multidomain one is due to demagnetization effect. If the film is sufficiently thick, there is also a tendency for the magnetization to have a component in a direction perpendicular to the plane of the film due to the lowering of

---

[5] E. Huber and D. O. Smith, *J. Appl. Phys.*, **30**: 267S (1959).

the perpendicular component of the demagnetization energy. In practice it has been found that for a $\frac{1}{16}$ in. spot the thickness must be less than 200 Å for the film to stay in single domain state.

3·2 EDGE DOMAINS

In the last paragraph, we have already touched upon the shapes of the edge domains in a thin film. It has been experimentally found that these domains are somewhat irregular in shape but resemble closure domains observed in bulk matter if the minimum-energy ferromagnetic state in the film is attained. In this section we shall describe further their shapes and their dominant role in the magnetization reversal process.

(a) Shape of Edge Domains

Figure 3.3 shows typical configurations of thin film edge domains after easy-axis saturation and reduction to zero field. They are highly irregular in shape. As we have already discussed in the last section, these edge domains arise due to the demagnetizing field in the plane of the film and to film-edge imperfections. If a small ac field is applied perpendicular to the easy axis or along the hard axis, the domain

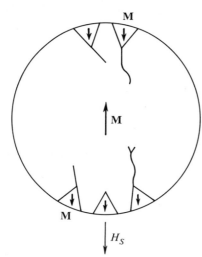

FIG. 3.3. Typical configuration of edge domains after saturation in easy direction.

walls begin to creep and the shapes of the edge domains will change to those corresponding to minimum energy. The shapes of the resulting domains resemble those of the closure domains shown in Fig. 3.1. In contrast with the 90° closure domains of Fig. 3.1 or the edge domains of the minimum-energy state, the edge domains of the remanent state shown in Fig. 3.3 are, by and large, 180° reversed domain, as can be verified by their modes of growth during magnetization reversal, to be discussed below.

(b) Growth of Edge Domains

If a magnetic field H slightly larger than the coercive force H_c is applied in the direction opposite to that of the magnetization in the main body of the film (see

Fig. 3.3), the edge domains are observed to grow inward toward each other indicating that these domains are not 90° closure domains but are reversed 180° domains oriented along the easy axis. Eventually, the tips of the edge domains on the opposite sides of the film will join with each other forming several long reversed domains oriented along the easy axis. Subsequent to this edge-to-edge reversed domain formation, the reversed domains grow into each other via the hard axis direction, thus completing the process of magnetization reversal. The growth of the reversed edge domains constitutes the most common domain wall motion magnetization reversal sequence, although it has been found that some films start their magnetization reversal process from some imperfection nucleating center away from the edge of the film. Since the nucleation field is usually higher than the critical field for motion of the domain walls of the edge domains the coercive force is determined by the critical field. Consequently, the edge domains play a dominant role in the magnetization reversal process via domain wall motion.

3·3 MAGNETIZATION DISTRIBUTION

In Sec. 3.1, we briefly considered the domain configuration after saturation in the hard direction. We found that the film is composed of many fine elongated domains, whose long axes are parallel to the easy axis. The widths of these domains vary from film to film, ranging from a few to tens of microns. The origin of these elongated domains is of considerable interest in the study of domain configurations in thin films and will be discussed in this section.

(a) After Saturation in Hard Direction

If the anisotropy field is constant in magnitude and direction throughout the film, it should be in a predominantly single domain state after saturation in the hard direction and subsequent reduction to zero field. Since the local field is in this case uniform throughout the sample, the magnetization as a whole rotates in unison reversibly back to the easy direction when the hard axis saturation field is reduced to zero. Therefore, to explain the existence of the experimentally observed multidomain state after saturation in the hard direction, it must be assumed that the magnitude and direction of the anisotropy field has a spatial dependence. The local anisotropy energy of the film is equal to the sum of the induced and local stray anisotropies. There may be a contribution to the local stray anisotropy due to the fact that the first-order magnetocrystalline anisotropy and magnetostriction do not vanish at the same Permalloy composition. Furthermore, the easy axis of the induced anisotropy depends not only upon the deposition field direction but upon the orientation of the crystal axes with respect to the field as well; although, dependent upon the nature of the amorphous substrate, these may be randomly oriented. Differences in the coefficients of expansion between substrate and film lead to an isotropic strain. As a result, however, compositional changes, crystal defects, mechanical disturbances, etc., in the film can in turn give rise to stray anisotropy.

(b) Easy-Axis Dispersion

If the crystalline anisotropy is the cause of the total anisotropy variations, it is possible that the easy direction changes from crystal to crystal. This results in an easy-direction dispersion wave whose wavelength is of the order of the crystal size (~ 500 Å).

In the presence of strong exchange forces, the wave will be modified so that the width of the actual magnetization distribution becomes smaller than that of the original anisotropy variations. Middelhoek has calculated the influence of the exchange and stray field energies on the magnetization variation for anisotropy dispersion wave of different wavelengths.[6] His results show that for a magnetization wave whose wavelength is more than 2 μ, the wavelengths of the magnetization and anisotropy waves are practically identical so that the spatial dependence of the anisotropy direction can be ascertained by measuring the magnetization variations using the Bitter technique. In this way, qualitative agreement between theory and experiment is obtained.

A more direct method of determining easy-axis dispersion has been developed by Crowther using the hysteresis loop tracer.[7] In this method, angular dispersion is measured by rotating the film until all flux falls to the same easy-axis direction. The details of this method will be discussed in Chap. 7, in conjunction with our study of the origin of the uniaxial anisotropy in thin films.

3·4 METHODS OF OBSERVATION

There are three methods available for the observation of domains: (1) the Bitter pattern method, (2) the Kerr magneto-optic and the Faraday rotation method, and (3) the electron microscopy method. We shall discuss each of these methods in turn in what follows.

(a) Bitter Pattern Method

The Bitter magnetic powder technique for the observation of ferromagnetic domains consists of depositing a drop of colloidal suspension of very fine magnetite ($Fe_3 O_4$) particles on the surface of a specimen. Due to the ever present Brownian motion, the particles move about in the suspension until they are captured by the magnetic stray fields associated with the domain walls. With the domain boundaries indicated by the equilibrium positions of the magnetite particles, a visual picture of the domain configuration is obtained. Since the stray fields associated with the roughness of the sample surface would contribute spurious Bitter patterns which may obscure the desired ones, electropolishing of the surface of bulk samples is necessary. Because of its inherently smooth surface the domains of thin films can be easily observed by the Bitter technique.

A drop of thin colloidal suspension[8] is placed on the film, and is squeezed to a thin layer by a microscope cover glass. After the particles are captured by the stray fields of the domain walls due to Brownian motion, their concentration above the walls can be observed by dark-field microscopy. Most walls can be most easily observed by top field illumination, but double walls, which occur in very thin films, are better seen by optical transmission.

Since the magnetization of the colloidal particles is very low and the particle cloud represents a rather poor yoke, the powder above the walls does not appear to affect the wall stray fields and thereby change the wall configuration. On the other hand, observations should be made immediately after the solution is applied to the specimen so that the surface of the film will not be chemically affected by the solution.

[6] S. Middelhoek, *op. cit.*, p. 46.

[7] T. S. Crowther, *MIT Lincoln Lab. Group Rept. No. 51–2*, February, 1959.

[8] W. C. Elmore, *Phys. Rev.*, **51**: 982 (1937).

By using a water immersion lens and alteration of lighting condition, significant improvements in the Bitter technique which provide better resolution, contrast, and magnification can be obtained.[9]

(b) Kerr Magneto-Optic and Faraday Techniques

Kerr magneto-optic and Faraday techniques are other methods used for the observation of domains of thin films.[10] When linearly polarized light is reflected by (Kerr effect) or transmitted through (Faraday effect) a ferromagnetic sample, the plane of polarization is rotated through an angle which depends upon the magnetization direction in the sample. If the film is composed of domains of antiparallel magnetization, an analyzer can be adjusted in such a way that the light reflected from or transmitted through domains of one particular orientation is extinguished. Since the optical absorption is high in transmission, the Faraday effect, in contrast to the Kerr effect, which is due to reflection, is applicable only for rather thin films of a few hundred angstroms or less.

We may classify three kinds of Kerr effects, depending upon the direction of the magnetization with respect to the plane of the film and the plane of incidence:

1. Longitudinal effect, in which the magnetization is in the plane of the film and parallel to the plane of incidence;
2. Transverse effect, in which the magnetization is in the plane of the film but perpendicular to the plane of incidence;
3. Polar effect, in which the magnetization is perpendicular to the plane of the film.

The difference in the angle of rotation between two oppositely magnetized domains is very small, about 5′ for the longitudinal effect. Thus, a high-intensity light source and high-quality polaroid filters or nicol prisms must be used.

Compared to the Bitter technique, the Kerr and Faraday techniques have the advantage of not disturbing the sample during observation. On the other hand, the small contrast does not permit high magnification, although this contrast may be

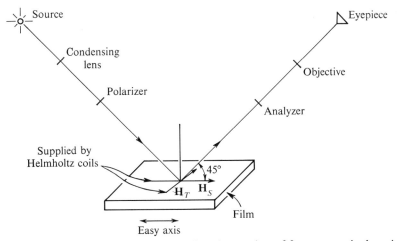

FIG. 3.4. Kerr magneto-optic apparatus for observation of ferromagnetic domains.

[9] R. M. Moon, *J. Appl. Phys.*, **30**: 82S (1959).
[10] C. A. Fowler and E. M. Fryer, *Phys. Rev.*, **100**: 746 (1955).

enhanced by using appropriate electronic circuits or by overcoating the film with a dielectric.[11] Furthermore, since the light is reflected at an angle of 45° to the film, it is difficult to take photographs which are sufficiently sharp over the whole plane. Thus, the two methods are complementary rather than duplicative and are, therefore, frequently used in combination. Figure 3.4 is a schematic diagram of the Kerr magneto-optic apparatus.

(c) Electron Microscopy

Electron microscopy methods of observing domains and domain walls in thin films appear to be extensions and complements to the Bitter pattern and Kerr magneto-optic or Faraday methods.

When an electron passes through a thin magnetized film the electron undergoes a deflection by interacting with the magnetization of the specimen, in addition to random deflections by normal scattering process. Experimentally, it has been found that the interaction could be represented, at least in a semiquantitative way, by the Lorentz force law:

$$\mathbf{F} = -\frac{e}{c}\mathbf{v} \times \mathbf{B} \tag{3.11}$$

where e is the absolute value of the electronic charge, $\mathbf{v}$ the electronic velocity, and $\mathbf{B}$ the flux density due to the film. Thus, the electron beam deflection in passing through a magnetic thin film could serve as a measurement of the magnetization distribution.

One general way of observing an image of the magnetization distribution in a thin film is to use a small aperture illuminating source and to focus the instrument on a plane other than the specimen plane.[12] Several other modes of operation of the microscope for thin-film magnetization distribution determination have also been successfully applied.[13]

---

[11] P. H. Lissberger, *J. Opt. Soc. Am.*, **51**: 948 (1961).

[12] M. E. Hale, H. W. Fuller, and H. Rubinstein, *J. Appl. Phys.*, **30**: 789 (1959).

[13] H. W. Fuller and M. E. Hale, *J. Appl. Phys.*, **31**: 308S (1960).

CHAPTER 4

DOMAIN WALLS

As discussed in Chap. 3, the minimum-energy state of a bulk ferromagnet is usually one of multidomains. Thin films, on the other hand, are usually composed of a single domain with its plane parallel to the surface of the film in the main body of the film, surrounded by small closure domains at the edges of the film. For thicker films or for films whose magnetoelastic easy axis is along the film normal, planar multi-domains or domains with their planes tilted away from the film surfaces, respectively, may exist. It is energetically more favorable for the spins to change their direction gradually rather than abruptly from that in a particular domain to the one in an adjacent domain. This means that there always exists a transition region of finite extent between any two domains within which the spins vary in direction. These regions are called domain walls, and their widths and spin configurations are determined by the relative spin orientation of the adjacent domains, the anisotropy, the exchange constant, as well as local imperfections and the geometry of the ferromagnet. In this chapter we shall examine the general problem of domain wall formation with particular reference to thin films. Various kinds of domain walls in thin films, e.g., Bloch walls, Néel walls, and cross-tie walls and means of observing them are discussed.

4·1 GENERAL THEORETICAL CONSIDERATIONS

Shape anisotropy is very pronounced in a thin film due to its extreme thinness compared to the other linear dimensions. As a consequence of this, the energies and widths of domain walls in thin films are quite different from those in bulk materials. Inside a bulk specimen, the spin direction in the wall changes in such a way that the component of the magnetization normal to the plane of the wall is constant in order to eliminate magnetic poles in the wall. Thus, the spins within these 180° walls rotate about an axis perpendicular to the plane of the wall; these types of walls are called Bloch walls.[1] Magnetic poles occurring at the intersection of a wall with the surface of the material give rise to stray fields external to the material. These stray fields can be eliminated by the introduction of 90° domains of closure at the surface of the specimen; if the magnetizations in the main and closure domains are at 45° to the intervening wall, the magnetization component normal to the wall is again continuous. In any event, the north and south poles on the surface of a bulk specimen, if they exist, are very far apart in comparison with the wall thickness so that the associated stray field energy is relatively small.

---

[1] F. Bloch, *Z. Physik*, **74**: 295 (1932).

On the other hand, the surface poles on the surface of a thin film, if they exist, are only separated by a distance equal to the film thickness so that relatively high stray field energy, which increases with decreasing thickness, is associated with them. Since the demagnetizing energy in the direction perpendicular to the film is very large ($\sim 2\pi M^2$ where M is the magnetization) compared to that in the plane of the film ($\sim 2\pi M^2 \, T/d$, where T is the thickness and d the linear dimensions of the film), it is reasonable to surmise that the spins would tend to lie in the plane of the film (see Eq. (5.9)). It then further follows that the spins in a domain wall rotate about an axis in the plane of the wall. Indeed, Néel demonstrated[2] in an approximate calculation that

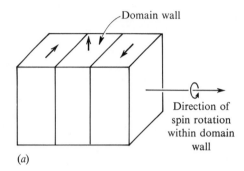

(a)

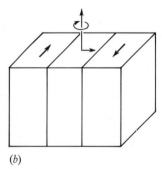

(b)

FIG. 4.1. Spin rotation in domain walls: (a) Bloch type and (b) Néel type.

in very thin films the energy can be minimized by having the component of the magnetization normal to the surfaces of the film vanish. Thus, the spins within the domain wall rotate in the plane of the film as expected. Since the component of the magnetization normal to the wall is no longer continuous, magnetic poles are created at the wall, inside the material. For these types of walls, called Néel walls, the domain wall energy decreases with decreasing film thickness.

In this section, we shall determine the thickness of domain walls as a function of other parameters of the film by an energy minimization process. In Fig. 4.1, we show the manner of rotation of the spins within both the Bloch and Néel wall to dramatize their difference.

(a) Energy Minimization

Consider the case of a Bloch wall within which the spin direction changes gradually about a direction perpendicular to the plane of the wall as shown in Fig. 4.2. The reason for the gradual change in the spin direction within the wall is the fact that the exchange energy is lower when the change is distributed over many atomic planes

---

[2] L. Néel, *Compt. Rend.*, **241**: 533 (1955).

instead of discontinuously. Of course, the anisotropy energy of the crystal is increased due to the fact that the spins within the wall must by necessity point in directions other than that of the easy axes.

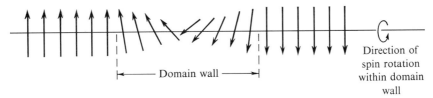

FIG. 4.2.   Schematic diagram of a Bloch wall.

(b) Thickness of Domain Walls

Consider the case of a ferromagnetic crystal with uniaxial anisotropy whose axis of easy magnetization is vertical as shown in Fig. 4.2. Since the exchange Hamiltonian is

$$\mathscr{H}_{\rm ex} = -2J \sum_{j>i} \mathbf{S}_i \cdot \mathbf{S}_j \tag{4.1}$$

The exchange energy $e_{\rm ex}$ between a pair of spins in the semiclassical treatment where the spins are considered as classical vectors follows from Eq. (4.1) as

$$e_{\rm ex} \simeq JS^2 \theta^2 \tag{4.2}$$

where θ is the angle that the adjacent spins make with each other and is assumed small. In Eq. (4.2), a constant term $2JS^2$ has been omitted as it is irrelevant to the following discussion. Now, let the total desired change of angle in a domain wall be θ_o (π for Fig. 4.1). If the change occurs in N equal steps, the angular change between adjacent spins is θ_o/N and the total exchange energy follows from Eq. (4.2) as

$$E'_{\rm ex} = (N+1)e_{\rm ex} \simeq JS^2 \frac{\theta_o^2}{N} \tag{4.3}$$

where the total number of spins $N+1$ has been assumed to be very large compared to unity.

We note from Eq. (4.3) that the total exchange energy is inversely proportional to the wall thickness D as $D = Na$, where a is the lattice constant. Thus, were it not for the increase in anisotropy energy, the wall would expand until it fills a sizable portion of the crystal. Actually, thickness of the domain wall is determined by the minimization of the total energy, exchange plus anisotropy. Since there are $1/a^2$ lines of atoms per unit area of the wall, we find from Eq. (4.3) that

$$E_{\rm ex} = \pi^2 \frac{JS^2}{Na^2} \tag{4.4}$$

for a 180° wall. The anisotropy energy density e_k is given by

$$E_k = \frac{1}{D} \int_{-D/2}^{D/2} K_1 \sin^2 \phi \, dx = \frac{K_1}{2} \tag{4.5}$$

where K_1 is the first order anisotropy constant and $\phi = \pi x/D$ is the angle between the spin and a direction in the plane of the wall. The total energy per unit wall area E_w is therefore

$$E_w = \frac{\pi^2 J S^2}{N a^2} + \frac{K_1}{2} N a \tag{4.6}$$

Differentiating E_w with respect to N, we easily find the domain wall width as

$$D = Na = \left(\frac{2\pi^2 J S^2}{K_1 a}\right)^{1/2} = \pi\left(\frac{A}{K_1}\right)^{1/2} \tag{4.7}$$

where $A = 2JS^2/a$ is the exchange constant. The total energy per unit wall area follows immediately from Eqs. (4.6) and (4.7) as

$$E_w = \pi\left(\frac{2JS^2 K_1}{a}\right)^{1/2} = \pi(Ak_1)^{1/2} \tag{4.8}$$

4·2 KINDS OF WALLS

As we pointed out at the beginning of the last section, at the intersection of a domain wall with the surface of the crystal, there will be free poles giving rise to stray fields. In bulk materials these poles are sufficiently far apart compared to the thickness of the wall that the stray field energy can be neglected in comparison with the anisotropy and exchange energies. Indeed, this has been implicitly assumed in Sec. 4.1 above so that the results there are strictly applicable only to bulk specimens. For thin films, on the other hand, the poles residing at the intersection of a wall with the surfaces, being separated by the film thickness, are very close together and the stray field energy cannot be a priori neglected. Indeed, as calculations below would show, the magneto-static energy associated with the stray fields in thin films plays an important role in the determination of the wall width.

(a) Bloch Walls

We shall begin our discussion of domain walls in this section by considering in more detail the case of Bloch walls within which the spin direction rotates about an axis perpendicular to the plane of the wall. To take adequate account of the magneto-static energy associated with the free poles, it would be simpler to treat the problem in the continuum approximation. Thus, in contrast with the semiclassical treatment given in Sec. 4.1 for the Bloch walls, we shall solve the problem in terms of the con-tinuous magnetization vector instead of the discrete spins.

Referring to Fig. 4.3, following Néel, we approximate the wall by an ellipsoidal cylinder. In this way, we can easily write down the magnetostatic energy in terms of the demagnetization factors of an ellipsoid which is well known. The magnetostatic energy E_m is equal to $-\frac{1}{2}H_m M_e$, where M_e is the effective magnetization perpendicular to the plane of the film and H_m is the demagnetizing field:

$$H_{m\perp} = -N_\perp M_e = -\frac{D}{T+D} 4\pi M_e \tag{4.9}$$

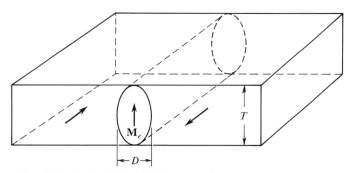

FIG. 4.3. Ellipsoidal cylinder approximation of a Bloch wall.

so that
$$E_{m\perp} = \frac{D}{T+D} 2\pi M_e^2 \tag{4.10}$$

If the angle ϕ between the magnetization and a direction in the plane of the wall and perpendicular to the plane of the film is given by

$$\phi = \pi \frac{x}{D} \tag{4.11}$$

for $-D/2 \le x \le D/2$, then $M_e = M_s \cos \phi$, where M_s is the saturation magnetization and $M_s \cos \phi$ represents the magnetization component perpendicular to the plane of the film. It follows that the local stray field for the case where $T \ll D$ (very thin films) is

$$H_{M\perp} = -N_1 M_e = -4\pi M_s \cos \frac{\pi x}{D} \tag{4.12}$$

The total magnetostatic energy density becomes

$$E_{M\perp} = \frac{1}{D} \int_{-D/2}^{D/2} 2\pi M_s^2 \cos^2 \frac{\pi x}{D} dx = \pi M_s^2 \tag{4.13}$$

Expression (4.13) should be equal to the limiting expression given by Eq. (4.10). Thus, for $T \ll D$,

$$2\pi M_e^2 = \pi M_s^2 \quad \text{or} \quad M_e = \frac{M_s}{\sqrt{2}} \tag{4.14}$$

The total energy of the system is given by

$$E_B = A\left(\frac{\pi}{D}\right)^2 D + \frac{K_1}{2} D + \frac{\pi D^2}{T+D} M_s^2 \tag{4.15}$$

since we are working with surface energy density of the wall. The first term in Eq. (4.15) was obtained from Eq. (4.2) by noting that $\theta = a(d\phi/dx)$ and $A = 2JS^2/a$ so that $e_{ex} = A(d\phi/dx)$. The continuum expression for the exchange energy $A(\pi/D)^2$ was obtained from the semiclassical expression $e_{ex} = JS^2\theta^2$ by replacing θ by $a(d\phi/dx)$ and noting that there are $2S$ spins in volume a^3 and that each spin has two neighbors:

$$e_{ex} = \frac{2e_{ex}}{a^3} = \frac{2}{a^3} JS^2\theta^2 = \frac{2JS^2}{a}\left(\frac{d\phi}{dx}\right)^2 \tag{4.16}$$

But $A = 2JS^2/a$, so that Eq. (4.16) becomes

$$e_{ex} = A\left(\frac{d\phi}{dx}\right)^2 = A\left(\frac{\pi}{D}\right)^2 \tag{4.17}$$

since ϕ was assumed to be equal to $\pi x/D$. The domain thickness D may be found by minimizing the total energy given by Eq. (4.15) with respect to D, giving

$$\frac{A\pi^2}{D^2} - \pi M_s^2 \frac{D^2 + 2DT}{(D + T)^2} = \frac{K_1}{2} \tag{4.18}$$

For given values of A, T, K_1, we could find D by plotting both sides of Eq. (4.18) vs D. Likewise the total energy E_B given by Eq. (4.15) could be obtained by using the expression for D given by Eq. (4.18). For a typical Permalloy film, $A = 10^{-6}$ erg/cm^3, $K_1 = 10^3$ ergs/cm^3 and $M_s = 800$ gauss. Using these values, we can plot D and E_B for 180° Bloch walls as a function of the thickness T as shown in Figs. 4.4 and 4.5.

For bulk material $T \gg D$ so that the magnetostatic energy term in Eqs. (4.15) and (4.18) can be neglected giving

$$D = \sqrt{2}\pi\left(\frac{A}{K_1}\right)^{1/2} \tag{4.19}$$

$$E_B = \sqrt{2}\pi(AK_1)^{1/2} \tag{4.20}$$

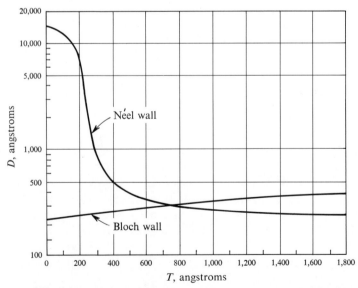

FIG. 4.4. Domain wall widths as a function of film thickness (after Middelhoek, Ref. 6).

From the exact solution of the Bloch wall in a uniaxial single crystal, we found that $D = \pi(A/K_1)^{1/2}$ and $E_B = \pi(AK_1)^{1/2}$. Thus, the continuum approximation used in this section to determine D and E_B gives reasonably good results. For a very thin film, on

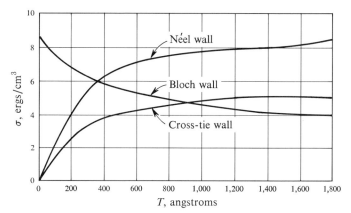

FIG. 4.5. Domain wall energies as a function of film thickness (after Middelhoek, Ref. 6).

the other hand, the anisotropy energy can be neglected providing $K_1 \ll 2\pi M_s^2$, which is usually the case for Permalloy films, and we find from Eq. (4.18) that

$$D = \pi\left(\frac{2A}{2\pi M_s^2}\right)^{1/2} \tag{4.21}$$

$$E_B = \pi[2A(2\pi M_s^2)]^{1/2} \tag{4.22}$$

Landau and Lifshitz have shown that the correct expression for ϕ should be given by[3]

$$\cos\phi = \frac{1}{\cosh(x\sqrt{K_1/A})} \tag{4.23}$$

instead of $\phi = x/\sqrt{2A/K_1}$ as obtained from the Néel assumption that $\phi = \pi x/D$. If ϕ were plotted vs x using Eq. (4.23), $\phi \to \pm\pi/2$ as $x \to \pm\infty$ so that an arbitrary definition of the wall thickness must be used. The wall thickness for the correct solution Eq. (4.23) is obtained by drawing a tangent to the ϕ vs x curve at the origin; the x at which this tangent intersects the horizontal line $\phi = \pm\pi/2$ is, by definition, the half-wall thickness.

(b) Néel Walls

For very thin films, the demagnetizing field in the direction normal to the plane of the film is practically $4\pi M_s$ which is equal to about 10^4 gauss. Because of such a high demagnetizing field, it may be energetically unfavorable to have the spin directions depart from that in the film plane, as is required in a Bloch wall. Thus, it is not unreasonable to expect that for a film thickness below a certain value, the magnetization,

---

[3] L. Landau and E. Lifshitz, *Physik Z. Sowjetunion*, **8**: 153 (1935).

in contrast to the case of the Bloch walls, turns about an axis which is perpendicular to the plane of the film as shown in Fig. 4.1.

In what follows, we shall calculate the width and energy of these Néel walls in a manner analogous to that used in the analysis of the Bloch walls. To begin with, let us refer to Fig. 4.6 and let

$$\phi = \frac{\pi x}{D} \tag{4.24}$$

for $-D/2 \leq x \leq D/2$ as before except ϕ is now taken to represent the angle between the magnetization and a direction normal to the wall and in the plane of the film. It follows that $e_{ex} = A(\pi/D)^2$ and $e_k = K_1/2$ as before. For the magnetostatic energy, we again approximate the wall by a cylinder with ellipsoidal cross section except now its long axis lies in the plane of the film as shown in Fig. 4.6. In this case, the demagnetization factor in the plane of the film is given by[2]

$$N_\parallel = \frac{4\pi T}{D + T} \tag{4.25}$$

so that the magnetostatic energy is given by

$$E_{M\parallel} = \frac{2\pi T}{D + T} M_e^2 \tag{4.26}$$

where $M_e = M_s/\sqrt{2}$ as before. Thus, the total wall energy is given by

$$E_N = A\left(\frac{\pi}{D}\right)^2 D + \frac{K_1}{2} D + \frac{\pi D T}{D + T} M_s^2 \tag{4.27}$$

Minimizing E_N with respect to D, we find

$$\frac{A\pi^2}{D^2} - \frac{\pi T^2}{(D + T)^2} M_s^2 = \frac{K_1}{2} \tag{4.28}$$

Using the expression for D in Eq. (4.28), we may in turn evaluate E_N given by Eq. (4.27). Both D and E_N for the Néel walls have been plotted in Figs. 4.4 and 4.5 for comparison with the results for Bloch walls. It is seen from Fig. 4.4. that the critical film thickness is about 350 Å below which the Néel wall has a lower energy than the Bloch wall.

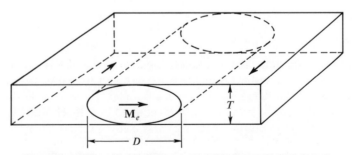

FIG. 4.6.   Ellipsoidal cylinder approximation of a Néel wall.

For $T \gg D$, we may neglect the anisotropy term in Eqs. (4.27) and (4.28) and obtain

$$D = \pi \sqrt{\frac{2A}{2\pi M_s^2}} \tag{4.29}$$

and

$$E_N = \pi \sqrt{(2A)(2\pi M_s^2)} \tag{4.30}$$

which are the same expressions as Eqs. (4.21) and (4.22) for the Bloch walls at very small film thickness. For very thin films, $T \ll D$, we may neglect the magnetostatic energy term in Eqs. (4.27) and (4.28) giving

$$D = \pi \sqrt{\frac{2A}{K_1}} \tag{4.31}$$

and

$$E_N = \pi \sqrt{2A K_1} \tag{4.32}$$

which are the same as those for a Bloch wall in a bulk material.

(c) Cross-Tie Walls

A new type of 180° domain wall was observed by Huber, Smith, and Goodenough;[4] the main wall is cut at regular intervals by short, right angle "cross ties" which terminate in free single ends. The cross-tie period and length are dependent upon film thickness, each becoming shorter with decreasing thickness. The observed patterns can be understood in terms of a new model wherein the axis of rotation of the spins is itself thought to rotate about the axis of the wall to give a corkscrew configuration of spins and a large decrease in associated magnetostatic energy.

A wall in which the spins spiral about the axis of the wall as shown in Fig. 4.7(a) could reduce the magnetostatic energy. The alternating polarity of the wall, both at the surface and in the plane of the film, provides short flux-closure paths outside the wall so that associated stray field energy is much smaller than $2\pi M_s^2$. If the anisotropy of the material is low, as is the case with Permalloy near the 80% Ni–20% Fe composition, the magnetization can rotate into the direction of the wall demagnetizing fields which are in the plane of the film to give the flux closure represented by the arrows in Fig. 4.7(a). However, such flux closure is only possible in alternate intervals, and a relatively high energy density results between these regions, i.e., in the area enclosed by the dotted lines in Fig. 4.7(a). The flux discontinuity in these regions can be accommodated by the configuration shown in Fig. 4.7(b), a configuration that is consistent with the appearance of the experimentally found cross-tie walls. It may be noted from Fig. 4.7(b) that the angular change in the direction of the flux across a cross-tie wall diminishes to zero in a direction normal to the main wall.

The question as to under what conditions cross-tie walls would exist in thin films naturally arises. The configuration of Fig. 4.7(b) has been proposed to yield qualitative agreement with experiments. We must next investigate the reasons for the existence of these walls and to calculate their associated energies.

Due to the thickness dependence of the magnetostatic energy, we can expect, on the basis of the discussion carried out in this chapter so far, a transition from Bloch to

---

[4] E. E. Huber, D. O. Smith, and J. B. Goodenough, *J. Appl. Phys.*, **29**: 294 (1958).

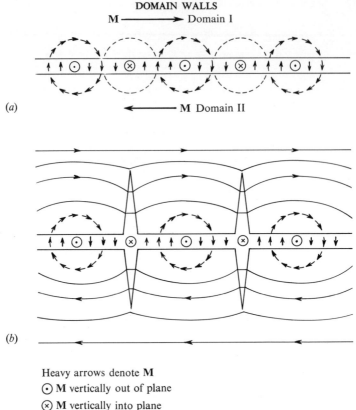

FIG. 4.7.   Schematic diagram of a cross-tie wall (after Huber, Smith, and Goodenough, Ref. 4).

Néel walls as the thickness of the film is decreased. Methfessel *et al.*[5] have suggested that the cross-tie walls observed in Permalloy films with uniaxial anisotropy correspond to such a transition, in which the cross ties serve to decrease the magnetostatic energy. Accordingly, for a film of given composition, cross-tie walls should occur within a certain thickness range only. Indeed, experimental observations on Permalloy films with a thickness gradient across the plane of film show the occurrence of the cross-tie walls in the thickness range of 400–900 Å, in approximate agreement with theoretical predictions.

To calculate the length p of the cross tie and the average magnetization direction β between the cross ties as shown in Fig. 4.7(b), the energy of the cross-tie wall as a function of p and β has to be known.[6] Minimization of the total energy with respect to p and β then required that $(\partial E/\partial p)\beta = 0$ and $(\partial E/\partial \beta)p = 0$. According to Fig. 4.7(b), the cross-tie walls consist of crosses of Néel walls, with legs of the same length p. The Néel wall segments with opposite magnetization are separated by Bloch lines, whose energies are neglected in the first approximation. Furthermore, the magnetization direction between the cross-tie walls is assumed to lie, for reasons of favorable flux closure, along concentric circles with centers below the main wall. The angle α between the magnetization and the easy axis at the intersection of the cross ties with the

[5] S. Methfessel, S. Middelhoek, and H. Thomas, *J. Appl. Phys.*, **31**: 302S (1960).
[6] S. Middelhoek, *J. Appl. Phys.*, **34**: 1054 (1963).

main wall is assumed to be $\pi/4$ in agreement with experimental observation.[7] The average magnetization direction between the cross-tie walls has to be approximately $\pi/8$ due to the circular flux lines. In this model, magnetic charges will occur at four places: at the main wall, at the cross-tie walls, on lines at a distance $p/2$ at both sides of the main wall, and on the whole area between the cross ties, when the average magnetization direction is varied while leaving α fixed.

The total energy of one complete cross consists of the energy of the main wall, $Dpe_N(180°)(1 - \sin\beta)^2$; the energy of the cross tie, $Dpe_N(180°)(1 - \cos\beta)^2$; and the anisotropy energy, $Dp^2K_1 \sin^2\beta$; where $e_N(180°)$ is the energy density of a 180° Néel wall. The free poles at the lines where the flux lines change from circular to straight ones lead to a stray field energy. To calculate this energy E_M, the volume between these lines is approximated by a flat cylinder with elliptic cross section with major and minor axes p and D respectively, so that $E_M = 2\pi D^2 p M_s^2 \sin^2\beta$. Since the polarity changes sign for each $p/2$ distance, this approximation is not in accord with the model. To account for this discrepancy, it is assumed that the real stray field in the area is lowered by a factor of two. In any event, this approximation does not affect the final result very much. The other component of stray field energy, which is due to the magnetic charges in the area between the cross ties when $\beta \neq \pi/8$, may be approximated on dimensional grounds by $Dp^2 e_\beta \sin^2(\beta - \pi/8)$, where e_β is an unknown magnetostatic energy density constant.

The total energy for a complete cross is

$$E_{c\,t.} = e_N(1 - \sin\beta)^2 + e_N(1 - \cos\beta)^2 + pK_1 \sin^2\beta$$
$$+ pe_\beta \sin^2\left(\beta - \frac{\pi}{8}\right) + \pi DM_s^2 \sin^2\beta \quad (4.33)$$

Minimizing $E_{\text{cross tie}}$ with respect to β yields

$$2e_N(1 - \sin\beta)(-\cos\beta) + 2e_N(1 - \cos\beta)\sin\beta$$
$$+ pK_1 \sin\beta + pe_\beta \sin 2\left(\beta - \frac{\pi}{8}\right) + \pi DM_s^2 \sin\beta = 0 \quad (4.34)$$

while minimizing with respect to p gives

$$e_\beta \sin^2\left(\beta - \frac{\pi}{8}\right) + K_1 \sin^2\beta = 0 \quad (4.35)$$

Assuming $e_\beta \gg K_1$, which is not unreasonable for thin films, the stray field energy terms are in most cases much larger than the anisotropy energy, β being $\pi/8$. Substituting this angle in Eq. (4.34), we find

$$p = \frac{1.6}{K_1}[e_N(180) - 2DM_s^2] \quad (4.36)$$

and

$$E_{c.t.} \simeq 0.6e_N(180) \quad (4.37)$$

[7] E. Feldtkeller, *Symposium on the Electric and Magnetic Properties of Thin Metallic Layers,* Leuven, Belgium, 1961, p. 100.

In Fig. 4.5, the energy of the cross-tie wall is plotted vs thickness and compared with that for the Bloch and Néel walls. It is seen from the figure that for thickness below about 900Å cross-tie walls occur, and Bloch walls exist for thickness above 900 Å. Furthermore, Néel walls do not occur at all in contradiction with experiment. This disagreement may be due to the fact that in the above calculation, the Bloch lines between different Néel wall segments are neglected.[8] Calculation of the Bloch line energy, assuming that the cross section of the Bloch line is determined by the width of the surrounding 90° Néel walls, shows that for film thickness above 450 Å, the Bloch line energy is negligible.

(d) Double Walls

According to Fig. 4.5 only Néel walls would occur in films whose thickness is less than about 350 Å. Therefore, long unipolar Néel walls can occur in films of this thickness range.[9] If two such walls are brought together by the application of a magnetic field, they would attract or repel each other depending upon their relative polarity.

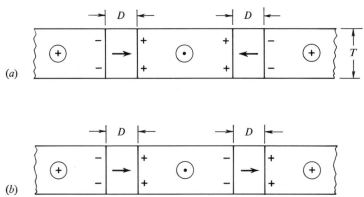

Fig. 4.8.   Double Néel walls in thin films: (a) repulsive nonunwinding walls and (b) attractive unwinding walls (after Middelhoek, Ref. 9).

Walls that repel each other are nonunwinding, as shown in Fig. 4.8(a), which means that the sense of rotation of the magnetization in both walls is the same; while the walls that attract each other are unwinding as shown in Fig. 4.8(b). Unwinding attractive walls will disappear when an external field is applied while the nonunwinding repulsive walls can be identified as double walls.

4·3 DOMAIN WALLS IN MAGNETIC FIELDS

In the previous section, we have determined the domain wall configuration under the influence of the exchange, anisotropy, and magnetostatic energies. The domain wall configuration so calculated, therefore, represents states of minimum free energy in the absence of an external field. As a prelude to the understanding of domain wall motion under external stimulus, it would be instructive to calculate the energy of the

[8] W. Schuppel and V. Kambersky, *Phys. Stat. Solids*, **2**: 345 (1962).

[9] S. Middelhoek, *Ferromagnetic Domains in Thin Ni-Fe Films*, Drukkerij Wed. G. Van Soest, N.V., Amsterdam, 1961, p. 111.

domain wall as a function of the angle through which the magnetization turns in the wall when a static magnetic field is applied in the hard direction. Following Middel-hoek,[6] we shall calculate the energies of the Bloch, Néel, and cross-tie walls for an arbitrary hard-axis applied field.

(a) Bloch, Néel, and Cross-Tie Walls

Let us first consider the case of a Bloch wall. Let the angle that the magnetization in the domains on both sides of the wall makes with the hard axis be $+\phi_o$ and $-\phi_o$. In order that the magnetization component perpendicular to the plane of the wall be continuous, the direction of the magnetization within the wall must turn on a cone-shaped shell from $+\phi_o$ to $-\phi_o$ as shown in Fig. 4.9(a). Thus, the total angle ϕ_t through which the magnetizations turns on the shell is $\phi_t = \pi \sin \phi_o$ and the associated

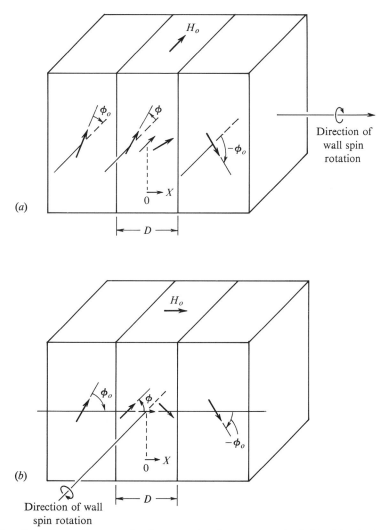

FIG. 4.9.   Domain wall magnetization rotation in a magnetic field: (a) Bloch wall and (b) Néel wall.

exchange energy density e_{ex} is equal to $A(\pi \sin \phi_o / D)^2$. The component of magnetization giving rise to surface charges is $M_s \sin \phi_o$ and the magnetostatic energy becomes

$$E_M = \frac{D}{D + T} M_s^2 \sin^2 \phi_o \qquad (4.38)$$

and the total Bloch wall energy is given by

$$E_B = \left(\frac{A\pi^2}{D} + \frac{\pi D^2}{D + T} M_s^2 \right) \sin^2 \phi_o \qquad (4.39)$$

where we have neglected the anisotropy energy with respect to the exchange and electrostatic energies.

Setting $\partial E_B / \partial D = 0$ using Eq. (4.39), we find that the domain wall width D is independent of ϕ_o. It therefore follows that the total Bloch wall energy $E_B(\phi_o)$ is equal to $E_B(180°) \sin^2 \phi_o$ where $E_B(180°)$ is the energy of the 180° Bloch wall. In Fig. 4.10, we have plotted $E_B(\phi_o)$ as a function of film thickness for various values of the angle $2\phi_o$ through which the magnetization turns in the wall.

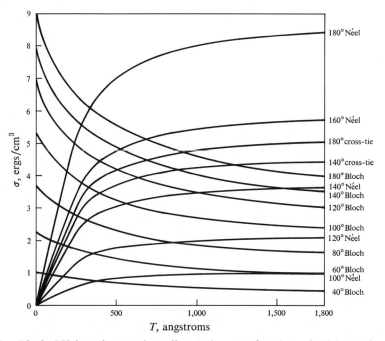

FIG. 4.10. Bloch, Néel, and cross-tie wall energies as a function of thickness for various angles through which the magnetization turns in the wall (after Middelhoek, Ref. 6).

In the case of the Néel wall, let $\phi = (2x/D)\phi_o$ for $-D/2 \le x \le D/2$ where D is the wall width and ϕ is the angle between the magnetization and an axis perpendicular to the plane of the wall as shown in Fig. 4.9(b). Since the component of the magnetization perpendicular to the Néel wall is not constant within the wall, there will be a magnetostatic energy associated with the resulting poles at the boundaries of the wall.

The difference between the magnetization component normal to the wall plane in and outside the wall is $M_S \cos[(2x/D)\phi_o] - M_S \cos \phi_o$. Thus, the stray field energy per unit wall area $E_N(\phi_o)$ can be approximated by $E_N(180°)(1 - \cos \phi_o)^2$ where $E_N(180°)$ is given by Eqs. (4.27) and (4.28). In Fig. 4.10, we have plotted $E_N(\phi_o)$ as a function of film thickness for various values of ϕ_o.

When a magnetic field is applied in the hard direction of a film containing cross-tie walls, the magnetization on either side of the wall will rotate. This rotation causes the total angle through which the magnetization turns in the wall to increase in one half of the main wall and to decrease in the other half. Thus, to a first approximation, we might expect the cross-tie wall energy to remain constant were it not for the fact that the Bloch lines separating the negative and positive Néel wall segments move in such a way as to shorten the Néel wall segments with the largest angle and highest energy.[6] The net result is a decrease in the total energy of the cross-tie wall. Since the energy, like that of a Bloch wall, is maximum at zero field, it does not seem unreasonable to approximate the angular dependence of the cross-tie wall energy $E_{c.t.}(\phi_o)$ by an expression similar to that for a Bloch wall, that is, by $E_{c.t.}(180°)\sin^2 \phi_o$. $E_{c.t.}(\phi_o)$ is plotted in Fig. 4.10 as a function of film thickness for various values of $2\phi_o$.

Comparison of the $E_B(\phi_o)$, $E_N(\phi_o)$, and $E_{c.t.}(\phi_o)$ vs T curves with ϕ_o as a constant parameter, all shown in Fig. 4.10, enables us to decide which wall has the minimum energy for a given thickness T and given angle $2\phi_o$ between the magnetization directions on both sides of the wall. It is seen from the figure that in the thickness range $T < 1200$ Å, Néel walls dominate when $2\phi_o$ is approximately less than 150°. For $2\phi_o > 150°$, Bloch walls occur for $T > 900$ Å while cross-tie walls occur for $T < 900$ Å.

Experimentally, it has been found that the thicknesses at which the transitions from cross-tie walls to Bloch walls, from Bloch walls to Néel walls, and from cross-tie to Néel walls occur are in approximate accord with theory. Furthermore, the typical cross-tie lengths p of about 3.4×10^{-4} cm predicted by theory are also of the same order of magnitude as the experimentally observed ones.[6]

(b) Spiral and Concentric Walls

In Sec. 4.2(d) we briefly indicated the possible existence of long unipolar double Néel walls in very thin films (thickness < 350 Å). When a field is applied at an angle to the easy axis, the sign of the field component along the easy direction determines in which direction the walls will move, and the sign of the field component in the hard direction determines which of the walls takes part in the reversal process. Thus, when alternating fields are applied at an angle to the easy axis, the elongated domains should move about, continuously changing their surrounding walls. However, the Bitter patterns observed[10] in a very thin Permalloy film (thickness 150 Å) after demagnetization at an angle to the easy direction do not show such simple elongated domains, but rather a high density of walls which seem to spiral around central points in the film. This discrepancy may be attributed to the existence of regions of high coercive force of different anisotropy (either in magnitude or in direction of easy axis). When an ac field is applied at an angle to the easy axis, a pair of Néel walls surrounding small regions of high coercive force or anisotropy is formed per cycle. Since the inside walls do not move due to the high coercive force or different anisotropy near the small region, the double Néel wall configuration grows and spirals outward from the

[10] H. J. Williams and R. C. Sherwood, *J. Appl. Phys.*, **28**: 548 (1957).

imperfection center giving rise to a high density of spiral and concentric type of walls, as has been observed by the Bitter technique.[9-11]

Spiral and concentric walls could also be observed by electron microscopy.[12] Permalloy films, which are thin enough to support 360° walls and which possess easy-axis dispersion especially near the film edge, specially prepared by vacuum deposition on thin carbon substrates supported on electron-microscope specimen grids, showed inward growing spiral or concentric-circle walls when rotated in a constant field. Whether spirals or concentric circles are exhibited depends upon the degree of easy-axis dispersion in the center of the film. The high dispersion near the edge of a film (which has small dispersion near the center) causes the magnetization **M** there to remain in its original direction during rotation. **M** in the central region, however, can follow the direction of the field applied parallel to the film plane as the film is rotated. Therefore, **M** twists gradually, due to exchange coupling, to form 180° walls as the film rotates. Upon further rotation, **M** near the periphery of the central region gradually begins to twist into the 180° wall; another 180° wall is thus formed inside the first wall. This spiral continues to grow as the film is rotated and can be unwound by reversing the direction of rotation.

On the other hand, concentric-circle walls exist in films having high easy axis dispersion near the edge and a comparatively lower dispersion near the center of the film. The high dispersion near the edge causes a high wall coercive force in that region, while the lower dispersion in the central region permits the nucleation of successive reverse domains. In the concentric-circle domain creation process, the film is first saturated parallel to the film edge and then the applied field is subsequently reduced to zero. On field reversal, the direction of **M** changes first in the center of the film and the reverse domain grows outward. Upon another reversal of the applied field, this domain contracts, but a new reverse domain nucleates in the center before the original domain collapses. As the reversed field increases, the two circular 180° walls move together until a 360° wall is formed and this process can be repeated again. Concentric-circle walls can also be formed in these films by rotating the film in a field applied in the film plane.

4·4   OBSERVATION OF DOMAIN WALLS

As we discussed in Sec. 3.4(a), the stray field associated with the free poles existing at the intersection of a domain wall with the surface of the specimen attracts the magnetite colloidal suspension. Thus, domain walls can be seen using this Bitter powder technique on the domain walls in thin films. The observed walls include Néel walls,[13-15] cross-tie walls,[4,14,16,17] spiral or concentric walls,[10,11,18,19] and perturbation walls.[19]

---

[11] H. W. Fuller, H. Rubinstein, and D. L. Sullivan, *J. Appl. Phys.*, **32**: 286S (1961); E. Feldtkeller and W. Liesk, *Z. Angew Phys.*, **14**: 195 (1962).

[12] M. S. Cohen, *J. Appl. Phys.*, **34**: 1221 (1963).

[13] H. Rubinstein, H. W. Fuller, and M. H. Hale, *J. Appl. Phys.*, **31**: 437 (1960).

[14] S. Methfessel, S. Middelhoek, and H. Thomas, *IBM J. Res. Develop.*, **4**: 96 (1960).

[15] E. Feldtkeller, *Z. Angew Phys.*, **13**: 161 (1961).

[16] R. M. Moon, *J. Appl. Phys.*, **30**: 82S (1959).

[17] H. W. Fuller and H. Rubinstein, *J. Appl. Phys.*, **30**: 84S (1959).

[18] M. E. Hale, *1958 Vacuum Symposium Transactions*, Pergamon Press, New York, 1959, p. 215.

[19] D. O. Smith and K. J. Harte, *J. Appl. Phys.*, **33**: 1399 (1962).

By electron microscopy domain walls can be observed on a finer scale than that possible with the Bitter technique. This method is based upon the existence of the Lorentz force on the electron $-(e/c)\mathbf{v} \times \mathbf{B}$ due to the magnetization of the film as discussed in Sec. 3.4(c). Static and dynamic magnetization distribution in a thin film[20] as well as spiral and concentric walls have been observed using electron microscopy.

---

[20] M. E. Hale, H. W. Fuller, and H. Rubinstein, *J. Appl. Phys.*, **30**: 789 (1959); H. W. Fuller and M. E. Hale, *J. Appl. Phys.*, **31**: 308S (1960).

CHAPTER 5

IMPERFECTIONS

In this chapter, we shall take up the topic of imperfections in thin films. These imperfections could be of macroscopic or microscopic origin and of nonmagnetic or magnetic character. Since reversed domains near an imperfection may determine the critical field for commencement of domain wall motion, imperfections may expedite as well as impede the process of magnetization reversal. Furthermore, many of the peculiar domain wall configurations observed in Permalloy films are related to the presence of these imperfections. Therefore, we shall study here both the static and dynamic configuration of domain walls about imperfections of magnetic thin films. The micromagnetics problem associated with these imperfections and the method of determination of their distribution will also be examined in this chapter.

5·1 MICROMAGNETICS OF THIN FILMS

From the results of thin-film switching experiments, it is concluded that there are three principal mechanisms of magnetization reversal, depending upon the excess switching field $H_s - H_{th}$ where H_s is the applied field and H_{th} is the threshold field. When $H_s - H_{th}$ is small, the magnetization reverses from one easy direction to another by domain wall motion; when $H_s - H_{th}$ is large, the magnetization reverses by coherent rotation. For intermediate values of $H_s - H_{th}$, the reversal process is presumably one of partial or incoherent rotation, a process which is comparatively complicated. In Chap. 9, we shall study these magnetization reversal mechanisms in detail. We shall only briefly study the role of imperfections in the magnetization reversal process in this chapter.

Let us consider the magnetization reversal behavior for small excess switching field $H_s - H_{th}$ so that the reversal process is one of domain wall motion. For domain wall motion to occur, there must exist regions of reverse magnetization such as that shown in Fig. 3.3 for otherwise a wall must first be nucleated somewhere in the film. Since the nucleation field is usually larger than the critical field for domain wall motion, the threshold field is equal to the critical field for commencement of motion of the walls of the reversed domains. Actual Bitter patterns, as exemplified by Fig. 3.3, show that the edge domains of thin films are far from simple and are in fact highly irregular even after saturation in the easy direction and subsequent reduction to zero field. The calculation of the length and form of these irregular demagnetizing domains is still largely an unsolved problem in micromagnetics. The core of the difficulty appears to lie in the evidence that these irregular domain configurations do not represent states of minimum energy. Thus, when a small alternating field is applied in the hard direction, the walls start to creep and after an elapse of time, the domain configuration with the lowest energy is assumed. The minimum-energy configuration, as approximately illustrated in Fig. 5.1, is composed of small 90° closure domains, regions of reversed magnetization, and a large central region of nonreversed magnetization.

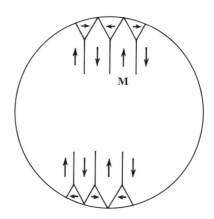

FIG. 5.1. Minimum-energy domain configuration in thin films.

(a) Role of Imperfections

It is logical to surmise from the above discussion that there are imperfections at the edges of the film which prevent the minimum-energy domain configuration from being assumed. Of course, imperfections, dislocations, nonmagnetic and magnetic inclusions, vacancies, etc., may occur in the body as well as at the edges of the film. In fact, other things being equal, we would expect these imperfections to be randomly distributed over the film in view of the rather random process of film formation. However, due to the imperfect masking of the substrate during deposition, films inevitably have a thickness gradient at the edge of the film. Since the imperfections of the substrate may be expected to greatly influence the structure of the first few layers of the film, we may surmise that films tend to be less perfect near the edges due to the thickness gradient and consequent smaller thickness there.

A very convincing piece of related evidence with regard to the nonattainment of the minimum-energy state in as-evaporated thin films due to the presence of imperfections is afforded by demagnetizing experiments using thin-film single crystals. Consider a single-crystal thin film with cubic anisotropy. If two easy axes are in the plane of the film, then 90° checkerboard domain patterns should be expected from considerations of symmetry. However, when domain patterns in an as-evaporated film are observed using the Bitter technique, no such clear checkerboard domain patterns were found.[1,2] Instead, the domain pattern is highly irregular and contains many intricate spike domains. However, when an ac field of sufficient amplitude to saturate the sample is applied to the film and subsequently is reduced to zero, very clear 90° checkerboard patterns are observed.[1]

There are several reasons why actual domain patterns deviate from the anticipated ones. Most obvious of these is the existence of macroscopic imperfections such as steps

[1] H. Sato, *J. Appl. Phys.*, **33**: 2956 (1962).

[2] H. Sato, R. S. Toth, and R. W. Astrue, *J. Appl. Phys.*, **33**: 1113 (1962).

and tear lines on the cleavage surface of the MgO single-crystal substrate from which spike domains may nucleate. Even without these macroscopic imperfections, the substrate is not free from microscopic imperfections and strain. In an as-evaporated film, domains nucleate wherever possible in a random manner. As the thickness of the film decreases, the nucleation process becomes more sensitive to imperfections of the substrate causing the number of potential domain nuclei to increase as the film becomes thinner. Also, as the film becomes thinner, demagnetizing field in the plane of the film, which is responsible for the formation of 90° closure domains, decreases. As a consequence of this, irregular nucleation of domains is not prevented resulting in smaller domain, in thinner film, and also in leaving 180° walls where the form of 90° domains is geometrically unfavorable. Thus, it is concluded that the formation of steplike or acicular domains in a cubic single-crystal film is definitely due to the lack of sufficient demagnetizing field. Thus, an external force, supplied by the demagnetizing ac field, is required to prevent irregular nucleation and assist closure domain formation.

From the discussion above, it may be surmised that the nonappearance of 90° closure domains in as-evaporated uniaxial Permalloy film is also due to imperfections and the lack of sufficient demagnetizing energy at the edge of the film. For a film without any thickness gradient at its edges, the assumption of small demagnetizing field at the edges is probably untenable since the film geometry is not one of a perfect ellipsoid. Consider, for example, the case of a single domain film. Since the thickness of a film is very small compared to its diameter, the magnetization along the easy direction would induce a very high density of poles at the edges giving rise to very high demagnetizing field ($\sim 2\pi M$ as we shall show below). Thus, it may be energetically favorable for 90° closure domains to form to minimize this high magnetostatic energy. However, if the film thickness is too small, imperfections and nucleating centers become more numerous due to the important influence of substrate imperfections so that spike-like reversed domains instead of 90° closure domains may nucleate near the film edge. The picture becomes quite different when unavoidable thickness gradient at the film edge is considered. In this case, we may think of the shape of the film as approaching closer to that of a true ellipsoid so that the demagnetizing field near the edge becomes smaller. If this field were sufficiently small at the edge where the role of imperfections is most important, we would expect irregular reversed domains rather than 90° closure domains to nucleate there.

(b) Inhomogeneous Demagnetizing Fields

At this point, it seems appropriate to attempt to calculate the demagnetizing field distribution in a nonellipsoidal sample such as a thin film. For the single domain state where the magnetization is saturated along the easy axis, the calculation is straightforward. Consider the disk configuration and the coordinate system of Fig. 5.2 with the saturation magnetization pointing in the z direction. Since this is a static problem, the demagnetizing field $\mathbf{H}$ can be expressed as the gradient of a magnetostatic potential ψ or

$$\mathbf{H} = \nabla\psi \tag{5.1}$$

Making use of the Maxwell's equation,

$$\nabla\cdot\mathbf{B} = \nabla\cdot(\mathbf{H} + 4\pi\mathbf{M}) = 0 \tag{5.2}$$

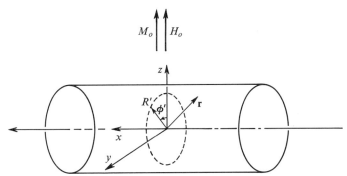

FIG. 5.2.   Coordinate system associated with magnetized cylinder.

we obtain from Eq. (5.1)

$$\nabla^2\psi = -4\pi\nabla\cdot\mathbf{M} \tag{5.3}$$

The solution of Eq. (5.3) can be obtained by noting that

$$\nabla^2\left(\frac{1}{|\mathbf{r}-\mathbf{r}'|}\right) = -4\pi\delta(\mathbf{r}-\mathbf{r}') \tag{5.4}$$

where $\delta(\mathbf{r}-\mathbf{r}')$ is the delta function. Thus, according to Eqs. (5.3) and (5.4), we have[3,4]

$$\psi(\mathbf{r}) = \int \frac{(\nabla\cdot\mathbf{M})_{\mathbf{r}'}}{|\mathbf{r}-\mathbf{r}'|}\, d^3\mathbf{r}' = -\int_s \frac{\mathbf{M}\cdot\mathbf{n}(\mathbf{r}')}{|\mathbf{r}-\mathbf{r}'|}\, d^2\mathbf{r}' \tag{5.5}$$

where we have used the fact that M vanishes everywhere except at the surface of the sample. The last integration has to be carried out over the surface S and $\mathbf{n}(\mathbf{r}')$ is the surface normal pointing away from the film.

The z component of the demagnetizing field follows from Eq. (5.5):

$$H_z = -M_o \int \frac{z-z'}{|\mathbf{r}-\mathbf{r}'|^3}(\nabla\cdot\mathbf{M})_{\mathbf{r}'}\, d^3\mathbf{r}' \tag{5.6}$$

We now proceed to solve Eq. (5.6) for our problem. According to Fig. 5.2, we have

$$(\nabla\cdot\mathbf{M})_{\mathbf{r}'} = \frac{\partial M_z}{\partial z'}\bigg|_{\mathbf{r}'} = -M_o\delta(|\mathbf{r}'| - R)\cos\phi' \tag{5.7}$$

where R is the radius of the film and r' and ϕ' are cylindrical coordinates of the point $\mathbf{r}'$ at which $\nabla\cdot\mathbf{M}$ is being evaluated. Since $d^3r' = dx'\, r'\, dr'\, d\phi'$, and $y' = R\sin\phi'$, $z' = R\cos\phi'$, we find

$$H_z = -M_o \int \frac{(z'-z)\, dx' r'\, dr'\, d\phi'\delta(r'-R)\cos\phi'}{[(x'-x)^2 + (y'-y)^2 + (z'-z)^2]^{3/2}} \tag{5.8}$$

[3] E. Schlomann in *Advances in Quantum Electronics*, J. R. Singer (ed.), Columbia University Press, New York, 1961, p. 450.
[4] E. Schlomann, *J. Appl. Phys.*, **33**; 2825 (1962).

The general solution of Eq. (5.8) applicable to any value of y and z is given in Appendix A. For the special case where $x = y = z = 0$ (near the center of the film) the integral of Eq. (5.8) can be readily evaluated to give

$$H_z|_{x=y=z=0} = -2\pi M_o \frac{T}{\sqrt{d^2 + T^2}} \simeq -2\pi M_o \left(\frac{T}{d}\right) \tag{5.9}$$

where $d = 2R$ is the diameter of the film. For another special case where $y = \pm R$, $z = 0$, and $y = 0$, $z = \pm R$ (i.e., points at the edge of the film), Eq. (5.8) yields the result for H_z

$$H_z|_{y=\pm R, z=0} \quad \ll -2\pi M_o$$
$$H_z|_{y=0, z=\pm R} \quad \simeq -2\pi M_o \tag{5.10}$$

From symmetry arguments, we find also $H_y \ll -2\pi M_o$ at $y = 0$, $z = \pm R$, and $H_y = -2\pi M_o$ at $y = \pm R$, $z = 0$ for the case where the film is saturated in the y direction. Thus, we see that the demagnetizing field in the z direction at $y = 0$ and $z = \pm R$ is several orders of magnitudes larger than that at the center, while H_y is probably comparable to it. Therefore, for the minimum energy state, we should expect the formation of 90° closure domains near $y = 0$, $z = \pm R$ to minimize this comparatively enormous magnetostatic energy at the points $y = 0$, $z = \pm R$ at the edge of the film. This conclusion, as we have seen, is consistent with experimental observations.

To determine the kind of closure domain walls that would be formed for this case, we need to determine also the demagnetizing field at the film edge in the direction of the film normal. A calculation entirely anologous to that given above for the parallel demagnetizing field may be carried out by assuming that the magnetization is saturated instead in the x direction. Alternatively, we may calculate its value by means of the sum rule for the demagnetizing field in nonellipsoidal samples.[4] Like the case of the uniformly magnetized ellipsoidal sample, this rule states that the diagonal sum of the demagnetizing tensor, that is, $\sum_i N_{ii}(\mathbf{r})$, is unity inside the sample and zero outside. In this notation, the component of the demagnetizing field H_i is given by

$$H_i = -4\pi \sum_k N_{ik} M_k \tag{5.11}$$

where
$$N_{ik}(\mathbf{r}) = \frac{1}{4\pi} \int_s \frac{r_i' - r_i}{|\mathbf{r}' - \mathbf{r}|} \cdot \mathbf{n}_k(\mathbf{r}') \, d^2 r' \tag{5.12}$$

and $\mathbf{N}$ is the demagnetizing tensor.

Using the sum rule $\sum_i N_{ii}(\mathbf{r}) = 1$ everywhere inside the sample, we easily find that the $H_x \simeq -2\pi M_o$ at the edge as compared to $-4\pi M_o$ at the center of the film. Actually, as shown in Appendix A, it is more expedient to obtain H_x by integration and then determine H_z at $y = 0$, $z = \pm R$ by the sum rule. Since H_z (at $y = 0$, $z = \pm R$) and H_x are quite comparable, we can not say a priori that the spins in the edge domain walls would not have a component perpendicular to the plane of the film. Thus, Bloch walls and cross-tie walls as well as Néel walls may form at the edge of the film. The existence of these 90° walls must be accompanied by regions of reversed magnetization in their vicinity. These reverse domains need not be of closed configuration, however. The magnetization distribution of these open domains may in principle be determined by a micromagnetics calculation. An example of this kind of calculation using the concept of magnetization curling is carried out in the next section for the case of magnetizing distribution near a domain tip. It should also be mentioned here that, according to a recent calculation, a 90° magnetization curling state near the film edge has a lower energy than that with 90° closure domains for films less than about 550 Å thick.[5] This curling state could explain, among other things, the ending of domain walls before the film edge. However, this calculation does not take into account the high demagnetizing field and the thickness gradient near the edge and the accompanying importance of the edge imperfections. It is conceivable that the curling state, when it exists, may be a consequence of the high demagnetizing field and imperfections near the edge; a curling magnetization may reduce the influence of both.

In addition to edge domains, there may also be peculiar domains nucleated in the film proper near imperfections and scratches. The domain wall shapes of these noneigen states, along with that of the irregular edge domains are very difficult to calculate from first principles.

5·2 DOMAIN CONFIGURATION NEAR IMPERFECTIONS

In this section, we shall study the domain configuration in the vicinity of different kinds of imperfections, both nonmagnetic and magnetic. Thus, these imperfections include cavities, scratches, anisotropy dispersions, etc.

(a) Nonmagnetic Imperfections

Consider the magnetization distribution about a circular cavity in a thin film. If the anisotropy energy and the magnetostatic energy associated with the poles at the remote film edge are neglected in the calculation of the flux configuration near the cavity, the flux lines would evidently be concentric circles about the cavity for there would then be no free poles. However, since the film is saturated in one of the directions in the plane of the film, there must be a smooth transition from the circular to the straight flux line configuration so as to minimize the magnetostatic energy.[6]

The direction of the wall at x_o, y_o shown in Fig. 5.3 is determined by the condition that the component of the magnetization normal to the wall must be continuous, i.e.,

$$\frac{dy}{dx}\bigg|_{x_o,y_o} = \tan\left(90° - \frac{\theta}{2}\right) = \cot\frac{\theta}{2} \tag{5.13}$$

But since

$$\frac{y_o}{x_o} = \cot\theta \tag{5.14}$$

and $\cot\theta = (\cot^2\theta/2 - 1)/2\cot\theta/2$, we find the differential equation for this micromagnetics problem as

$$x\left(\frac{dy}{dx}\right)^2 - 2y\left(\frac{dy}{dx}\right) - x = 0 \tag{5.15}$$

[5] R. M. Hornreich, *J. Appl. Phys.*, **34**: 1071 (1963).

[6] S. Middelhoek, *Ferromagnetic Domains in Thin Ni-Fe Films*, Drukkerij Wed. G. Van Soest, N.V., Amsterdam, 1961, p. 39.

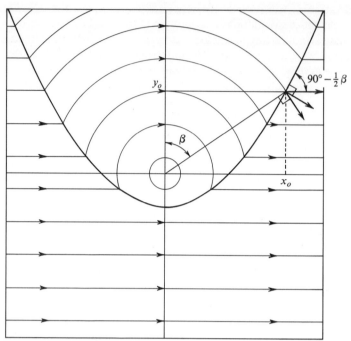

FIG. 5.3. Magnetization distribution about a circular cavity (after Middelhoek, Ref. 11).

The solution of Eq. (5.15) is a set of parabolas with vertexes at $y = -c/2$ where c could be either positive or negative:

$$x^2 = 2cy + c^2 \qquad (5.16)$$

Fig. 5.4 shows some of the observed Bitter patterns about a cavity along with proper interpretations. The wall shape observed, however, is not exactly parabolic since anisotropy energy, though small in comparison, can not totally be neglected. In a micromagnetics problem of this kind, it is usually not possible to write down the free energy of the domain system and minimize it to obtain the proper configuration. This is because the free energy expression can only be written down if the sought-after domain configuration is already known. Thus, one usually starts with logical assumptions about the probable domain configuration and then finding the minimum-energy configuration by requiring the continuity of the normal component of the flux at the domain boundary as illustrated above.

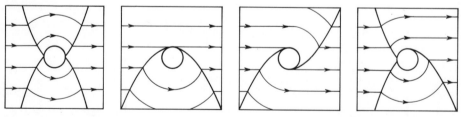

FIG. 5.4. Bitter patterns and interpretation of magnetization distribution about a cavity (after Middelhoek, Ref. 11).

As discussed in Sec. 5.1 and illustrated in Fig. 3.3, the edge domains have triangular forms with a small top angle and with the edge of the film as the base. The magnetization distribution at the domain tip may again be determined by the procedure used for the cavity problem above. If we require that the normal component of the magnetization be continuous across the domain wall boundary, the micromagnetics problem is formally identical to that of the cavity imperfection. Thus, those parabolas which fit the observed domain walls represent physical solutions. If the distance between the two walls of the domain of reversed magnetization is D, the parabolas are given by the expressions

$$x^2 = 4Dy + 4D^2$$
$$x^2 = -4Dy$$

(5.17)

Fig. 5.5 shows the observed Bitter pattern of such a parabola together with magnetization direction interpretations.[6]

The effect of dislocations on the magnetization curve at high fields has been calculated by direct application of dislocation theory.[7] The deviation from saturation is

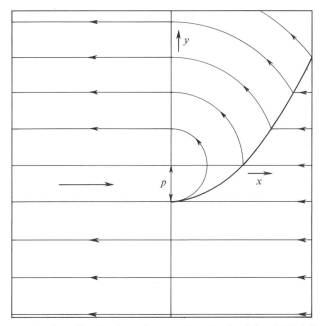

FIG. 5.5.   Magnetization distribution about a domain tip (after Middelhoek, Ref. 11).

assumed to be due to magnetostrictive forces, localized in the stress field about the dislocation. Pairs of dislocations of opposite sign, separated by a short distance, were found to contribute a term a/H to the deviation from saturation. Pairs separated by a long distance and surplus dislocations of one sign contribute a term b/H^2 with b theoretically not a constant but a logarithmically varying function of H. This calculation was aimed at estimating the effect of randomly distributed deviating source,

---

[7] W. F. Brown, *Phys. Rev.*, **60**: 139 (1941).

and more specifically of dislocations on the approach to saturation. Thus, the applied field is assumed to be very large so that the magnetization vector everywhere is in approximate coincidence with its own directions. This situation should be satisfied when a saturating field is applied to the film in a given direction and nearly satisfied in the easy-axis remanent state due to the presence of uniaxial anisotropy. In this case, the film is nearly in a single-domain state and the closure domains at the edges occupy only a small fractional volume of the film. The source of dislocations in thin films may be attributed to the imperfections of the substrate and internal strains set up in the film due to magnetostriction and difference in the thermal expansion coefficients of the films and the substrate.

Observation of domain walls near scratches has been carried out on both evaporated[8] and electrodeposited[9] films. For the evaporated films, it has been found that cross walls occur on scratches in the easy direction in Permalloy films with negative magnetostriction. Due to the difference between the coefficients of expansion between the film and the substrate, there is an isotropic tension in the plane of the film. A scratch relieves the component of tension perpendicular to it leaving the parallel one unchanged. Both the pressure perpendicular to the scratch resulting from the inelastic deformation and the tension parallel to the scratch resulting from the partial relief of the isotropic tension cause a narrow band parallel to the scratch to have an easy direction perpendicular to the scratch, when material with negative magnetostriction is used.

Three different forms of walls can occur depending upon the size of the scratch. When the scratch is not very heavy or when the anisotropy constant is high, the common form with only cross walls occurs. For a heavier scratch, half-moon shaped domains divided by cross walls occur, while for a very heavy scratch, only half-moons remain. For the last case, the requirement of the continuity of the normal component of the magnetization indicates that the half-moons must be parabolic. Although the state of stress around a scratch should in principle lead to cross-wall structure only for films with a negative magnetostrictive coefficient, similar structures have sometimes been observed in films with positive magnetostrictive coefficient. This is presumably due to the fact that compressive stress associated with the scratch need not be exactly perpendicular to it. Thus, the magnetization even in this case could have a small component perpendicular to the scratch leading to asymmetric cross-wall structures.

For electrodeposited films with a positive magnetostrictive coefficient, it has been found that the easy axis is parallel to the scratches on the substrates and the domain walls fall into these scratches. On the other hand, for electrodeposited films with a negative magnetostrictive coefficient, an average easy direction is induced perpendicular to the scratches in some films, whereas in other films it is not well established. Thus, we conclude that magnetoelastic and shape anisotropies are both induced in an electrodeposited film, accompanying the scratches on the surface of the substrate.

(b) Magnetic Imperfections

The problem of magnetic imperfections is considerably more complicated than the nonmagnetic one. These imperfections may take on several forms. The chemical

---

[8] Y. Gomi and Y. Odani, *J. Phys. Soc. Japan*, **15**: 535 (1960); S. Methfessel, S. Middelhoek, and H. Thomas, *IBM J. Res. Develop.*, **4**: 96 (1960).

[9] S. Kainuma and N. Tsuya, *J. Appl. Phys.*, **34**: 795 (1963).

composition may vary rather abruptly at various locations giving rise to abrupt changes in magnetization and anisotropy in local regions. Or, the chemical composition may vary continuously giving rise to "anisotropy and magnetization ripples."

Consider, for example, a ferromagnetic material infinite in all directions with uniaxial anisotropy $K_1(x)$ which is some arbitrary function of x.[10] Let an external field H be applied in the z direction of easy magnetization. For the mode of magnetization change by rotation of the spins in the $y - z$ plane or the plane of the film, we have

$$\alpha_x = 1 \qquad \alpha_y = \sin \theta \qquad \alpha_z = \cos \theta$$

where α's are the directional cosines and θ, the angle between $\mathbf{M}$ and the $+z$ axis, is taken to be a function of x only. Neglecting demagnetizing effects (approximately zero in the plane of the film), the energy of the system is given by

$$E = \int_0^\infty \left[A\left(\frac{d\theta}{dx}\right)^2 + K_1(x)\sin^2\theta - HM_s\cos\theta \right] dx \tag{5.18}$$

where we have implicitly assumed that $K_1(x) = K_1(-x)$ so that only $x \geq 0$ need be considered. Setting $\partial E/\partial x = 0$, we find from Eq. (5.18) that

$$\frac{d^2\theta}{dt^2} - hT^2\sin\theta - \frac{1}{2}T^2\sin 2\theta = 0 \tag{5.19}$$

where

$$t = \frac{x}{d} \qquad h = \frac{HM_s}{2K_1} \qquad T = \frac{dK_1^{1/2}}{A^{1/2}} \tag{5.20}$$

where d is some linear dimension which will be later related to the size of the defect. The boundary conditions are

$$\theta'(0) = \theta'(\infty) = 0 \tag{5.21}$$

Now, let the anisotropy imperfection be represented by the step function

$$\begin{aligned} K_1 &= 0 && \text{for } t \leq 1 \\ &= K_1' && \text{for } t > 1 \end{aligned} \tag{5.22}$$

For small angles θ and for $|h| < 1$, the solution of Eq. (5.19) which satisfies Eq. (5.21) and is continuous at $t = 1$ is given by

$$\theta = C\cos\frac{T\sqrt{-ht}}{\cos T\sqrt{-h}} \qquad t \leq 1 \tag{5.23}$$

$$\theta = C\exp\left[-T\sqrt{1 + h}(t - 1)\right] \qquad t \geq 1 \tag{5.24}$$

---

[10] A. Aharoni, *J. Appl. Phys.*, **30**: 70S (1959).

Since $d\theta/dx$ must be continuous at $t = 1$, we find from Eqs. (5.23) and (5.24) that

$$-h_n = \cos^2(T\sqrt{-h_n}) \tag{5.25}$$

where h_n is the nucleation field and is plotted in Fig. 5.6.

The jump K_1 assumed above might be too severe for physical understanding. Therefore, for comparison purposes let us assume

$$\begin{aligned} K_1 &= K_1' t \quad && \text{for} \quad t \le 1 \\ &= K_1' \quad && \text{for} \quad t \ge 1 \end{aligned} \tag{5.26}$$

The solution of Eq. (5.19) for this case is

$$\theta = T(-h-t)^{1/2} \left\{ C_1 J_{1/3}\left[\frac{2}{3} T(-h-t)^{3/2}\right] \right.$$
$$\left. + C_2 J_{-1/3}\left[\frac{2}{3} T(-h-t)^{3/2}\right] \right\} \quad \text{for } t \le 1 \tag{5.27}$$

and
$$\theta = C_3 \exp[-(-h+1)^{1/2} t] \quad \text{for } t \ge 1 \tag{5.28}$$

The nucleation field is given by

$$J_{2/3}(\mu_1)[I_{1/3}(\mu_2) - I_{-2/3}(\mu_2)] + J_{-2/3}(\mu_1)[I_{-1/3}(\mu_2) + I_{2/3}(\mu_2)] = 0 \tag{5.29}$$

where

$$\mu_1 = \frac{2}{3}(-h_n)^{3/2} T \tag{5.30}$$

$$\mu_2 = \frac{2}{3}(1 + h_n)^{3/2} T$$

h_n is plotted in Fig. 5.6. It is seen that the nucleation field decreases with anisotropy defect.

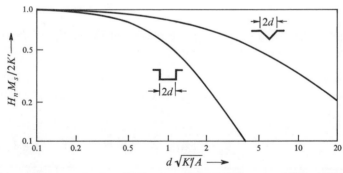

FIG. 5.6. Normalized nucleation field vs normalized defect size (after Aharoni, Ref. 10).

Another type of magnetic imperfection is the anisotropy easy-axis dispersion. The effect of this dispersion upon the magnetization reversal process can best be understood by examining the reversal behavior of inverted films ($H_c > H_k$). In the region where $H_k < H_s < H_c$ where H_s is the easy-axis switching field, the magnetization reversal should occur by coherent rotation if imperfections were neglected. Experimental evidence, indicates, however, that the reversal process first proceeds by incoherent rotation and then follows by wall motion. By incoherent rotation, we mean that the magnetization in different parts of the film rotates in opposite directions. This discrepancy between theory and experiment could be resolved by taking the dispersion of the local values of the anisotropy constant and easy direction, as well as the internal exchange and magnetostatic coupling into account.[11]

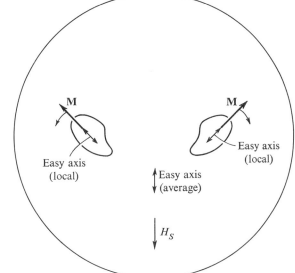

FIG. 5.7. Local easy-axis dispersion in thin films.

When a field $H < H_c$ but $> H_k$ is applied in the easy direction of an inverted film, the magnetization direction opposite to the field direction becomes unstable and rotation should occur. As a consequence of the dispersion of the anisotropy direction in the film, the magnetization in parts of the film will rotate clockwise toward the applied field direction while that in the remaining part of the film will rotate counterclockwise. This situation is depicted in Fig. 5.7. If the magnitude of the anisotropy should vary from one part of the film to another, then the amount of rotation of **M** for a given H_s would also be different for different regions of the film. If we postulate that these local anisotropy variations are due to random deviations such as spatial variation of composition, imperfections, inclusions, dislocations, etc., the magnetization distribution at a given time would be very complicated indeed. However, if we take into account the tendency of neighboring spins to align with each other due to exchange forces and the smoothing effect of the long range dipolar forces, it is not unreasonable to suppose that "magnetization ripples" such as that shown in Fig. 5.8 could result. Since the angle through which the magnetization turns in the wall separating parts of the film of different rotation is very small, these walls should be of the Néel type. As

[11] Middelhoek, *op. cit.*, p. 111.

detail calculations would show,[12] the magnetostatic coupling in a direction perpendicular to the magnetization direction is much stronger than in a direction parallel to the magnetization. As a consequence of this, the longitudinal magnetization ripples prevail over the transverse ones, both of which are depicted in Fig. 5.8. Therefore, the

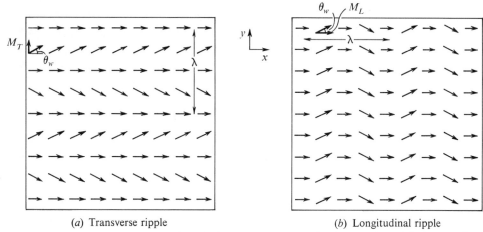

(a) Transverse ripple   (b) Longitudinal ripple

FIG. 5.8. Schematic representation of (a) transverse magnetization ripple and (b) longitudinal magnetization ripple (after Middelhoek, Ref. 11).

film splits up into elongated domains, the axes of which are perpendicular to the easy axis and the widths of which are determined by the wavelength of the anisotropy direction variation. As a result of the high energy of the walls which separates these domains further rotation is blocked. If H_s is increased to the value H_c, the magnetization reversal process consisting of domain wall motion preceded by inhomogeneous partial rotation will be discussed in more detail in Chap. 9 wherein the different reversal processes are subjected to close scrutiny. Here, we are mainly interested in the nature of the imperfection which gives rise to this peculiar process of reversal, i.e., inhomogeneous partial rotation followed by wall motion. In this connection, it should be recalled here that the hard-axis saturation and field reduction process, discussed in Sec. 3.3(a), is also associated with a splitting up of the film into elongated domains oriented parallel to the easy axis.[13] Thus, the hard-axis magnetization process in either normal ($H_c < H_k$) or inverted films ($H_c > H_k$) and the easy-axis reversal in inverted films have similar behavior and are presumably related to anisotropy dispersion. In other words, when the hard-axis saturation field decreases toward zero, the magnetization in each domain rotates to that easy direction closest to the field direction and splitting occurs.

A careful examination of the experimental evidence on easy- and hard-axis magnetization reversal in thin films would indicate that there are anisotropy axis variations over the film. However, the extent of this easy-axis dispersion and the possible spatial dependence of the magnitude of the anisotropy constant itself must be further ascertained. The methods for measuring easy-axis dispersion have been briefly mentioned in Sec. 3.3(b) and will be further examined in detail in Chap. 7. Here we

[12] *Ibid.*, p. 46.
[13] R. J. Spain and H. Rubinstein, *J. Appl. Phys.*, **32**: 288S (1961).

shall try to ascertain the extent of the local anisotropy axis variations from the results of switching experiments.

As mentioned in Sec. 3.3(a) and (b), the local anisotropy in a film is determined by the uniaxial anisotropy and local crystal and stress anisotropies. Furthermore, for Permalloy, zero uniaxial anisotropy and magnetostriction do not occur at the same composition. Because of the difference in thermal expansion of the film and substrate, the film is under isotropic tension in its plane. If the magnetostrictive constant is positive or negative, the film normals are the direction of hard and easy directions respectively. In the plane of the film, this isotropic stress will lead to stray anisotropies due to compositional changes and other crystal imperfections. It may then be expected that the variation of the easy direction in a film as a function of position is very complicated. It is therefore very difficult to investigate the influence of the exchange and the stray field couplings on these spatial anisotropy (and magnetization) variations in any simple quantitative manner, although it is obvious that the resulting magnetization distribution would be a function of the Fourier wavelengths associated with the easy-direction variation. Whereas simplified calculations could be made for the case where a particular wavelength is dominant to show the magnetization variation is diminished by the exchange and dipolar forces, it seems difficult to relate these results in any quantitative way to experimental observations. This is due to the fact that for these calculations we must assume a priori that spatial anisotropy variations do exist; and yet we have at present no direct evidence of these variations. Furthermore, a rather different explanation for the so-called related "locking patterns" in inverted films after saturation in a direction making an arbitrary angle with the easy axis has been advanced by other workers.[14]

According to the "magnetization ripple" theory discussed above, the dispersion of the anisotropy direction causes the hard-axis saturation and field reduction process and the reversal process in the easy direction for inverted films to be associated with a splitting up of the film into elongated domains. The reversal process in inverted films at various angles of applied field with respect to the easy axis, is thought to be due to the same mechanisms.[15] In fact, magnetization ripples under these conditions seem to have been observed.[16]

On the other hand, Smith[13] proposed that regions of negative H_k exist throughout the film, presumably due to the presence of impurities, and are responsible for these bands or "locking patterns" after saturation in an arbitrary direction and with subsequent reduction to zero field. In the negative H_k regions, the easy axis is oriented perpendicular to that in the positive H_k regions. The appearance of short disconnected segments can be interpreted by assuming the existence of regions of negative H_k which cause kinks in $\mathbf{M}$. For a reversing field in the locking section shown in Fig. 5.9, $\mathbf{M}$ will rotate in opposite directions in neighboring positive and negative H_k regions accompanied by the formation of local wall segments; further rotation is inhibited by magnetostatic interaction and the film is in the locked state. The angular extent of the locking sector can be determined by saturating in the easy direction and applying a reversing field at increasing angles to the easy axis until locking disappears. These experiments show that $\mathbf{M}$ kinks are in fact nearly 90° domains even before a reversing field is applied. Furthermore, experiments have shown that negative H_k regions are present

[14] D. O. Smith, *J. Appl. Phys.*, **32**: 70S (1961); *J. Appl. Phys. Letters*, **2**: 191 (1963).

[15] Middelhoek, *op. cit.*, p. 153.

[16] H. W. Fuller and M. E. Hale, *J. Appl. Phys.*, **31**: 238 (1960); E. Fuchs, *Z. Angew Phys.*, **13**: 157 (1961).

to an increasing extent as H_w/H_k increases and locking patterns have been observed for $H_w/H_k = 0.86$.

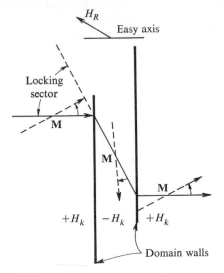

FIG. 5.9. Schematic representation of "locking" due to the presence of negative H_k regions (after D. O. Smith, Ref. 14).

Although it appears from the discussion above that difference in hypothesis could lead to plausible results in qualitative accord with experiment, it seems that the assumption of some anisotropy variation, whatever its cause, over the plane of the film is not unreasonable. We shall return to a more detailed discussion of this subject in Chap. 7.

5·3 DOMAIN WALL PASSING AN IMPERFECTION

When a domain wall passes an imperfection, both the shape of the wall and the magnetization distribution around the imperfection change as a function of time. The nature of these changes, of course, depends upon the type of wall being considered and the size and character of the local defect. Both the Bitter pattern and the method of electron microscopy may be used to study this type of dynamic behavior. As an example of the dynamic behavior of a wall in motion near an imperfection, Fig. 5.10 shows a

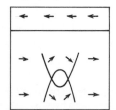  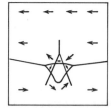 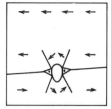

FIG. 5.10. Bitter patterns and magnetization distribution for a cross-tie wall passing a nearly circular cavity (after Middelhoek, Ref. 11).

sequence of Bitter patterns and the associated magnetization distribution for the case of a cross-tie wall passing a nearly circular cavity.[17]

Many more Bitter patterns showing the interaction of domain walls with nonmagnetic inclusions or cavity and negative H_k imperfections have been published by

---

[17] Middelhoek, *op. cit.*, p. 40.

Smith and Harte.[18] In films thin enough to support Néel walls, long perturbation walls are observed to be generated when such walls collide with a nonmagnetic inclusion or cavity. The perturbation walls appear to be some form of 360° or integral multiple of 360° wall separating head-on parallel domains. For perturbation walls to form, the size of the inclusion should be of the order of the wall thickness. In the presence of different H_k regions, magnetization reversal takes place by labyrinth propagation, in which the walls remain relatively fixed, and long slender domains develop from the tip, leaving behind regions of unswitched material, resulting in a labyrinth-like flux pattern.

As another example of the behavior of a wall passing an imperfection, we may examine the electron micrograph of Fuller and Hale.[19] It is seen from these micrographs that a simple wall becomes a cross-tie bearing wall as it passes an apparently highly stressed region.

5·4 DETERMINATION OF IMPERFECTION DISTRIBUTION

Imperfection distribution may be determined by several techniques. These are the Bitter pattern technique, the electron micrograph method and the microwave magnetic microscope method.

(a) Bitter Patterns

As discussed in Sec. 5.2, we can surmise the existence of anisotropy dispersion from the appearance of locking patterns which appear after saturation at an arbitrary angle with respect to the easy axis in a normal or an inverted film. The anisotropy dispersion can also be inferred from the long domain pattern after saturation in the hard direction in a normal film. Furthermore, using the Bitter technique, we can determine the location of holes, nonmagnetic inclusions, and different H_k regions as discussed in Sec. 5.3.

(b) Electron Micrographs

As discussed in Sec. 5.3, imperfections such as highly stressed regions could be located by the method of electron microscopy. Since the resolution of an electron microscope could be as high as 50 Å, much detail on imperfections could in principle be obtained. For polycrystalline films, electron micrographs give the crystallite size distribution and their preferred orientations, if any exist. For example, the so-called angle of incidence anisotropy effect (see Chap. 7) due to the preferred orientation of crystallines in the direction of the vapor beam can be directly verified by means of electron microscopy.

(c) Microwave Magnetic Microscope

Using selective resonance absorption technique whereby small regions of the film are examined consecutively, it is possible to determine the spatial variation of H_k, M, etc., by using the microwave magnetic microscope.[20] In contrast to other forms of microscopes, this instrument measures the spatial variation of the important properties

[18] D. O. Smith and K. J. Harte, *J. Appl. Phys.*, **33**: 1399 (1962).
[19] H. W. Fuller and M. E. Hale, *J. Appl. Phys.*, **31**: 308S (1960).
[20] R. F. Soohoo, *J. Appl. Phys.*, **33**: 1276 (1962).

of a magnetic sample directly. To date, clear resonances in portions of Permalloy films (~ 1000 Å thick) with a cross-sectional diameter of 0.010 in. have been observed.

By observing the spin-wave resonances with the static magnetic field parallel and perpendicular to the plane of the film at different locations independently, the spatial variation of the magnetization, relaxation time, gyromagnetic ratio, anisotropy magnitude and easy direction, exchange constant, and surface anisotropy energy, etc., of a thin film can be directly determined. The details of this method will be discussed in Chap. 11.

CHAPTER 6

MAGNETIZATION
OF THIN FILMS

One of the central problems in bulk ferromagnetism is the determination of the magnetization as a function of temperature. In the low-temperature region, i.e., at temperatures T that are low compared to the Curie temperature T_c of the ferromagnet, the temperature dependence of the magnetization M can be computed by the use of noninteracting spin-wave theory leading to the well-known Bloch $3/2$ power law $(M \sim T^{3/2})$. When the dynamic interaction between spin waves is included, Dyson found by series expansion in powers of T valid at low temperatures that there are in addition $T^{5/2}$, $T^{7/2}$, and T^4 terms in the temperature dependence of M. On the other hand, Opechowski has obtained an expression for $M(T)$ valid at very high temperatures by a series expansion in $1/T$. The functional behavior of the magnetization at intermediate temperature is much more difficult to calculate. However, an approximate expression for this temperature range including the interesting region near the Curie point has also recently been obtained by Callen using the Green's function method.

In the case of the magnetization in thin films, rigorous theoretical calculation to date is based upon the results of spin-wave theory and is therefore only applicable to temperatures low compared to the Curie point. However, an attempt to extend the valid temperature range by means of molecular field theory has also been made. In this chapter, after a brief discussion of the general theory of magnetization, we shall study the magnetization of thin films as a function of temperature, thickness, and composition. The Klein and Smith theory of the magnetization of thin films will be discussed in detail together with a careful consideration of the appropriate film exchange boundary condition. The discrepancies between theory and experiment with regard to the thin-film magnetization behavior as a function of temperature will also be examined.

6·1 GENERAL THEORY OF MAGNETIZATION

In order for an assembly of spins to be aligned spontaneously, there must exist some very strong forces between them. An estimate of the order of magnitude of the equivalent field may be obtained by observing that the thermal agitation energy is nearly equal to the Zeeman energy of a magnetic moment in this field at the order-disorder transition point. Thus,

$$H \simeq \frac{k_B T_c}{\mu_B} = 4.5 \times 10^6 \text{ Oe} \tag{6.1}$$

for $T_c = 300°K$. Here k_B is the Boltzmann's constant and μ_B, the Bohr magneton, is the magnetic moment of an electron spin. The origin of this enormous field is of obvious importance in the theory of magnetism. Now, for any magnetized medium, there is always a Lorentz field acting on a dipole in the direction of the magnetization.[1] For magnetic materials that are either isotropic or with cubic symmetry, the Lorentz field is equal to $4\pi M/3$. Such a dipolar field, being in the order of 10^3 Oe, is several orders of magnitude too small to account for the apparent field required for spontaneous magnetization given by Eq. (6.1).

Weiss, in his phenomenological theory of magnetism, arbitrarily dismisses this difficulty and assumes that there exists a very large field, which, like the Lorentz field, is proportional to the magnetization.[2] In this way, he derived an expression for the magnetization which is in good agreement with experiment. The physical origin of this Weiss molecular field, however, remained unclear until 1928 when Heisenberg pointed out that it is related to the quantum-mechanical exchange integral. It can be shown that semiclassically[3]

$$E_{ex} = -2J\mathbf{S}_i \cdot \mathbf{S}_j \qquad (6.2)$$

where E_{ex} is the exchange energy between atoms i and j bearing vector spins $\mathbf{S}_i$ and $\mathbf{S}_j$ respectively, while J, known as the exchange integral, has no classical analogue. (A constant term which is of no consequence to the discussion is omitted in Eq. (6.2).) J expresses the difference in coulomb interaction energy of the system when the spins are parallel or antiparallel. It is a consequence of the Pauli exclusion principle that in quantum mechanics we cannot usually change the relative direction of two spins without making changes in the spatial charge distribution in the overlap region. The resulting changes in the coulomb energy of the system may conveniently be written in the form of Eq. (6.2) so that it appears as if there were a direct coupling between $\mathbf{S}_i$ and $\mathbf{S}_j$. If the exchange integral J is positive, parallel alignment of spin or ferromagnetism results. On the other hand, if J is negative, antiparallel spins or antiferromagnetism results. In the ferromagnetic case there is, of course, a resultant spontaneous magnetization while in the antiferromagnetic case there is no net magnetic moment since, on the average, there are an equal number of spins oriented in opposite directions. In general J is negative, favoring the nonferromagnetic state. However, for certain elements such as Fe, Co, and Ni, the ratio between the radius of the 3d orbit and the interatomic separation is within the proper range for ferromagnetism to occur. In this chapter, we are particularly interested in the magnetization behavior of ferromagnets as a function of temperature, thickness, and composition.

The magnetization of a magnetic material is defined as the magnetic moment per unit volume and is in general a decreasing function of temperature. The decrease of the magnetization as temperature is increased is interpreted as departure from saturation due to the excitation of spin waves.[4] The probability $\langle n \rangle$ that a particular spin wave of energy $\hbar\omega$ will be occupied at a given temperature T is given by

[1] H. A. Lorentz, *The Theory of Electrons*, Teubner, Leipzig, 1906.
[2] P. Weiss, *J. Phys.*, **6**: 667 (1907).
[3] See, e.g., J. H. Van Vleck, *Rev. Mod. Phys.*, **17**: 27 (1945).
[4] F. Bloch, *Z. Physik*, **61**: 206 (1930); **74**: 295 (1932).

$$\langle n \rangle = \frac{1}{e^{\hbar\omega/k_B T} - 1} \tag{6.3}$$

for a system at thermal equilibrium at temperature T. Here k_B is Boltzmann's constant, $\hbar$ is Planck's constant h divided by 2π, and ω is the frequency of the spin wave. Equation (6.3) is applicable to spin waves or magnons because these psuedoparticles, being macroscopically observable, are not subjected to the Pauli exclusion principle. Therefore, they should obey Bose-Einstein statistics. Since $\langle n \rangle$ is equal to the equivalent number of reversed spins, the difference between the saturation magnetization at °K, $M_s(0)$, and that at temperature T, $M_s(T)$, is given by

$$M_s(0) - M_s(T) = \frac{2\mu_B}{V} \sum_k \langle n \rangle \tag{6.4}$$

where $\mu_B = e\hbar/2mc$ is the magnetic moment of a free electron, V is the volume of the specimen and k is the spin-wave wave vector. The factor of 2 appears in Eq. (6.2) because a spin reversal corresponds to a change of $2\mu_B$. For a three-dimensional lattice, the number of energy states per unit volume with wave number less than k is $(1/2\pi)^3(4\pi/3)k^3$. This result follows from the fact that the number of normal modes per unit volume is $4\pi/3\lambda^3$ and $\lambda = 2\pi/k$. Thus, we find from Eqs. (6.3) and (6.4) that

$$M_s(0) - M_s(T) = \frac{8\pi\mu_B}{(2\pi)^3} \int_0^\infty \frac{k^2 \, dk}{e^{\hbar\omega/k_B T} - 1} \tag{6.5}$$

Now, the energy of a spin wave of frequency ω, according to spin-wave theory (Chap. 11), is given by

$$\hbar\omega = (2S)J(ka)^2 = \hbar\gamma \frac{2A}{M_s(T)} k^2 \tag{6.6}$$

where J is the exchange integral, A the exchange constant, a the lattice constant, γ the gyromagnetic ratio, and S the spin. Noting that $2S = 1$ for $S = \frac{1}{2}$ and letting $K = ka$, Eq. (6.5) may be transformed to

$$M_s(0) - M_s(T) = \frac{8\pi M_s(0)}{(2\pi)^3} \int_0^\infty \frac{K^2 \, dK}{e^{JK^2/k_B T} - 1} \tag{6.7}$$

where we have identified μ_B/a^3 as the saturation magnetic moment per unit volume at °K or $M_s(0)$ since there are $2S$ spins per atom. Integrating Eq. (6.7), we readily find for an sc (simple cubic) crystal,

$$M_{s3}(T) = M_s(0)\left[1 - 0.1174\left(\frac{k_B T}{J}\right)^{3/2}\right] \tag{6.8}$$

This is Bloch's $\frac{3}{2}$ power law. For bcc (body-centered cubic) and fcc (face-centered cubic) crystals, the constant 0.1174 should be replaced by 0.0587 and 0.0294, respectively.

6·2   THIN FILMS

Similarly, for a two-dimensional lattice,

$$M_{s2}(T) = M_s(0)\left[1 - \frac{2(2\pi)}{(2\pi)^2}\int_0^\infty \frac{K\,dK}{e^{JK^2/k_BT} - 1}\right] \tag{6.9}$$

This integral diverges at the lower limit, a result which is interpreted to mean that the plane lattice has no spontaneous magnetization. For this case the basic assumption of the Bloch theory, that the magnetization is close to the saturation value, is invalid. Therefore, in order to examine the behavior of the magnetization as a function of temperature for thin films, we must take into account the discrete nature of the lattice.

(a) Theory of Klein and Smith

To begin with, let us consider a three-dimensional ferromagnet in a magnetic field. The quantum mechanical Hamiltonian is given by

$$\mathscr{H} = -\frac{1}{2}\sum_{i,j=1}^{N}{}' 2J_{ij}(R_{ij})\mathbf{S}_i\cdot\mathbf{S}_j$$

$$+ \frac{1}{2}\sum_{i,j=1}^{N}{}' \frac{4\mu_B^2}{R_{ij}^5}(R_{ij}^2\mathbf{S}_i\cdot\mathbf{S}_j - 3\mathbf{S}_i\cdot\mathbf{R}_{ij}\mathbf{S}_j\cdot\mathbf{R}_{ij}) - \sum_{i=1}^{N} 2\mu_B S_i^{(z)}H \tag{6.10}$$

Here N is the total number of atoms while the sums over i and j each run from 1 to N, summands with $i = j$ being omitted. $R_{ij} = |\mathbf{R}_i - \mathbf{R}_j|$ is the distance between the centers of gravity of the ith and j^{th} atoms, J_{ij} the exchange integral between these atoms, S_i the spin-angular momentum operator of the atom at R_l in units of $\hbar = h/2\pi$ and H the z directed magnetic field.

The first term in the Hamiltonian of Eq. (6.10) is the Heisenberg exchange energy expressed in terms of the atomic spin operators while the second term is due to magnetic dipole-dipole interaction between electrons on different atoms. The effects of exchange and of higher magnetic poles on the magnetic interaction are both neglected; hence, the centers of gravity of the atoms constitute the locations of magnetic dipoles, each with moment $2\mu_B S$. The last term is the Zeeman energy of interaction between the magnetic moment of each atom and the external magnetic field. It should be noted that energy due to spin-orbit coupling, which has only a small influence upon the magnetization behavior of the ferromagnet, has not been included in Eq. (6.10). Furthermore, the dipole-dipole term in Eq. (6.10) also has only a small influence upon the magnetization at low temperatures and can therefore be neglected for our purposes.

Diagonalizing the Hamiltonian (6.10), neglecting the dipole-dipole terms, we obtain its eigenvalues E as[5]

$$E = C + \frac{1}{2}\sum_\lambda A_\lambda N_\lambda \tag{6.11}$$

---

[5] T. Holstein and H. Primakoff, *Phys. Rev.*, **58**: 1098 (1940). See also Chap. 11.

where $N = 0, 1, 2, \ldots$ and

$$C = -\sum_{i,j}' J_{ij}S^2 - 2\mu_B SNH \tag{6.12}$$

and

$$A_\lambda = \sum_\lambda 2SJ_h(R_h)(1 - e^{i\mathbf{K}_\lambda \cdot \mathbf{R}_h}) + 2\mu_B H \tag{6.13}$$

where $\mathbf{R}_h = \mathbf{R}_i - \mathbf{R}_j$ and $\mathbf{K}_\lambda$ is the reduced wave vector. The usual periodicity conditions require its components to take the values $K_\lambda^i = 2\pi n_i/G_i$ where $i = x, y, z$ and where G_i is the linear dimension of the specimen in the ith direction in units of the lattice constant. Thus, n_i assumes integral values between $-\frac{1}{2}G_i$ and $\frac{1}{2}G_i - 1$.

The spontaneous magnetization M_s as a function of temperature T can now be obtained from the partition function Z by the relation

$$M_s(T) = \frac{k_B T}{V} \frac{\partial}{\partial H} \ln Z \tag{6.14}$$

where V is the volume of the sample. According to Eq. (6.11) and (6.13), Z is given by

$$Z = \sum_E e^{-E/k_B T} = e^{-C/k_B T} \prod_\lambda (1 - e^{A_\lambda/k_B T})^{-1} \tag{6.15}$$

For an sc lattice of atoms with spin $\frac{1}{2}$, the spontaneous magnetization is given by

$$M_s(T) = \frac{N\mu_B}{V} \left\{ 1 - \frac{2}{N} \sum_{n_x, n_y, n_z} \left\{ \exp\left[\frac{2J}{k_B T} \sum_{i=x,y,z} \left(1 - \cos\frac{2\pi n_i}{G_i} \right) \right] - 1 \right\}^{-1} \right\} \tag{6.16}$$

Since N is the total number of atoms in the crystal, $N\mu_B/V$ is equal to the saturation magnetization at $°K$ $M_s(0)$. For ordinary crystals G_x, G_y, and G_z, the x, y, and z dimensions of the crystal in units of the lattice constant, are very large so that the cosine expression in Eq. (6.16) may be expanded in a series in $2\pi n_i/G_i$, retaining only the constant and quadratic terms. If the summations in Eq. (6.16) are further replaced by integrals (the intervals between K states being equal to $2\pi/G_i$ are so small that the discrete K states could be approximated by a continuum), then Eq. (6.16) reduces to Eq. (6.5) for the magnetization of a three-dimensional crystal formulated by very simple arguments.

Consider now a thin film with its surface normal in the z direction. G_x and G_y, taken equal to G for convenience, are still very large numbers. On the other hand, since the film is thin in the z dimension, G_z need not be a large number, and is in any event much smaller than G. Therefore, we can integrate over n_x and n_y but not over n_z. We then obtain from Eq. (6.16)[6]

$$M_s(T) = \frac{N\mu_B}{V} \left\{ 1 - \frac{2G^2(2\pi)}{N(2\pi)^2} \sum_{n_z=0}^{G_z-1} \int_{2\pi/G}^{\infty} \frac{K\, dK}{e^{(J/k_B T)/[K^2 + 2 - 2\cos(2\pi n_z/G_z)]}} \right\} \tag{6.17}$$

---

[6] M. J. Klein and R. S. Smith, *Phys. Rev.*, **81**: 378 (1951).

Klein and Smith have set the lower limit on the integral of Eq. (6.17) nonzero because they observed that the state with $n_x = n_y = n_z = 0$, corresponding to the classical picture of all spins being parallel with the spin system aligned in an arbitrary direction, makes an infinite contribution to the magnetization as given by Eq. (6.16). The origin of this unrealistic infinite term can be traced to the incorrect method of evaluating the partition sum in the original derivation of Eq. (6.16) by Holstein and Primakoff. The sum of the N's (the occupation numbers of the spin-wave states) is a measure of the number of reversed spins in the lattice. Consequently, this sum has a maximum value. In carrying out the partition sum from which Eq. (6.16) is derived, we should therefore impose a restriction on the possible values of N_λ; namely, their sum should be less than a fixed number, proportional to N. Actually, the partition sum is evaluated without imposing this restriction; the N's are allowed to take on all integer values from zero to infinity. This method of evaluating the partition sum leads directly to the infinity in question. Klein and Smith did not succeed in evaluating the partition sum rigorously so they set the sum of N_λ to a fixed value determined to fit experimental data for the spontaneous magnetization. In this way, they found that the troublesome state, with $n_x = n_y = n_z = 0$, makes a negligible rather than an infinite contribution to the magnetization.

The upper limit in Eq. (6.17) is set equal to infinity without appreciable error because the important contributions to the integral come from the region of small K when $J/k_B T \gg 1$, a necessary condition for the applicability of the Bloch theory. The integrand of Eq. (6.17) can now be evaluated with the following result:

$$M_s(T) = \frac{N\mu_B}{V}\left\{1 - \frac{k_B T}{J}\frac{1}{2\pi G_z}\sum_{n_z=0}^{G_z-1}(-)\ln\left[1 - \left(1 - \frac{J}{k_B T}\frac{4\pi^2}{G^2}\right) \times e^{-f(n_z)}\right]\right\} \quad (6.18)$$

where

$$f(n_z) = \frac{2J}{k_B T}\left(1 - \cos\frac{2\pi n_z}{G}\right) \quad (6.19)$$

Since G is very large, we have retained only the first-order term in the series for $e^{(J/k_B T)(4\pi^2/G^2)}$.

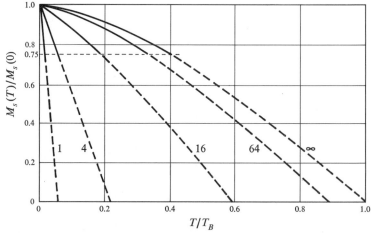

FIG. 6.1.   Normalized magnetization vs normalized temperature for sc square films (2×10^7 atoms on a side) of varying thickness. The integers on the curves denote the film thickness in number of atom layers (after Klein and Smith, Ref. 6).

Klein and Smith[6] have carried out the summation in Eq. (6.18) by numerical methods for films varying in thickness from 1 to 128 atom layers with representative results shown in Fig. 6.1. Here T_B is the characteristic temperature determined by setting $M_{s3}(T)$ equal to zero in Eq. (6.8), giving $T_B = 3.9J/k_B$. For $M_s(T)/M_s(0)$ less than about 0.75, the results of spin-wave theory are no longer strictly valid and the curves below this value have been drawn dotted for emphasizing this point. The plot of $G_z = \infty$ is merely a plot of Eq. (6.8).

It is seen from Fig. 6.1 that for films thinner than about 60 atom layers, there is a significant deviation of the magnetization from the three-dimensional value at a

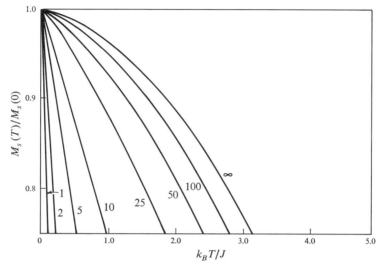

FIG. 6.2.   Normalized magnetization vs normalized temperature for bcc square films (3×10^7 atoms on a side) of varying thickness. The integers on the curves denote the film thickness in number of atom layers (after Glass and Klein, Ref. 7).

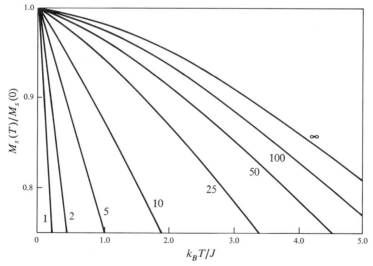

FIG. 6.3.   Normalized magnetization vs normalized temperature for fcc square films (3×10^7 atoms on a side) of varying thickness. The integers on the curves denote the film thickness in number of atom layers (after Glass and Klein, Ref. 7).

given temperature. Furthermore, for these sufficiently thin films $M_s(T)$ falls off more sharply with temperature than $T^{3/2}$ given by the Bloch law.

Permalloy, the nickel-iron alloy, is either bcc or fcc depending upon the relative composition of nickel and iron. Thus, the theory developed above for simple cubic lattices could not be strictly applicable to these alloys of interest to magnetic thin films. Glass and Klein,[7] however, have studied theoretically the magnetization behavior of thin films for both the body-centered and the face-centered lattices. The calculation involved is quite analogous to that for the simple cubic case discussed above. Figures 6.2 and 6.3 give the reduced magnetization $M_s(T)/M_s(0)$ as a function of the reduced temperature $k_B T/J$. It is seen that the temperature behavior of the bcc and fcc films is similar to that for sc films.

(b) Exchange Boundary Condition

In Sec. 6.2(a) we found that the magnetization of a thin film decreases as a function of increasing temperature faster than that of bulk matter. Before we attempt to compare the theoretical results of Klein-Smith and Glass-Klein with experiments, it would be of interest to examine whether the use of periodic boundary conditions in their calculation is physically justified.

To begin with, let us examine the physical reasons why the magnetization of a thin film decreases faster with temperature than that of bulk matter.[8] For a film that is $G \times G$ atoms in area and G_z atoms thick, the total number of atoms in the film N would be equal to $G^2 G_z$. For $k_z = 0$, if periodic boundary condition is used, the number of spin-wave states of wave number n_f less than k for the film is

$$n_f = \left(\frac{1}{2\pi}\right)^2 \pi k^2 (Ga)^2 \tag{6.20}$$

where a is the lattice constant. Likewise, the number of spin-wave states of wave number n_B less than k in a bulk cube sample is

$$n_B = \left(\frac{1}{2\pi}\right)^3 \frac{4\pi}{3} k^3 (N^{1/3}a)^3 \tag{6.21}$$

The ratio $n_f/n_B = (3/2)(\pi G^2/Na)(1/k)$ is very large until k reaches the order of $\pi G^2/Na = \pi/G_z a$. This value of k is exactly equal to the first allowed value for k_z in the film for a completely pinned surface boundary condition. (See Chap. 11. In this case k_x and k_y are assumed zero as the rf magnetic field h is assumed uniform in the x–y plane.)

From the above discussion we may therefore conclude that if periodic boundary conditions are used for k_z, there will be a piling up of low-energy modes with $k_z = 0$, which will cause the magnetization of the film to fall below the Bloch $T^{3/2}$ curve for bulk samples. This then is the physical reason for the results of Klein-Smith and Glass-Klein as exemplified by the normalized magnetization vs normalized temperature curves of Figs. 6.1–6.3. Furthermore, we conclude that if pinned boundary

[7] S. J. Glass and M. J. Klein, *Phys. Rev.*, **109**: 288 (1958).
[8] J. A. Davis and F. Keffer, *J. Appl. Phys.*, **34**: 1135 (1963).

conditions are used, there will be a gap in the spectrum which will cause the magnet-ization to fall off more slowly than $T^{3/2}$. If there are no complications in the energy spectrum and in the density of states other than that introduced by the gap, then at a temperature such that k_BT is large compared to the energy k_BT_o of the first allowed mode, the density of important thin-film states will catch up with that of bulk states, and the thin-film magnetization vs temperature characteristic will follow the Bloch $T^{3/2}$ law for bulk samples. For nickel, T_o is about $2300°\text{K}/(G_z)^2$.

Let us now return to Eq. (6.17). We recall that Klein and Smith discarded the $n_x = n_y = n_z = 0$ states on the ground that these states make an infinite contribution to the magnetization of a sample, an impossible result. Hence, they let the minimum value of k ($= K/a$) $= 2\pi/Ga$ rather than zero. Since Ga, the linear cross-sectional dimension of the film, is very much larger than the film thickness G_za, the lower limit of k used by Klein and Smith is several orders of magnitudes lower than the lowest allowable value of k_z ($= \pi/G_za$) for the pinned boundary condition. Thus, consistent with the discussion of the last paragraph, the elimination of the $k = 0$ mode is in itself insufficient in drastically reducing the high density of states below $k \sim \pi/G_za$ for $k_z = 0$. To see whether the film magnetization decreases slower or faster than $T^{3/2}$ at low temperatures, we must therefore examine more closely the exchange boundary condition for the surface spins.

To begin with, we observe that in contrast to the case of spins in the interior of the film, surface spins have exchange interactions with interior spins only. As a consequence of this asymmetry, relatively large anisotropies can act on the surface spins since interactions which cancel in the interior as a result of cubic symmetry will not cancel at the film surface.[9] An antiferromagnetic oxide layer on the surface of a metallic film can also give rise to an exchange anisotropy[10] which tends to pin the end spins. Of course, the actual boundary conditions depend upon the nature of the surface anisotropy which may only be large enough to cause partial pinning.

The allowable values of the z component of the wave vector depend upon the degree of surface spin pinning involved. Thus, the expression for the magnetization given by Eq. (6.18) should be rewritten to read

$$M_s(T) = \frac{N\mu_B}{V}\left\{1 - \frac{k_BT}{J}\frac{1}{2\pi G_z}\sum_{k_z}(-)\ln\left[1 - \left(1 - \frac{J}{k_BT}\frac{4\pi^2}{G^2}\right)e^{-f(k_z)}\right]\right\} \quad (6.22)$$

where

$$f(k_z) = \frac{2J}{k_BT}(1 - \cos k_za) \quad (6.23)$$

(Dipolar fields given by the second term of Eq. (6.10) are again neglected on the grounds that the resultant spread in the spin-wave energies is small compared to the effect of the surface anisotropy field considered.) The allowable values of k_z for a given degree of pinning depend upon the crystal structure considered. For an sc lat-tice with spin $\frac{1}{2}$ and with $k_z \neq 0$, we find in Chap. 11 that in the continuum approxi-mation (or equivalently $G \gg k_za$), k_z is determined by the transcendental equation

$$\tan(k_zT') = \frac{2\varepsilon k_za}{(k_za)^2 - \varepsilon^2} \quad (6.24)$$

---

[9] L. Néel, *Compt. Rend.*, **237**: 1468 (1953); *J. Phys. Radium*, **15**: 225 (1954).
[10] W. H. Meiklejohn and C. P. Bean, *Phys. Rev.*, **102**: 1413 (1956); *J. Appl. Phys.*, **29**: 454 (1958).

where $\varepsilon = \mu_B H_s/2J$, the ratio of the surface energy to the exchange energy, and T' is the thickness of the film. Equation (6.24) is applicable for the uniaxial surface anisotropy case with the easy axis perpendicular and a hard plane parallel to the film plane and with the applied field in the film plane. By comparing theoretical calculations with the results of ferromagnetic resonance experiments, we have identified the type of the surface anisotropy energy in thin films as of the aforementioned type.[11,12] Actually, in these calculations, the field was applied at some arbitrary angle with respect to the film surface. However, for magnetization determination using the torque magnetometer as discussed in the next section, it is possible to consider only the case where the applied field is parallel to the film plane to which Eq. (6.24) corresponds. If ε is small and there is no restriction on the value of $k_z a$, an analogous calculation would show that expression (6.24) should be replaced by

$$\cot(k_z T') = -\frac{2(1-\varepsilon)}{\varepsilon(\varepsilon-2)}\tan\left(\frac{k_z a}{2}\right) + \frac{\varepsilon^2}{\varepsilon(\varepsilon-2)}\cot(k_z a) \qquad (6.25)$$

The magnetization may be calculated from Eq. (6.22) and (6.25) for various values of ε. $M(T)/M(0)$ vs T/T_c for $G_z = 1, 3, 6$, and 12 with $\varepsilon = 0.01$ are plotted in Fig. 6.4. Shown also is the case for $\varepsilon = 0.1$ and $G_z = 6$. It is seen from this figure that for high values of H_s, the magnetization of a thin film with $G_z = 6$ is essentially indistinguishable from the bulk value. If $\varepsilon = 1$, corresponding to very strong pinnings,

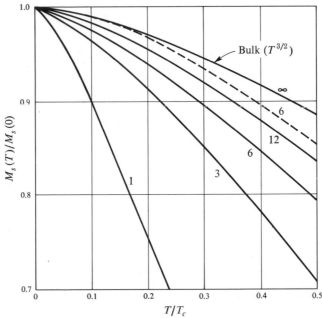

FIG. 6.4. Normalized magnetization vs normalized temperature for sc films $(k_B T_c/J = 2)$ of varying thickness. The integers on the curves denote film thickness in number of atom layers. Solid curves are for $\varepsilon = 0.01$ where dashed curve is for $\varepsilon = 0.1$ (after Davis and Keffer, Ref. 8).

[11] R. F. Soohoo, *Phys. Rev.*, **131**: 594 (1963).
[12] R. F. Soohoo, *J. Appl. Phys.*, **34**: 1149 (1963).

the film magnetization falls off more slowly than bulk magnetization for the low temperature ($T/T_c \leq 0.5$) investigated, approaching the Bloch law as G_z increases, consistent with the qualitative prediction at the beginning of this section.

(c) Theory of Valenta

The theory of the magnetization of thin films developed by Klein and Smith as well as subsequent modifications to the theory is based upon the spin-wave approach. Therefore, the results of their theory are strictly applicable only to temperatures that are low compared to the Curie point. Drigo[13] and Crittenden and Hoffman,[14] have attempted to modify the Klein and Smith theory so that it would be applicable to higher temperatures. Drigo attempted to relate more closely the results of Klein and Smith to that of the well-established Weiss theory for bulk samples. Thus, he identified the point at which the magnetization curves of Klein and Smith intersect the temperature axis with the Curie temperature. To obtain the magnetization at a given temperature, he then multiplied the Klein-Smith value of the magnetization by the ratio of the magnetization of Klein and Smith and Weiss for an infinitely thick sample. The agreement between theory and experiment which was achieved by Drigo in this way was satisfactory for some cases. Crittenden and Hoffman attempted to use a similar correction except for constant magnetization. In this case, the agreement between theory and experiment was less satisfactory. As pointed out by these authors themselves, these means of correction to the Klein-Smith results must be considered provisory. With Drigo's correction, he worked mainly with that part of the Klein-Smith magnetization curve which is not reliable, i.e., in the temperature range about the Curie point. Furthermore, Drigo identified the Curie temperature T_c with the Bloch temperature T_B, which are quantities that differ from each other by almost an order of magnitude.

In recognizing the inadequacies of these methods of correction to the Klein-Smith theory, Valenta[15] tried to develop a theory for the magnetization of thin films applicable at higher temperature by invoking the concept of Néel sublattices.[16] In essence, Néel's theory of magnetic sublattices consists of the division of all the atoms of the material into several groups or sublattices formed by physically equivalent particles, i.e., equivalent particles situated at identical physical environments. It is therefore possible to consider the film as if it consists of a number of magnetic sublattices formed by atomic planes parallel to the surface. In contrast to the ferrimagnetic case originally considered by Néel, the sublattices do not interlace but gradually pass from one to the other. Thus, atomic planes at equal distance below the surfaces of the film formed equivalent sublattices.

Let us consider the film to be composed of n sublattices or atomic planes. Division into sublattices implied the assumption that the total wave function of the electrons of a thin film differs negligibly from that of the state in which the components of magnetic moment of the individual atomic planes have well-defined values. The exchange part of the diagonal matrix element of the exchange energy operator is

[13] A. Drigo, *Nuovo Cimento*, **8**: 498 (1951).
[14] E. C. Crittenden, Jr., and R. W. Hoffman, *Rev. Mod. Phys.*, **25**: 310 (1958).
[15] L. Valenta, *Czech. J. Phys.*, **2**: 127 (1957).
[16] L. Néel, *Ann. Phys.*, **3**: 137 (1948).

given by

$$E_{ex} = - \sum_{-spin} J_{ik} - \sum_{+spin} J_{ik} \tag{6.26}$$

where J_{ik} denotes the exchange integral formed from the wave functions of electrons of the ith and k^{th} atom and addition is carried out over all pairs of atoms with spin components equal to $-\frac{1}{2}$ or $+\frac{1}{2}$. The assumption of magnetic sublattices means that when introducing the energy centers of gravity, we must consider how many times, with states characterized by $+$ and $-$ spins on the individual sublattices, there occurs an exchange integral of a certain type. For the distribution with r_1, $r_2, \ldots, r_n, -\frac{1}{2}-$ spins on the individual sublattices, we then obtain a rather lengthy expression for the mean value of the diagonal matrix element of the energy operator. We may then obtain the partition function Z by adding to this energy the Zeeman energy of the spins in an external magnetic field. The normalized magnetization at a given temperature T can then be obtained by means of Eq. (6.14) giving

$$\frac{M_s(T)}{M_s(0)} = B_{1/2}\left\{\frac{1}{k_BT}\left[\left(\frac{J}{2}\sum_{i=1}^{n} s_{ik}y_k\right) + \mu_BH\right]\right\} \tag{6.27}$$

where $B_{1/2}$ is the special Brillouin function analogous to that for bulk samples and where we have considered nearest-neighbor interaction with exchange integral J only.

From Eq. (6.27), we see that introducing the concept of magnetic sublattices in thin films, a solution is offered for the problem of the spontaneous magnetization of thin films at higher temperature by generalizing the Weiss-Néel theory of molecular field. The intensity of the molecular field acting on the atoms of a given layer due to the particles of another layer is assumed to be proportional to the magnetization of this layer and the number of nearest neighbors of the particular atom contained in this layer. At the same time, the number of nearest neighbors in the atom layers adjoining the layer of the atom under investigation is characterized by the number s_{ik} or s_k $(i, k = 1, 2, \ldots, n)$ denoting the number of nearest neighbors of the atom of the ith atom layer in the kth atom layer. Thus, the spontaneous magnetization of the individual layers is given by

$$\frac{M_s(T)}{M_s(0)} = B_J\left(\frac{\alpha}{T}s_{ik}y_k\right) \tag{6.28}$$

where α is a constant. The solution of Eq. (6.28) may be found by plotting $y = B_J(x)$ and $y = \text{const } x$ vs x as is done for bulk specimens.[17] The value of the constant is determined by the type of crystal structure involved and the Curie temperature of the bulk specimen. Valenta has solved Eq. (6.28) for the following single-crystal cases: Fe(100), Fe(111), Co(0001), and Ni(111). The case of the 111-plane nickel is plotted in Fig. 6.5. Comparison of Fig. 6.5 with Fig. 6.2 shows that the spontaneous magnetization decreases more slowly with temperature than that given by the Klein-Smith theory.

---

[17] See, e.g., R. F. Soohoo, *Theory and Application of Ferrites*, Prentice-Hall, Inc., Englewood Cliffs, N.J., 1960, p. 42.

Let us recapitulate the method used by Valenta in calculating the magnetization of thin films. He used the Néel sublattice model to construct a Heisenberg type quantum-mechanical theory for the magnetization in thin films. The solution for the magnetization of a given sublattice is equivalent to that derived from molecular-field theory. The sublattice molecular field is proportional to its magnetization.

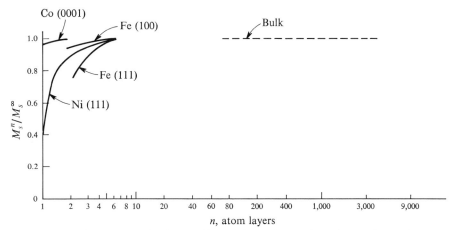

FIG. 6.5.   Normalized magnetization vs film thickness in number of atom layers for Fe, Co, and Ni single crystals at 16°C. For a Ni(111) film, the (111) crystallographic axis is along the film normal, etc. (after Valenta, Ref. 15). M_s^n and M_s^∞ represent magnetization of an n-layer film and bulk material, respectively.

Since the surface atoms have fewer nearest neighbors than the interior ones, the Curie temperature and therefore the magnetization at a given temperature is reduced. This reduction of the surface layer magnetization in turn lowers the molecular fields, being proportional to M, acting on the adjacent layer. This effect further propagates from layer to layer and, due to the stronger exchange interaction between layers, a net Curie temperature which is lower than that for bulk material is therefore obtained. In this connection, it may be pointed out that the Néel sublattices or atom layers of the film become equivalent as the thickness of the film approaches infinity and the Curie temperature would approach that of bulk matter.

We shall conclude our discussion of the general theory of the magnetization of ferromagnetic materials by briefly examining other related theories involved, mainly for bulk matter. Dyson,[18] in his study of the interaction between spin waves, observed that the Holstein and Primakoff result as exemplified by Eq. (6.16) is only valid for noninteracting spin waves, identical with the results of the linearized theory of Bloch. However, it is found that the dynamic spin-wave interaction is weak and the temperature dependence of the low-temperature magnetization is only slightly modified due to its presence. The normalized magnetization as a function of temperature is given by

$$\frac{M_s(T)}{M_s(0)} = S - a_0\theta^{3/2} - a_1\theta^{5/2} - a_2\theta^{7/2} - a_3S^{-1}\theta^4 + O(\theta^{9/2}) \tag{6.29}$$

[18] F. J. Dyson, *Phys. Rev.* **102**: 1217, 1230 (1956).

where θ is the temperature in dimensionless units, and a_0, a_1, a_2, a_3 are positive numerical coefficients whose values are dependent upon the types of crystal lattices. Callen,[19] in a recent calculation using Green's function theory of ferromagnetism succeeded in deriving approximate expressions for the magnetization for any temperature. His result agrees with Dyson's result series expansion in T in the lower temperature limit and with the Opechowski result by series expansion of M in $1/T$ in the high temperature limit.[20]

6·3   MAGNETIZATION AS A FUNCTION OF TEMPERATURE

The theoretical behavior of the magnetization as a function of temperature has been adequately discussed in Sec. 6.2. The experimental situation is far from clear. In fact, various investigators have found rather divergent results. In what follows, we shall try to discuss these experimental results and try to collaborate them with theory.

The theoretical behavior of the magnetization as a function of temperature has already been indicated in Figs. 6.1 to 6.5. The calculations involved for the fcc and bcc lattices described above have assumed that the film plane is perpendicular to one of the basis vectors of the cubic lattice. On the other hand, the films studied experimentally are normally polycrystalline with more or less randomly oriented crystallite. This fact will introduce complications in the correlation between theory and experiment on the magnetization of thin films. However, Glass and Klein[7] found in preliminary calculations for films a few atom layers thick, whose base plane is (100), that only small changes in the magnetization curve would result if the magnetization of polycrystalline films could be calculated.

The most careful experimental data on the magnetization of thin films as a function of temperature has been obtained by Neugebauer.[21] The relative magnetization of nickel films of various thicknesses is shown in Fig. 6.6. It is seen that the magnetization of a thin film is essentially indistinguishable from that of bulk matter for films more than 30 Å thick. For thicknesses less than 30 Å, the film structures are no longer continuous. Islands of materials are formed on the substrate, which cause the films to be superparamagnetic. Therefore, it would not be very meaningful to compare the experimental magnetization of thin films <30 Å thick with theory, although it has been found that for films in this thickness range, the magnetization decreases with thickness.

The films used by Neugebauer are polycrystalline samples prepared by vacuum deposition. The substrate is suspended on a calibrated torsion wire, and while still in vacuum can be placed in a variable field between the pole pieces of an electromagnet. When the film is positioned at an angle α to the field direction, its energy at saturation, is given by[21]

$$E = -M_s H \cos\theta + 2\pi M_s^2 \sin^2(\alpha - \theta) + K_1 \sin^2(\alpha - \theta) \tag{6.30}$$

where M_s is the saturation magnetization, H the external field, θ the angle between

---

[19] H. Callen, *Phys. Rev.*, **130**: 890 (1963).

[20] W. Opechowski, *Physica*, **4**: 181 (1937); **6**: 1112 (1938).

[21] C. A. Neugebauer, *Gen. Elec. Res. Lab. Sci. Rept. No. 2*, Schenectady, N.Y., 1961; *Phys. Rev.*, **116**: 1441 (1959).

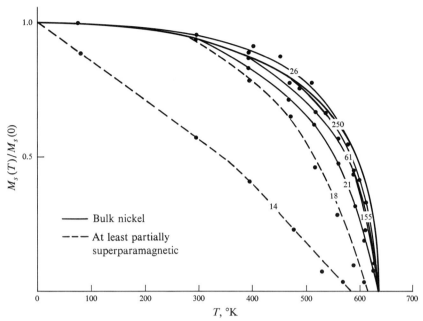

FIG. 6.6.   Normalized magnetization of nickel films of various thicknesses vs temperature (after Neugebauer, Ref. 21).

the magnetization and the field, and K_1 is an anisotropy constant inserted to accommodate a possible easy or hard direction of magnetization perpendicular to the plane of the film. According to Chap. 8, the torque τ acting on the magnetization is proportional to $\delta E/\delta \theta$. Therefore, setting $\delta E/\delta \theta = 0$ and letting $\alpha = 45°$, we find

$$\sin \theta = \frac{-M_s H \pm [M_s^2 H^2 + 8(2\pi M_s^2 + K_1)^2]^{1/2}}{4(2\pi M_s^2 + K_1)} \qquad (6.31)$$

The torque $\tau = \mathbf{M} \times \mathbf{H}$ exerted on the torsion wire by a film of volume V in a field H is

$$\tau = M_s H \sin \theta \qquad (6.32)$$

Equation (6.32) may be solved with the aid of Eq. (6.31) giving

$$\frac{\tau}{H} = -\frac{M_s^2 V}{4(2\pi M_s^2 + K_1)} H + \frac{1}{\sqrt{2}} M_s V \qquad (6.33)$$

at low fields where the H^2 term can be neglected. Thus, the vertical intercept of a τ/H vs H plot yields $\tau/H_o = M_s V/\sqrt{2}$ constituting a measurement of M_s. Note that in this method, the value of K_1 does not influence the measured value of M_s. This fact is pertinent when we recall the influence of a surface anisotropy upon the value of the magnetization as discussed in Sec. 6.2. It should be mentioned that at very low fields, $M < M_s$ and the values of τ/H_o are too low compared to the theoretical predictions so we have to determine the τ/H ordinate intercept by extrapolation of the curve at higher fields.

At a field $H = (2\pi M_s^2 + K_1)/M_s$, the solution of the torque equation, Eq. (6.32), gives

$$\frac{\tau}{H} = 0.707 \frac{\tau}{H_o} \qquad (6.34)$$

Thus, the anisotropy constant K_1 can be measured by finding the field H corresponding to the value of τ/H equal to 0.707 (τ/H_o).

On the other hand, at high fields, $\sin\theta$ can be rewritten to read

$$\sin\theta = \frac{M_s H}{4(2\pi M_s^2 + K_1)} \pm \left[\frac{M_s^2 H^2}{16(2\pi M_s^2 + K_1)^2} + \frac{1}{2}\right]^{1/2} \qquad (6.35)$$

Letting $a = M_s H/4(2\pi M_s^2 + K_1)$, Eq. (6.35) becomes

$$\sin\theta = a \pm \left(a^2 + \frac{1}{2}\right)^{1/2} = a \pm a\left(1 + \frac{1}{2a^2}\right)^{1/2} \qquad (6.36)$$

If $H > 9$ kOe at $K_1 = 0$, or if $H > 6$ kOe at $K_1 = -5 \times 10^5$ ergs/cm^3, $1/2a^2$ is less than unity and $(1 + 1/2a)^{1/2}$ in Eq. (6.36) can be expanded in a binomial series. Expanding and substituting in this way, we find for very high fields

$$\tau = -(2\pi M_s^2 + K_1)V + 2(2\pi M_s^2 + K_1)^3 \frac{V}{M_s^2 H^2} \qquad (6.37)$$

Thus, if τ is plotted against $1/H^2$, the intercept of the straight line with the τ axis yields the saturation torque τ_∞

$$\tau_\infty = (2\pi M_s^2 + K_1)V \qquad (6.38)$$

Actually, the torque at 10 kOe, τ_{10}, the maximum value of field used by Neugebauer in his experiments, is within 15% of τ_∞ at $K_1 = 0$. If $K_1 = -5 \times 10^5$ ergs/cm^3, τ_{10}/τ_∞ is equal to 0.93. Extrapolation of the torque from 6 to 10 kOe, although not always strictly valid in this range, nevertheless yields a value of τ_∞ which is at most 7% too low. Also, at higher temperatures, where M_s is small, τ_{10} is very close to the value of τ_∞. Thus, the saturation magnetization at different temperatures is given by

$$2\pi M_s^2(T) + K_1(T) \propto \tau_\infty(T) \qquad (6.39)$$

and if $K_1(T) \ll 2\pi M_s^2(T)$, then

$$M_s(T) \propto [\tau_\infty(T)]^{1/2} \qquad (6.40)$$

The reduced magnetization vs temperature curves of Fig. 6.6 were plotted using Eq. (6.40).

When oxygen is let into the vacuum system, M_s was observed to decrease. This is thought to be due to the formation of an oxidized layer (NiO) on the surface of the nickel film, about 10 Å thick which reduces the net volume of the ferromagnetic film. We therefore conclude that a thin film with a clean surface, i.e., devoid of appreciable oxidation, has indistinguishable magnetization from that of bulk matter. These results are in direct contradiction with the predictions of the original Klein-Smith theory using periodic boundary conditions and may or may not be consistent with the results of the modified Klein-Smith theory using partially pinned boundary condition depending upon the possible values of the surface anisotropy. It is therefore of interest to examine the correlation between theory and experiment in this regard in more detail.

Before Neugebauer's experiments were performed, there was ample experimental evidence to indicate that the magnetization of a thin film deviates significantly from that of the bulk material when the thickness of the film is less than about 100 Å in qualitative support of the theory of Klein and Smith.[13,14,22-30] In view of the new results of Neugebauer which demonstrated in a rather convincing way that the deviation of the magnetization of a continuous film from its bulk value is due to surface oxidation, we may reasonably surmise that the reported deviations of film magnetization from the bulk value[13,14,22-30] is due to the fact that these films were deposited in vacuums which are not sufficient to prevent oxidation. Furthermore, before the magnetization of these films was measured, they were removed from the vacuum deposition chamber and exposed to air for an indefinite length of time which causes further oxidation. It may be recalled here that in Neugebauer's experiments, the films were deposited in an ultrahigh vacuum of 10^{-9} mm Hg and the magnetization of the film was measured subsequent to deposition without removing it from the vacuum chamber. It may be of interest to examine here the manner in which this was accomplished by looking at his experimental apparatus, i.e., the vacuum torsion magnetometer shown in Fig. 6.7.

As shown in the figure, a mirror and lamp-scale combination allows detection of any changes in the position of the film and substrate which are oriented at 45° with respect to the field direction at zero field. When a field is applied, the film tends to twist itself parallel with the field. This tendency is counteracted by applying an equal and opposite torque by twisting the torsion wire through the required number of degrees. This is accomplished by adjusting a calibrated turn table on which are positioned a magnet, which transmits the angular motion by coupling with a third magnet in the vacuum, which, in turn, transmits it to the torsion wire. By observing this torque required to keep the film at 45° to the field direction as a function of increasing field, a τ/H vs H relationship can be found.

By means of a magnetically operated pulley, the substrate can be raised and positioned in front of the evaporation slit. Before depositing nickel on the substrate, a portion of the filament is evaporated to coat the glass walls with nickel and getter residual gases, until the pressure drops to 10^{-9} mm of Hg while the filament is still evaporating. A shutter in front of the slit is then opened for the required length of time to give a film of the desired thickness. The rate of film growth has been varied

[22] L. Reimer, *Z. Naturforsch.*, **12a**: 550 (1957).
[23] W. Ruske, *Ann. Phys.*, **2**: 274 (1958).
[24] H. J. Bauer, *Z. Physik.*, **153**: 484 (1959).
[25] A. Colombani, G. Goureaux, and P. Huet, *J. Phys. Radium*, **20**: 303 (1959).
[26] W. Hellenthal, *Z. Naturforsch.*, **13a**: 566 (1958).
[27] W. Reincke, *Z. Physik*, **137**: 169 (1954).
[28] M. H. Seavey, Jr., and P. E. Tannenwald, *J. Appl. Phys.*, **29**: 292 (1958).
[29] K. Kuwahara, *J. Phys. Soc. Japan*, **14**: 1247 (1959).
[30] M. Kuriyama, H. Yamanouchi, and S. Hosoya, *J. Phys. Soc. Japan*, **16**: 701 (1961).

from 2 Å/min to about 200 Å/min. In order to obtain a vacuum of the order of 10^{-9} mm of Hg, the system has to be baked out at 450°C for 16 hr, and metal parts must be carefully outgassed.[31]

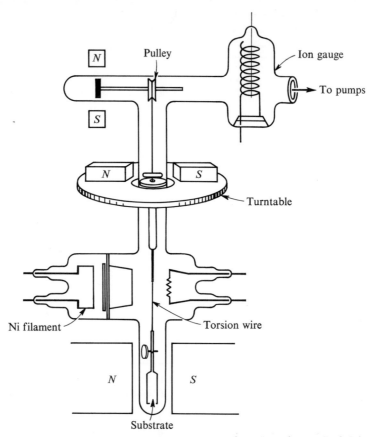

FIG. 6.7.   Vacuum torsion magnetometer (after Neugebauer, Ref. 21).

The final thickness of the film is determined after all magnetic measurements are completed and the vacuum system is open. In addition, since all results depend most critically on an accurate knowledge of the film thickness, a method of thickness measurement whose accuracy does not deteriorate with decreasing thickness in the less than 100 Å range has to be used. Since the accuracy of the Tolansky interferometer method of thickness measurement is probably not much better than 20 Å, X-ray fluorescence analysis has to be used. In this method, a polychromatic X-ray beam excites the K line of nickel, whose intensity is measured by scintillation counting. The intensity increases linearly with the thickness of the film up to several thousand angstroms. A typical count rate is 80 counts/μg/sec. The spectrometer was calibrated against known weights of solution of nickel salts. The maximum error in this method of thickness determination is about 10% of the measured thickness.

Let us now return to the discussion of the reasons for the absence of the "thin-film effect," i.e., no decrease of film magnetization with decreasing film thickness.

[31] D. Alpert, *J. Appl. Phys.*, **24**: 860 (1953).

First, it may be noted from Eq. (6.33) that τ/H is a function of the anisotropy constant K_1. Thus, the value of K_1 is usually chosen to give the best fit to the experimental τ/H vs H curve. In this way, the value of K_1 for as-evaporated films ranges from about -5×10^5 to -9×10^5 ergs/cm^3; the negative sign indicating that the easy axis corresponding to this uniaxial anisotropy is along the film normal. The origin of this anisotropy is attributed to magnetostriction in nickel. Thus, the film is under a high tensile stress of some 10^{10} dynes/cm^2 and it can be partially relieved by subsequent anneal. Of course, in the case of Permalloy film of interest, i.e., those in the 80% Ni-20% Fe composition range, the magnetostrictive coefficient is very small so that the corresponding value K_1 should also be much smaller than that for nickel quoted above.

Of particular interest is the increase in the value of K_1 of nickel films when oxygen or hydrogen is admitted to the vacuum system or if a copper film is deposited on top of the nickel. For example, after oxygen is admitted to the vacuum system, the value of K_1 of the film changes from -6.6×10^5 to -9.5×10^5 ergs/cm^3, a relatively large change indeed. Several explanations may be given for this observed change in K_1.[21] First, it is conceivable that the atoms in the underlying nickel film will try to match the larger Ni-Ni distances in the oxide, thus leading to a tensile strain in the film, and thus to a larger K_1. Second, a more negative K_1 after oxidation could be explained if the surface roughness was increased during oxidation. For instance, if the film was reasonably flat before oxidation, and acquired a mountain-valley structure after oxidation, it now becomes easier for the magnetization vector to swing into a direction perpendicular to the film plane since the shape demagnetizing energy is lowered in the direction of the peaks. Such a roughening of the surface can only come about by the preferential oxidation at certain locations at the surface. It is difficult, however, to assess the importance of this in an already highly disordered and random structure of an evaporated film. Third, there may be an exchange interaction between the ferromagnetic nickel and the antiferromagnetic nickel oxide at their interface giving rise to an exchange anisotropy.[10] In order to get more negative K_1's during oxidation, we have to postulate that the ferromagnetic sheets in the NiO lie parallel to the protruding peaks at the surface of the nickel film, and that the moments of the nickel ions in the oxide are aligned in a parallel direction. At first sight, however, one would expect the ferromagnetic sheets of the NiO to be distributed randomly and not to give rise to a preferred direction of magnetization. Nevertheless, the energetics of the situation are far from clear since the interface between a ferromagnetic and an antiferromagnetic region may be very complicated indeed.

Still a fourth explanation can be advanced for the observed changes in the anisotropy, and this has to do with the change in surface anisotropy of the film as the interface changes from metal/vacuum to metal/oxide. Néel has pointed out that although anisotropic interaction, such as pseudodipolar coupling in cubic lattices, may sum to zero by symmetry in first approximation at interior lattice points, it need not sum to zero at surfaces.[9] This anisotropy is associated with certain crystallographic planes and can make K_1 either more positive or negative, depending upon the crystal face and metal in question. Therefore, it can be expected that the sign and magnitude of this anisotropy would depend rather sensitively upon the detail environment of the surfaces. Thus, changes in the surface anisotropy should certainly occur when originally clean nickel surfaces are covered with oxide or are altered in any way; but it is difficult to estimate the magnitude of this effect in the absence of a detailed calculation in this regard.

If the observed magnetic anisotropy of nickel arises in second order from pseudo-dipolar coupling, then the coupling strength is required to be $\sim 30°K$. Taking this as a measure of the surface anisotropy energy, and $J \sim 300°K$, we arrived at a crude estimate of ε, the ratio of surface anisotropy energy to exchange energy [see Eq. (6.25)], of about 0.1 for clean smooth surfaces of nickel. Wolfram and Lehman have recently made a calculation, similar to that of Davis and Keffer for sc crystals, on the spin pinning and size effect in thin ferromagnetic films of sc, fcc, and bcc structures.[32] They found that for an ε of $> 10^{-3}$, the magnetization of a 15 atom-layer film is within 5% of that of the bulk value. Thus, the magnetization of thin films is likely to be indistinguishable from that of bulk matter as an ε of 10^{-3} can be amply supplied by the estimated Néel surface anisotropy energy of 0.1 that of the exchange energy of nickel. According to the results of theoretical calculation using partially pinned rather than periodic boundary condition, we then indeed should expect the magnetization of a nonoxidized thin film to be independent of thickness, consistent with the experimental results of Neugebauer. For an oxidized film, on the other hand, we can interpret, at least qualitatively, the decrease in magnetization from the bulk value as due to the formation of an oxidized surface layer accompanied perhaps by an antiferromagnetic to ferromagnetic transition region. The oxidation reduces the net volume of ferromagnetic material and an apparent decrease in the magnetization if the volume of the entire film is used in the interpretation of the torque data. The actual situation is probably much more complicated than this. For example, if oxygen diffuses into the nickel via grain boundaries, the magnetization decrease may be due to a volume rather than a surface effect. However, since the magnetization was observed to decrease very quickly after admission of oxygen into the vacuum system, this is probably not the case. On the other hand, when hydrogen instead of oxygen was admitted, the magnetization decrease was observed to occur slowly indicating some degree of volume chemical absorption of hydrogen.

Inasmuch as the magnetostrictive constant in a Permalloy film is in general not zero, a volume uniaxial anisotropy energy of the form $K_1 \sin^2(\alpha - \theta)$ as given by Eq. (6.30) should be included in a magnetization calculation. This effect has recently been considered in detail by Doring, who adds a small anisotropy field, uniform across the film.[33] By treating the surface field H_s as a perturbation on Doring's solution, Davis and Keffer[8] found practically identical results for the film magnetization as that obtained by assuming a mixed z-directed sine and cosine spin waves leading to the transcendental equation, Eq. (6.25), for the allowed values of k_z.

6·4 MAGNETIZATION AS A FUNCTION OF THICKNESS

Whereas a comparison between theory and experiment of the thin-film magnetization as a function of temperature was done in the last section, it is more convenient to replot Figs. 6.1 to 6.5 as a function of thickness with the temperature as a constant parameter. This is so because most experiments in this connection were carried out

[32] T. Wolfram and G. W. Lehman, *Bull. Am. Phys. Soc.*, Ser. II, **8**: 439 (1963).
[33] W. Doring, *Z. Naturforsch.*, **16S**: 1146 (1961).

at liquid helium, liquid nitrogen, or room temperatures for films of various thicknesses.

By replotting some of the curves in Figs. 6.1 to 6.5, we obtain $M_s(T)/M_s(0)$ as a function of the thickness in units of the lattice constant as shown in Fig. 6.8. Some representative experimental results[13, 14, 21, 28] are also plotted in Fig. 6.8 for comparison with theory. It is seen that the results on nonoxidized nickel films[21] agree well with the modified Klein-Smith theory using partially pinned boundary condition. On the other hand, the oxidized films[13, 14, 28] also have the qualitative

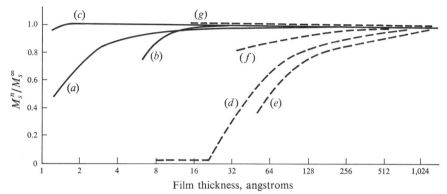

FIG. 6.8.   Normalized magnetization vs film thickness: (a) Ni(111) at 289°K (after Valenta, Ref. 15); (b) Ni(100) at 223°K (after Glass and Klein, Ref. 7); (c) sc lattice at 4°K; lattice constant of nickel is used here (after Davis and Keffer, Ref. 8); (d) polycrystalline nickel at 293°K (after Crittenden and Hoffman, Ref. 14); (e) polycrystalline nickel at 293°K (after Drigo, Ref. 13); (f) polycrystalline 80–20 Permalloy at 293°K (after Seavey and Tannenwald, Ref. 28); (g) polycrystalline nickel (after Neugebauer, Ref. 21).

Solid curves and dashed curves represent theoretical and experimental data, respectively. M_s^n and M_s^∞ represent magnetization of an n-layer film and bulk material, respectively.

behavior of the original Klein-Smith theory. However, as we discussed at length in the last section, this agreement is probably more accidental than real. The decrease in the experimental value of the magnetization from bulk value is due to surface oxidation while the corresponding decrease in the Klein-Smith theory is due to the unpermissible use of the periodic boundary condition. Valenta's calculation is based upon the approximate molecular-field Néel sublattice method. It is seen from Fig. 6.8 that the agreement between Valenta's theory and experiment, using Neugebauer's results, is better than that with original Klein-Smith theory but not as good with the modified Klein-Smith theory.

The constancy of the magnetization with film thickness agrees with the experimental results connected with the magnetization of fine ferromagnetic particles. Several investigators have studied the magnetic behavior of small ferromagnetic particles down to 15 Å radius and found no decrease in the magnetization from bulk value within an experimental accuracy of 10%.[34–37]

[34] C. P. Bean, J. D. Livingston, and D. S. Rodbell, *J. Phys. Radium*, **20**: 298 (1959).
[35] C. P. Bean and I. S. Jacobs, *J. Appl. Phys.*, **27**: 1448 (1956).
[36] F. Luborsky, *Phys. Rev.*, **109**: 40 (1958).
[37] J. J. Becker, *Trans. Am. Inst. Mining Met. Engr.*, **209**: 59 (1957).

6·5 MAGNETIZATION AS A FUNCTION OF COMPOSITION

Most magnetization measurements were carried out with nickel films although some were with Permalloy. In particular, the pertinent experiments of Neugebauer were concerned with the magnetization of nickel films. In principle, at least, the film magnetization as a function of composition cannot be completely settled in the absence of results of magnetization measurements with Permalloy of different composition. In this connection, it may be pointed out that a measurement in the change of the anisotropy constant K_1 for 80–20% composition range Permalloy with oxidation is of significance in determining the mechanism of spin pinning in spin-wave resonance experiments (see Chap. 11). However, from the theoretical standpoint, in view of the discussion in Secs. 6.2 to 6.4, there is no particular reason why the magnetization of thin films should not have the same compositional dependence as bulk material.

CHAPTER 7

ANISOTROPY

When a static magnetic field is applied parallel to the substrate during deposition of a thin Permalloy film, an easy axis is developed in the direction of the field giving rise to a uniaxial anisotropy. One of the most intriguing and interesting aspects of magnetic thin films is the origin of this uniaxial magnetic anisotropy.

The contributing sources to this anisotropy are at least fivefold: (1) Fe-pair formation in a nickel lattice, (2) preferential imperfection orientation, (3) magnetostriction due to induced stress, (4) local variations of the magnetocrystalline anisotropy, and (5) the vapor beam angle of incidence effect. In this chapter, we shall study the relative importance of these contributions to the magnitude and direction of the uniaxial anisotropy in Permalloy films with particular emphasis upon the pertinent theory and related experiments.

Some of the films, when subject to magnetic anneal either at room or at elevated temperatures for a sufficient length of time, change their direction of easy magnetization acquired during deposition to that of the subsequent annealing field. The origin of this "rotatable anisotropy" is of considerable interest; a careful study of its characteristics may help to decide which of the five mechanisms mentioned in the last paragraph is mainly responsible for the uniaxial anisotropy in thin films. Therefore, we shall examine this subject in some detail.

Several methods may be used for the measurement of the anisotropy. The most common techniques employed are the torque magnetometer, the hysteresis looper, and the ferromagnetic resonance spectrometer. We shall discuss each of these methods along with descriptions of the apparatus involved. In addition, we shall study the methods of measuring the anisotropy easy-axis dispersion often found in thin films, the origin of which will also be examined in connection with the theory of the anisotropy.

7·1 MAGNETOCRYSTALLINE ANISOTROPY

It is an experimental fact that ferromagnetic single crystals have easy and hard directions of magnetization; i.e., the energy required to magnetize the crystal depends upon the direction of the applied magnetic field relative to the crystalline axes. The difference between the energies required to magnetize the crystal in the hard and easy directions is termed the anisotropy energy. For single-crystal ferromagnetic metals such as nickel, iron, and their alloys (Permalloy) prepared in the absence of a magnetic field, their anisotropy has cubic symmetry. (Due to the random orientation of the axes of the constituent cubic crystallites, a polycrystal appears isotropic.) Neither the exchange interaction between spins nor the classical dipole-dipole interaction due to spin magnetic moments adequately accounts for the observed anisotropy. In the former case, the exchange interaction, in the semiclassical treatment, as given by Eq. (6.2), is proportional to the scaler product between the spin vectors but is independent of the angle between the spins and the crystalline axes. Therefore, its isotropic nature can not lead to anisotropic effect. In the latter case, the magnetic field acting on a spin due to its neighboring dipoles cancels to a first approximation when all the spins are assumed parallel due to the crystal's cubic symmetry and, therefore, cannot contribute to the anisotropy either. [See calculation, Sec. 7.2(a).] However, although the classical dipole-dipole coupling does not contribute to cubic anisotropy when the spins are all parallel, there is some contribution in the second approximation of quantum-mechanical perturbation theory in which complete parallelism is not assumed. Nevertheless, the main source of contribution to the cubic anisotropy obtained from second-order perturbation theory is due not to the classical dipole-dipole interaction but to interactions that are purely quantum mechanical in origin. These so-called "pseudodipole" and "pseudoquadrupole" couplings, although respectively identical in form to the ordinary magnetic dipole-dipole and quadrupole-quadrupole couplings with respect to the spin variables, are shorter in range and the pseudodipole interaction is 50 times larger in magnitude than the ordinary dipole-dipole interaction. The quantum-mechanical origin of these couplings is believed to be due to the combined effects of spin-orbit interaction and the partial quenching of the orbital angular momentum by inhomogeneous crystalline electric fields and by orbital exchange interaction with neighboring atoms.[1] To be more explicit, the spin and orbital angular momentum interact with each other via spin-orbit coupling, and orbital motion is in turn influenced by the electrostatic fields and overlapping wave functions associated with the neighboring atoms of the crystal lattice. Thus, the magnetization of the crystal, via the agency of the orbital motion of the electron, becomes aware of the presence of the crystal lattice and its symmetry.

In this section, we shall study the mathematical details of the theory of cubic anisotropy for two purposes. First, we wish to understand the physical origin of cubic anisotropy of single-crystal magnetic films deposited in the absence of a magnetic field. Secondly, we wish to acquaint ourselves with the mathematical formalism pertinent to the study of the all-important uniaxial anisotropy in thin films deposited in the presence of a magnetic field. In the next section, we shall show that due to the presence of pseudodipole interaction ferromagnetic metals and their solid solutions may have an anisotropic equilibrium distribution of atom pairs below the Curie temperature if they are formed in the presence of a magnetic field. This anisotropic distribution of atom pairs in turn gives rise to an anisotropy having a symmetry that is lower than cubic.

(a) General Discussion

The experimental results on the anisotropy of such cubic metals as nickel and iron can be expressed in terms of a free energy F of the form

$$F = F_0 + F_1 + F_2 \qquad (7.1)$$

---

[1] J. H. Van Vleck, *Phys. Rev.*, **52**: 1178 (1937).

F_0 is purely isotropic in origin while F_1 and F_2 are anisotropic and may be expressed in terms of the direction cosines α_1, α_2, and α_3 of the saturating applied field relative to the principal cubic axes:

$$F_1 = K_1(\alpha_1^2\alpha_2^2 + \alpha_2^2\alpha_3^2 + \alpha_3^2\alpha_1^2) \tag{7.2}$$

$$F_2 = K_2\alpha_1^2\alpha_2^2\alpha_3^2 \tag{7.3}$$

where K_1 and K_2, known as the first- and second-order anisotropy constants, are chosen to fit the experimental data.

It is easy to see that the forms in Eqs. (7.2) and (7.3) do indeed represent to a good approximation cubic symmetry. From considerations of cubic symmetry, the anisotropy energy must be an even power of α_i where $i = 1, 2, 3$; and it must be invariant under interchanges of the α_i's among themselves. The lowest-order combination satisfying this symmetry requirement is $\alpha_1^2 + \alpha_2^2 + \alpha_3^2$, but this is equal to unity and therefore does not enter into the description of anisotropic effects. The next combination is of the fourth degree, $\alpha_1^2\alpha_2^2 + \alpha_2^2\alpha_3^2 + \alpha_3^2\alpha_1^2$, and then of the sixth degree, $\alpha_1^2\alpha_2^2\alpha_3^2$. Thus, to a good approximation, the anisotropy energy may be expressed in the forms of Eqs. (7.2) and (7.3).

We now proceed to evaluate K_1 and K_2 in terms of fundamental atomic constants. The Hamiltonian of the spin system is given by[1]

$$\mathcal{H} = -2\sum_{i,j}' J_{ij}(\mathbf{r}_{ij})\mathbf{S}_i \cdot \mathbf{S}_j + \sum_{i,j}' C_{ij}[\mathbf{S}_i \cdot \mathbf{S}_j - 3r_{ij}^{-2}(\mathbf{S}_i \cdot \mathbf{r}_{ij})(\mathbf{S}_j \cdot \mathbf{r}_{ij})]$$

$$+ \sum_{ij}' \gamma_{ij} r_{ij}^{-4}(\mathbf{S}_i \cdot \mathbf{r}_{ij})^2(\mathbf{S}_j \cdot \mathbf{r}_{ij})^2 \tag{7.4}$$

where the first term represents the exchange energy while the second and third terms represent, respectively, the pseudodipole and pseudoquadrupole energies. J_{ij} is the exchange integral between spins i and j, while the summation $\sum_{i,j}'$ implies the exclusion in the sum of the self-energy terms $i = j$. S_i and S_j represent two spin operators denoted by i and j while r_{ij} is the corresponding separation between them. As we discussed earlier, the anisotropic terms in Eq. (7.4) are due to the interplay between spin-orbit coupling and orbital valence. The latter term refers to the fact that the mutual electrostatic energy of two atoms depends on the way their orbital angular momenta as well as their spins are aligned.

Since the Heisenberg exchange energy is usually much larger than the pseudo-dipole and pseudoquadrupole energies, the first term in Eq. (7.4) may be taken as the unperturbed part of the Hamiltonian in a perturbation calculation. For simplicity, we shall regard the exchange energy as equivalent to a Weiss molecular field proportional to the intensity of the magnetization. The constant of proportionality λ may, if desired, be a function of T. The use of a Weiss molecular field is somewhat phenomenological but has been shown by Heisenberg to be related to the exchange integral as we have discussed in Sec. 6.1. Thus, the first term of Eq. (7.4) may be replaced by $-g\mu_B\lambda\mathbf{M} \cdot \sum_i S_i$ where g is the Lande g factor ($=2$ for an electron spin), μ_B is the Bohr magneton, and $\mathbf{M}$ is the magnetization of the ferromagnet.

In the usual way, we proceed by diagonalizing the Hamiltonian of Eq. (7.4) obtaining its eigenvalues E_λ. Then, the free energy F may be found from the expression

$$F = -k_B T \log Z \tag{7.5}$$

where $Z = \sum_\lambda e^{-E_\lambda/k_B T}$ is the partition function while k_B is Boltzmann's constant and T is the absolute temperature. For generality, the molecular field λM may be augmented by an applied field H_{ex} so that Eq. (7.4) may be written compactly:

$$\mathscr{H} = -g\mu_B H \sum_i S_{zi} + \sum_{i,j}{}' w_{ij} \tag{7.6}$$

where $H = H_{ex} + \lambda M$ and w_{ij} is the interaction energy between atoms i and j. Let us now regard the first term of Eq. (7.6) as the unperturbed system. A system of representation can then be used in which each atom is space-quantized separately with the corresponding eigenvalues of S_{zi} being denoted by m_i. Thus, the unperturbed energy is simply

$$E_o = -g\mu_B H \sum_i m_i \tag{7.7}$$

Treating w_{ij} in Eq. (7.6) as the perturbation potential and carrying the calculation to the second order in C and first order in γ, we can find the complete set of eigenvalues E_λ and H. From these values of E_λ, we find a complicated expression for the partition function $Z = \sum_\lambda e^{-E_\lambda/k_B T}$. Then, using Eq. (7.5), we find that the expression for the free energy F, in the case of a cubic single crystal, is of the form of Eq. (7.1), consistent with experiment. The sign of K_1 due the pseudodipole term is negative for an fcc or bcc lattice and is positive for an sc one. The pseudodipole coupling gives a K_1 of the proper sign for nickel, since the latter has a face-centered lattice and negative K_1. Since nickel is the material most likely to have a spin of $\frac{1}{2}$ for which the pseudoquadrupole term vanishes, the agreement is indicative of the correctness of the general feature of the Van Vleck theory of anisotropy. For iron, which is bcc, on the other hand, the observed positive sign of K_1 does not check with the pseudodipole model, but is not inconsistent with the combination of pseudodipole and pseudoquadrupole couplings providing $S > \frac{1}{2}$ (likely in iron) and the pseudo-quadrupole effect is more important than that of the pseudodipole. Theoretical estimates of K_1 are of right order of magnitude when compared with the experimental values; on the other hand, the temperature dependence of K_1 proves correct only in a rough qualitative way. Of course, C and γ should really be taken as undetermined functions of T rather than as constant in the calculation of the anisotropy.

The perturbation calculation has not been carried out to sufficiently high order to say anything about the sign or temperature dependence of K_2. Furthermore, the theoretical values of K_2 are two or three orders of magnitude smaller than the experimental ones.

It may be of interest to quote the typical values of K_1 and K_2 for some cubic crystals. For iron, the easy axes of magnetization lie along the cube edges. At room temperature, for iron, $K_1 = 4.2 \times 10^5$ ergs/cm^3 and $K_2 = 1.5 \times 10^5$ ergs/cm^3. For nickel, on the other hand, the easy directions of magnetization are the body diagonals of the cubic crystal. Its K_1 is -5×10^4 ergs/cm^3.

(b) Local Variations

The discussion in the last subsection is mainly concerned with the anisotropy of single crystals. For fundamental studies, single crystals are usually used in order to minimize complications and to facilitate comparison between theory and experiment. On the other hand, polycrystalline samples are usually of more technological importance because of their larger size and simpler methods of mass preparation. It is therefore of some significance to inquire into the nature of the crystalline anisotropy in polycrystals.

Since the various crystallites in a polycrystalline sample are more or less randomly oriented, the anisotropy field in a saturated specimen may average nearly to zero. If the sample is not saturated, then the anisotropy field may not average to zero. In the case of insulating polycrystals like ferrites, an indirect qualitative determination of the anisotropy field can be made by observing the domain rotation resonance in polycrystalline samples.[2] For example, in this way it has been found that for several dense polycrystalline ferrites $K_e \sim 2K_1$, where K_e and K_1 are, respectively, polycrystalline and single-crystal anisotropy constants.[3] K_e and K_1 are different, owing to the demagnetizing fields introduced by the porosity and the grain structure of polycrystalline materials.

If the distribution of the easy axes of uniaxial crystals, say, is not random, then the spatial variation of the easy directions may be represented by a Fourier series; each of its components may be termed an "anisotropy easy-direction wave." If such waves do exist in polycrystalline Permalloy films, a number of magnetization reversal phenomena may be explained. We shall reserve this topic for a fuller discussion after we have discussed the theory of induced uniaxial anisotropy in magnetic films in the next section.

7·2 INDUCED UNIAXIAL ANISOTROPY

For hexagonal and uniaxial single crystals, etc., the dipole-dipole interaction (classical or pseudo), due to the loss of cubic symmetry, no longer vanishes in the first approximation when all spins are assumed parallel. In this section, we shall discuss in particular the Néel-Taniguchi theory of induced uniaxial anisotropy in bulk Permalloy formed in the presence of magnetic field which is related to the prominence of the pseudodipole term in the noncubic crystals. Comparing the results of this theory to the experimental observations on the uniaxial anistropy in thin films, we find that although this source of induced anisotropy is all important in bulk Permalloy, it is probably not the only mechanism which is responsible for the uniaxial anisotropy in Permalloy films. Therefore, subsequent to the discussion of the Néel-Taniguchi theory, we shall examine the possible contribution to the uniaxial anisotropy in thin films due to magnetostriction and imperfection orientation. The anisotropy related to the angle of incidence of the vapor beam and rotatable anisotropy (change of easy axis by annealing in a magnetic field at an angle to the easy axis after evaporation) will be separately treated in the following sections.

---

[2] See, e.g., R. F. Soohoo, *Theory and Application of Ferrites*, Prentice-Hall, Inc., Englewood Cliffs, N.J., (1960), p. 83.
[3] G. J. Kriesman, S. E. Harrison, and H. A. Bilson, *J. Appl. Phys.*, **29**: 452 (1958).

(a) Néel-Taniguchi Theory

When a binary alloy such as Permalloy is heat-treated in a magnetic field, a uniaxial anisotropy is developed therein. Néel[4] and Taniguchi[5] have interpreted this as the creation of a short-range directional order. They consider an alloy of two components, A and B, and assume that the energy of the link between two neighboring atoms depends both on their natures, and on the angle between the line joining them and the spontaneous magnetization. During the annealing in a strong magnetic field, the diffusion of the atoms on the lattice leads to anisotropic distributions of the $A–A$, $A–B$, and $B–B$ links, and this state can be conserved at room temperature by quenching. The same interaction energy between the nearest-neighbor links and the magnetization leads to a uniaxial anisotropy. We shall first give the mathematical formulation of the theory and then compare the theoretical results with experiment.

Starting with the Van Vleck Hamiltonian of Eq. (7.6), we may find its eigenvalues. Then, the partition function Z of the system can be obtained by expanding it in a power series of $(kT)^{-1}$:

$$\frac{Z}{Z_o} = 1 - \langle \sum_{i,j}' w_{ij} \rangle / k_B T + \langle (\sum_{i,j}' w_{ij})^2 \rangle / 2k_B^2 T^2 \cdots \tag{7.8}$$

where Z_o is partition function of the unperturbed system corresponding to the first term of Eq. (7.6) and $\langle \sum_{i,j}' w_{ij} \rangle$ denotes the expectation value of $\sum_{i,j}' w_{ij}$, etc. The free energy F of the system is then given by

$$F = -k_B T \ln Z = -k_B T \ln Z_o + \langle \sum_{i,j}' w_{ij} \rangle$$
$$- \langle (\sum_{i,j}' w_{ij})^2 \rangle / 2k_B T + \cdots \tag{7.9}$$

which shows that the anisotropy can be found if $\langle \sum_{i,j}' w_{ij} \rangle$, etc., can be evaluated.

Since the pseudodipole interaction is expected to be dominant in a noncubic crystal even to the first approximation, we may neglect the pseudoquadrupole term in w_{ij}. Then, it follows that

$$w_{ij} = \sum_{q, q' = x, y, z} a_{ij}^{qq'} S_{qi} S_{q'j} \tag{7.10}$$

where $a_{ij}^{qq'} (= a_{ij}^{q'q})$ is the qq' component of the coupling constant a_{ij} referred to the coordinate system (x, y, z) so oriented that the field is always in the z direction. S_{qi} and $S_{q'j}$ are, respectively, the q component of the spin of atom i and the q' component of the spin of atom j, and

$$\langle w_{ij} \rangle = \sum_{q, q'} a_{ij}^{qq'} \langle S_{qi} S_{q'j} \rangle = a_{ij}^{zz} B_1^2 \tag{7.11}$$

where
$$B_1 = SB(\theta) = \frac{2S+1}{2} \coth\left(\frac{2S+1}{2}\theta\right) - \frac{1}{2}\coth\left(\frac{\theta}{2}\right) \tag{7.12}$$

[4] L. Néel, *Compt. Rend.*, **237**: 1468, 1613 (1953); *J. Phys. Radium*, **15**: 225 (1954).
[5] S. Taniguchi, *Sci. Repts. Res. Insts.*, Tohoku Univ. Ser. A1, 269 (1955).

and $\theta = g\mu_B H/k_B T$. Here S is the spin quantum number of all atoms, and $B(\theta)$ is the usual Brillouin function.

To study anisotropy, it is necessary to express the interaction energy w_{ij} in terms of constant A_{ij} for a system of axes (X, Y, Z) fixed relative to the crystal instead of fixed relative to the field, i.e.,

$$w_{ij} = \sum_{q, q' = X, Y, Z} A_{ij}^{qq'} S_{qi} S_{q'j} \tag{7.13}$$

The transformation relation between the a_{ij}'s and the A_{ij}'s is

$$a_{ij}^{qq'} = \sum_{p, p' = X, Y, Z} \lambda_{qp} \lambda_{q'p'} A_{ij}^{pp'} \tag{7.14}$$

where λ_{qp} is the cosine of the angle between the q and p axes. Furthermore, for the dipole-dipole coupling, $A_{ij}^{pp'}$ is given by

$$A_{ij}^{pp'} = C_{ij}(\delta_{pp'} - 3n_{ij}^p n_{ij}^{p'}) \tag{7.15}$$

where C_{ij} is the coupling constant, $\delta_{pp'}$ the Kronecker delta, and n_{ij}^p the cosine of the angle between the direction of the atom pair (i,j) and that of the p axis. From Eq. (7.11) we have

$$\left\langle \sum_{i, j}' w_{ij} \right\rangle = \frac{N}{2} B_1^2 \sum_j a_{ij}^{zz} \tag{7.16}$$

where the summation $\sum_{i, j}'$ has been replaced by $\frac{N}{2} \sum_j$ and N is the number of atoms per unit volume, since all atoms are identical for the cubic lattice of concern here. Using Eqs. (7.14) and (7.15), Eq. (7.16) becomes

$$\left\langle \sum_{i, j}' w_{ij} \right\rangle = \frac{N}{2} B_1^2 (\alpha_1^2 \sum_j A_{ij}^{XX} + \alpha_2^2 \sum_j A_{ij}^{YY} + \alpha_3^2 \sum_j A_{ij}^{ZZ}$$
$$+ 2\alpha_1 \alpha_2 \sum_j A_{ij}^{XY} + 2\alpha_2 \alpha_3 \sum_j A_{ij}^{YZ} + 2\alpha_3 \alpha_1 \sum_j A_{ij}^{ZX}) \tag{7.17}$$

In Eq. (7.17), α_1, α_2, and α_3 have been used in place of λ_{zX}, λ_{zY}, and λ_{zZ}.

In cubic crystals, sums like $\sum A_{ij}^{XY}$ in which a letter in the superscript appears only once vanish while

$$\sum_j A_{ij}^{XX} = \sum_j A_{ij}^{YY} = \sum_j A_{ij}^{ZZ} = \frac{1}{3} \sum_j (A_{ij}^{XX} + A_{ij}^{YY} + A_{ij}^{ZZ}) = \Omega_o \tag{7.18}$$

For this case Eq. (7.17) simply becomes

$$\left\langle \sum_{i, j}' w_{ij} \right\rangle = \frac{N}{2} B_1^2 \Omega_o \tag{7.19}$$

which is independent of the direction of the magnetization. Thus, we have demonstrated the well-known result that the dipole-dipole coupling, to the first order, does not contribute to the magnetic anisotropy in cubic crystals composed of only one kind of atom.[6] The situation is quite different, however, for cubic solid solutions of the substitutional type as we shall now elaborate in what follows.

Consider a cubic solid solution of the substitutional type, composed of two kinds of atoms A and B. The energy of the pseudodipole due to the interplay between spin-orbit coupling and orbital valence, unlike the ordinary magnetic dipole-dipole interaction, decreases more rapidly than the inverse three power of the distance between atom pairs.[1] Thus, without great loss of generality, we may consider the pseudodipole interaction as existing between nearest neighbors only. Furthermore, we shall assume for simplicity that the spin quantum numbers are the same for the constituent atoms and only the coupling constant C_{ij}'s in Eq. (7.15) differ for different kinds of nearest-neighbor atom pairs. We then let C_{AA}, C_{BB}, and C_{AB} be the coupling constants of nearest-neighbor atom pairs A–A, B–B, and A–B. In the absence of anisotropic interaction among atoms, such as that associated with superlattice formation or precipitation other than that of magnetic origin, we may suppose that if the concentration of B atoms is n ($\ll 1$) and the total number of nearest-neighbor atoms is z, the nearest-neighbor atoms around a given atom are nz of B atoms and $(1 - n)z$ of A atoms. Since, within the framework of the nearest-neighbor approximation, only the distribution of B atoms in the neighbors of a given B atom may be responsible for the induced anisotropy, we may replace $(N/2) \sum_j$ in the previous equations by $(N/2) n \sum_j'$ where $\sum_j'$ denotes the summation over all nearest neighbors of a given B atom.

The diffusion of atoms during magnetic anneal takes place at high temperatures below the Curie point. An increase by unity in the number of B–B atom pairs in one of the nearest-neighbor directions through any interchange between A and B atoms results in an increase by unity in the number of A–A atom pairs and a decrease by two in the number of A–B atom pairs in the same direction. It follows that the change in the energy of the pseudodipole coupling due to an interchange between an A and a B atom at a temperature T' may be expressed as $CB_1^2(T')(1 - 3\cos^2 \phi)$ with the help of Eqs. (7.11), (7.14), and (7.15), where $C = C_{AA} + C_{BB} - 2C_{AB}$ and ϕ is the angle between the direction of the spontaneous magnetization and the direction of the B–B atom pair considered. Therefore, the probability that an B–B atom pair takes the direction specified by the angle ϕ in the equilibrium state, $\omega(\phi)$, is given approximately by

$$\omega(\phi) = \frac{1}{z} e^{-CB_1^2(T')(1 - 3\cos^2 \phi)/k_B T'} \tag{7.20}$$

since the pseudodipole coupling is very much smaller than the thermal agitation energy so that the deviation from isotropic distribution is very small. Accordingly, the equilibrium distribution of solute atom pairs becomes slightly anisotropic below the Curie temperature. Then, the result of our calculation for the cubic anisotropy for pure metals obtained above, which may also be applicable for solid solutions having the isotropic distribution of solute atom pairs, does not hold in this case. In contrast to the negative result expressed by Eq. (7.19) with regard to the first-order contribution of the pseudodipole interaction to the cubic anisotropy of a crystal

---

[6] See, e.g., R. Becker, *Zeits Physik*, **62**: 253 (1930); G. S. Mahajani, *Phil. Trans. Roy. Soc.*, **228**: 63 (1929).

of identical atoms, the first-order pseudodipole interaction in this case gives rise to an anisotropy of form, according to Eq. (7.17) and the discussion above:

$$F = F_0 + \alpha_1^2 \Omega^{XX} + \alpha_2^2 \Omega^{YY} + \alpha_3^2 \Omega^{ZZ}$$

$$+ 2\alpha_1\alpha_2 \Omega^{XY} + 2\alpha_2\alpha_3 \Omega^{YZ} + 2\alpha_3\alpha_1 \Omega^{ZX} \qquad (7.21)$$

where the isotropic term F_0 is equal to $-k_B T \ln Z_o$ and

$$\Omega^{pp'} = \frac{N}{2} n B_1^2(T) {\sum_j}' A_{ij}^{pp'} \qquad (7.22)$$

Since $A_{ij}^{pp'}$ in this case is given by

$$A_{ij}^{pp'} = zn\omega(\phi) C_{ij}(\delta_{pp'} - 3n_{ij}^p n_{ij}^{p'}) \qquad (7.23)$$

instead of by Eq. (7.15), we can calculate $\Omega^{pp'}$ by expanding the exponential in $\omega(\phi)$ given by Eq. (7.20) with respect to $(k_B T')^{-1}$. Since $|C|/k_B T' \ll 1$, we need to retain only the first-order term in the expansion and if we further replace C_{ij} by C, we find

$$\Omega^{pp'} = \frac{N}{2} n^2 C B_1^2(T) {\sum_j}' \{1 - C B_1^2(T')[1 - 3(n_{ij}^X)^2]/k_B T\}$$

$$\times (\delta_{pp'} - 3n_{ij}^p n_{ij}^{p'}) \qquad (7.24)$$

where the direction of the annealing field is assumed to be along the X axis. Furthermore, since the terms such as ${\sum_j}' (\delta_{pp'} - 3n_{ij}^p n_{ij}^{p'})$ vanish, Eq. (7.24) becomes

$$\Omega^{pp'} = -\frac{9Nn^2 C^2 B_1^2(T) B_1^2(T')}{2k_B T'} {\sum_j}' \left[(n_{ij}^X)^2 n_{ij}^p n_{ij}^{p'} - \frac{1}{3} n_{ij}^p n_{ij}^{p'} \right] \qquad (7.25)$$

For the various kinds of cubic lattices, we find from Eq. (7.25) that

$$\Omega^{XX} = -ANn^2 C^2 B_1^2(T) B_1^2(T') \frac{(\beta_1^2\beta_2^2 + \beta_2^2\beta_3^2 + \beta_3^2\beta_1^2 + B)}{k_B T'}$$

$$\Omega^{YY} = \frac{A}{2} Nn^2 C^2 B_1^2(T) B_1^2(T') \frac{(\beta_1^2\beta_1'^2 + \beta_2^2\beta_2'^2 + \beta_3^2\beta_3'^2 + B)}{k_B T'}$$

$$\Omega^{ZZ} = \frac{A}{2} Nn^2 C^2 B_1^2(T) B_1^2(T') \frac{(\beta_1^2\beta_1''^2 + \beta_2^2\beta_2''^2 + \beta_3^2\beta_3''^2 + B)}{k_B T'}$$

$$\Omega^{XY} = \frac{A}{2} Nn^2 C^2 B_1^2(T) B_1^2(T') \frac{(\beta_1^3\beta_1' + \beta_2^3\beta_2' + \beta_3^3\beta_3')}{k_B T'} \qquad (7.26)$$

$$\Omega^{YZ} = \frac{A}{2} Nn^2 C^2 B_1^2(T) B_1^2(T') \frac{(\beta_1^2\beta_1'\beta_1'' + \beta_2^2\beta_2'\beta_2'' + \beta_3^2\beta_3'\beta_3'')}{k_B T'}$$

$$\Omega^{ZX} = \frac{A}{2} Nn^2 C^2 B_1^2(T) B_1^2(T') \frac{(\beta_1^3\beta_1'' + \beta_2^3\beta_2'' + \beta_3^3\beta_3'')}{k_B T'}$$

where $(\beta_1, \beta_2, \beta_3)$, $(\beta_1', \beta_2', \beta_3')$, and $(\beta_1'', \beta_2'', \beta_3'')$, are the direction cosines of the X, Y, and Z axes, and $A = 9$, 16, -8, and $B = \frac{1}{3}$, 0, $-\frac{1}{3}$ for fcc, bcc, and sc lattices. There are twelve [110], eight [111], and six [100] nearest-neighbor directions for the fcc, bcc, and sc lattices, respectively. A table of values for the summations $\sum_j (n_{ij}^X)^2 n_{ij}^p n_{ij}^{p'}$ and $\sum_j n_{ij}^p n_{ij}^{p'}$ in terms of the direction cosines $(\beta_i, \beta_i', \beta_i''$ where $i = 1, 2, 3)$ may be found in Taniguchi.[5] It is of interest to note that the sc lattice is equivalent to the interstitial solid solution of the bcc lattice.

The anisotropy induced during magnetic anneal can now be calculated using Eqs. (7.21) and (7.26). For the specific case where the induced anisotropy is in the X-Y plane induced by an annealing field in this plane, F may be written as

$$F = F_0 - \Omega_1 \cos^2 \theta + \Omega_2 \cos \theta \sin \theta \tag{7.27}$$

where
$$\Omega_1 = \Omega^{YY} - \Omega^{XX}$$
$$\Omega_2 = 2\Omega^{XY} \tag{7.28}$$

and θ is the angle between the magnetization vector and the direction of the annealing field. For the induced anisotropy in which the X-Y plane corresponds to the $(1\bar{1}0)$ or (001) plane and where the X axis coincides with the [111], [110], or [001] direction, Eqs. (7.27) and (7.28) become

$$F = F_0 - \Omega_1 \cos^2 \theta \tag{7.29}$$

and
$$\Omega_1 = \frac{A'Nn^2C^2B_1^2(T)B_1^2(T')}{k_B T'} \tag{7.30}$$

and the value of A' is as given in Table 7.1 for various crystal lattices. Thus, the anisotropy in this case is uniaxial with its easy axis of magnetization lying along the direction of the annealing field and with its anisotropy constant given by Eq. (7.30).

Table 7.1 Values of A' for Various Cubic Lattices[5]

(X, Y) Plane	X Axis	fcc	bcc	sc
$(1\bar{1}0)$	[111]	9	8	0
	[110]	27/4	4	9/2
	[001]	9/2	0	9
(001)	[110]	9	8	0
	[100]	9/2	0	9

In the foregoing calculation, we have followed mainly the work of Taniguchi.[5] Independently, Néel has developed a similar theory.[4] Their results are in general agreement although they used slightly different approaches to the problem. In Taniguchi's theory, the starting point is the quantum-mechanical Hamiltonian of Eq. (7.6) which includes the exchange energy in the Weiss molecular field approximation and the interaction energy of an atom pair. In Néel's theory, on the other hand, the coupling energy of an atom pair is expanded in a series of Legendre polynomials, the first term of which corresponds to the ordinary magnetic dipole-dipole coupling. Since the magnetic dipole-dipole coupling is too small to account for the observed magnetostriction, another form of dipole-dipole interaction, probably of spin-orbit coupling origin, is introduced as parameter. To be more explicit, the energy of interaction $w(r, \phi)$ between two atoms is given by

$$w(r, \phi) = g_1(r)P_2(\cos \phi) + g_2(r)P_4(\cos \phi) + \cdots \tag{7.31}$$

where P_2, P_4 are Legendre polynomials. The coefficient of $P_2(\cos \phi)$, namely $g_1(r)$, is the sum of a term due to ordinary magnetic dipole-dipole coupling between atoms of moment μ and other terms, probably due to spin-orbit coupling. This rather phenomenological introduction of the dipole-dipole couplings responsible for the induced uniaxial anisotropy in cubic solid solutions of the substitutional type renders its temperature dependence obscure. Thus, the temperature dependence of the induced anisotropy and the dependence of its magnitude upon the annealing temperature cannot be deduced from Néel's theory. On the other hand, Néel has been able to estimate the coefficients of dipole-dipole coupling for various kinds of atom pairs in any solid solution by calculating the magnetostrictive constants. Furthermore, unlike the case with Taniguchi's theory, the result of Néel's calculation is applicable to nonideal as well as ideal solutions of any concentration. It may be recalled here that in Taniguchi's calculation the B-atom concentration n is much less than unity and the solid solution is implicitly assumed ideal. Since the spin-orbit interaction decreases more rapidly than $1/r^3$ at large distances,[1] it is sufficient to take only nearest neighbors into account for the spin-orbit term in Eq. (7.31). Letting the distance between two atoms be $r = r_o + \delta r$ where r_o is the average separation, we find from Eq. (7.31) that

$$w = \left(-\frac{3\mu^2}{r^3} + L + M\delta r\right)\left(\cos^2 \phi - \frac{1}{3}\right)$$
$$+ (Q + S\delta r)\left(\cos^4 \phi - \frac{30}{35}\cos^2 \phi + \frac{3}{35}\right) \tag{7.32}$$

where L, M, Q and S are coefficients dependent on r_o. Since $\delta r \ll r_o$, we have retained only first-order terms in δr in Eq. (7.32). The first term in Eq. (7.32) plays the dominant role in determining the magnetostriction of the material. However, since Becker[7] has shown the magnetic dipole-dipole interaction accounts for only a small part of the observed magnetostriction, we can ignore the μ^2 term in Eq. (7.32). For a cubic crystal of constant dimensions, that is, $\delta r = 0$, the mean value of $\cos^2 \phi$ is $\frac{1}{3}$ and the first term in Eq. (7.32) disappears. We then observe that the form of the cubic anisotropy energy density E_a must be determined by the mean value of $\cos^4 \phi$, which is proportional to $\sum_{ij}' \beta_i\beta_j$, where the β's are the direction cosines of the magnetization relative to the quaternary axes. The anisotropy constant K_1 is obtained by multiplying the mean value of w by the number $n Na/2V$ of liaisons contained within 1 cm^3 where $n = 12$, 8, and 6 for the fcc, bcc, and sc lattices. N_a is Avogadro's number and V

---

[7] R. Becker, *Z. Physik*, **62**: 253 (1930).

is the atomic volume. Thus, we find

$$E_a = K_1(\beta_1^2\beta_2^2 + \beta_2^2\beta_3^2 + \beta_3^2\beta_1^2) \tag{7.33}$$

with $K_1 = cN_aQ/V$ where c is a numerical coefficient equal to zero for an isotropic substance and equal to 1, $16\!\!/\!\!9$, and 2 for the face-centered, body-centered, and single-cubic lattices.

The foregoing theory could be easily extended to solid solutions of two constituents A and B. For a solid solution of a cubic system containing concentration c_a of A and c_b of B where $c_a + c_b = 1$, the constant then takes the values L_{aa}, L_{ab}, and L_{bb}, depending upon the nature of the interacting atoms. In the absence of ferromagnetism, the distribution of interactions in such a solid solution is isotropic among all the interactions of the same orientation, and the proportion of the number of A–A, A–B and B–B interactions is independent of the chosen orientation. This is no longer true when there is a spontaneous magnetization M_s, as the interaction is then dependent upon the interaction orientation with respect to M_s. If M_s is oriented by an external field H_1, and if the temperature T' is sufficiently high to facilitate atomic diffusion, the solid solution would acquire a uniaxial anisotropy with the easy axis parallel to H_1. If the sample is then quenched to a temperature sufficiently low (room temperature, say) to suppress diffusion, the solid solution then possesses a permanent anisotropy. Néel called this state of affairs "orientation superstructure."

Due to the anisotropic distribution of atom pairs in the case of a solid solution of two constituents annealed in a magnetic field, the pseudodipole term $L(\cos^2\phi - \frac{1}{3})$ of Eq. (7.32) is no longer zero to the first approximation ($\delta r = 0$) due to the lower than cubic symmetry. In fact, it plays a dominant role in contributing to the uniaxial anisotropy. It now follows from Eq. (7.32) that if $c_a \ll 1$ the probability of a single A–A interaction having the orientation ϕ is then

$$\omega(\phi) = \frac{1}{n} e^{-L'(\cos^2\phi - 1/3)/RT'} \tag{7.34}$$

since the pseudodipole coupling energy is much smaller than the thermal energy so that the deviation from isotropic distribution is small. Here n is the number of distinct orientations of the interactions of the number of nearest neighbors, R is the gas constant, and ϕ is the angle that the interaction makes with H_1. L' is the value at T' of

$$L' = N_a(L_{aa} + L_{bb} - 2L_{ab}) \tag{7.35}$$

Since $L'/RT' \ll 1$, we may expand the exponential in Eq. (7.34) and retain only up to the first-order term in L'/RT'. It is of interest to note that Eq. (7.34) derived by Néel is identical in form to expression (7.20) derived by Taniguchi. Thus, following a similar calculation as that used in deriving Eq. (7.27) from Eq. (7.20), we find that the anisotropy energy density E_u bound to the "orientation superstructure" is given by

$$E_u = \frac{nc_a^2 L'L_oQ}{2VRT'} \tag{7.36}$$

where $L_o = L$ when $T = T_o$, and where Q is given as a function of the direction cosines $\beta_1, \beta_2, \beta_3$ of the field H_1 and $\gamma_1, \gamma_2, \gamma_3$ of the direction of the magnetization by

$$Q = \frac{1}{9} - S_{22} + (S_{22} - S_4)(\beta_1^2\gamma_1^2 + \beta_2^2\gamma_2^2 + \beta_3^2\gamma_3^2)$$
$$- 4S_{22}(\beta_1\beta_2\gamma_1\gamma_2 + \beta_2\beta_3\gamma_2\gamma_3 + \beta_3\beta_1\gamma_3\gamma_1) \quad (7.37)$$

The quantities S_4 and S_{22} are the mean values of α_i^4 and of $\alpha_i^2\alpha_j^2$, for the n possible interaction directions, where $\alpha_1, \alpha_2, \alpha_3$ are the direction cosines of the interaction directions with respect to the quaternary axes. For an isotropic polycrystalline substance, $S_4 = \frac{1}{5}$ and $S_{22} = \frac{1}{15}$, while in a fcc lattice, $S_4 = \frac{1}{6}$ and $S_{22} = \frac{1}{12}$.

Eq. (7.36) valid for small values of c_a can be extended, to a first approximation, to the entire sample by replacing c_a^2 by $c_a^2 c_b^2$. In an isotropic substance, E_u then becomes

$$E_u = \frac{nc_a^2 c_b^2 L_o L'}{15VRT'} \cos^2\theta \quad (7.38)$$

where θ is the angle that the magnetization makes with the annealing field H_1 subsequent to quenching at temperature T_o.

(b) Comparison with Experiment for Bulk Permalloy

Néel believes that the magnetic anisotropy of diverse alloys of the types Fe-Si, Fe-Co, Fe-Co-Ni, acquired by cooling in a magnetic field, can be attributed to the "orientation superstructure" discussed above. Of particular interest to our study of magnetic films is the comparison between theory and experiment on the uniaxial anisotropy in the bulk Ni-Fe (Permalloy) system. In this subsection, we shall first discuss the case of bulk Permalloy. This discussion is followed by a careful comparison of the experimental evidence on the uniaxial anisotropy in thin films with the predictions of the Néel-Taniguchi theory.

In the case of bulk Permalloy, the Néel-Taniguchi theory has been confirmed by several investigators. Chikazumi and Oomura[8] found experimentally that the magnitude of the anisotropy in bulk Permalloy of various compositions heat-treated in a magnetic field is proportional neither to the magnetostriction nor to the saturation magnetization. The origin of this anisotropy, therefore, cannot be explained by either one of the earlier theories, namely, the "theory of strain of directional order"[9] or the theory of "elongated order phase."[10] However, their result can be explained by the pseudodipole interaction in directionally ordered arrangement of atoms. In other words, their result is consistent with the Néel-Taniguchi theory. The experiments in this case were performed by using polycrystalline Permalloy (60–100% Ni) prepared by melting the electrolytic nickel and iron in a vacuum-induction furnace. In a later report Chikazumi[11] made precise measurements on the anisotropy of magnetically annealed Ni_3Fe bulk single crystals by means of a high-temperature torque magnetometer. It was found that the magnitude of the anisotropy depends upon the direction of the annealing field relative to the crystallographic axes.

[8] S. Chikazumi and T. Oomura, *J. Phys. Soc. Japan*, **10**: 842 (1955).
[9] S. Chikazumi, *J. Phys. Soc. Japan*, **5**: 327, 333 (1950).
[10] S. Kaya, *Rev. Mod. Phys.*, **25**: 49 (1953).
[11] S. Chikazumi, *J. Phys. Soc. Japan*, **11**: 551 (1956).

The uniaxial anisotropy of a specimen with surfaces parallel to (110) was found to be the largest when the annealing field was applied along the [111], second for [110] and smallest for [100]. It was further found that if the direction of the annealing field does not coincide with the principle crystallographic directions, the minimum of the uniaxial anisotropy does not lie in the direction of the annealing field but in a direction nearer to the neighboring [110] direction. These results could again be explained qualitatively by the Néel-Taniguchi theory. Quantitative discrepancy between theory and experiment could be attributed to the nature of the fcc lattice wherein the nearest neighbors of one atom are also nearest neighbors of one another. (However, in a recent calculation Iwata[12] extended Néel's theory of nonideal solution to include the effect of both short- and long-range order upon the value of the uniaxial anisotropy in Ni_3Fe. He concluded that the nature of the fcc lattice could not account for the discrepancy between theory and experiment observed by Chikazumi.)

It may be of interest to point out that for polycrystalline samples, the cubic anisotropy is averaged out due to the random orientation of the constituent grains. On the other hand, in a single-crystal anneal in a magnetic field, both cubic and uniaxial anisotropies exist and are represented in that case by

$$E = E_c + E_u = K_1\left(\sin^4\frac{\theta}{4} + \sin^2\theta\cos^2\theta\right)$$

$$+ K_2\sin^4\theta\cos^2\frac{\theta}{4} - K_u\cos^2(\theta - \theta_o) \qquad (7.39)$$

where K_1 and K_2 are the usual first- and second-order cubic anisotropy constants, K_u is the uniaxial anisotropy constant, and θ is the magnetization direction relative to the [100] direction. The experimental torque curve could be converted into E vs θ curves by integration and these curves could then be Fourier analyzed in turn to obtain K_1, K_2, and K_u. It was found that K_2 is negligibly small and K_1 is independent of the direction of the annealing field as it should be. As we have mentioned previously K_u depends upon crystallographic direction of the annealing field, attaining its maximum and minimum values with the annealing field in the [111] and [100] directions, respectively. These findings are in agreement with the results of the Néel-Taniguchi theory.

Ferguson[13] has also performed similar experiments with bulk Permalloy. His samples were bulk Permalloy with 50, 60, 70, and 80 wt % Ni, with an addition of 0.5% Mn to render them workable. Nearly isotropic polycrystalline samples were prepared to reduce the cubic magnetocrystalline anisotropy. The influence of the residual anisotropy was further eliminated by two successive heat-treatments, with mutually orthogenal magnetic fields. Using a torque magnetometer, it was found that the anisotropy energy at some annealing temperature T' is proportional to $T_o - T'$ where $k_B T_o$ is the activation energy and T_o is near 35,000°K. Since Volkov et al.[14,15] have shown that the saturation magnetostriction λ_s is approximately proportional to $T_o - T$ or M_s^2, Ferguson's results are in agreement with the theories of Néel and

---

[12] T. Iwata, *Trans. Japan Inst. Metals,* **2**: 86 (1961).

[13] E. T. Ferguson, *J. Appl. Phys.,* **29**: 252 (1958).

[14] D. E. Volkov and V. E. Chichernekov, *J. Expt. Theo. Phys.* (USSR), **27**: 208 (1954).

[15] D. E. Volkov, V. E. Chichernekov, and V. B. Seeten, Publication Univ. of Moscow, *Phys. Ser., No. 2,* 21 (1956).

Taniguchi, predicting proportionality to λ_s/T' (Néel) or $M_s^2(T)/T'$ (Taniguchi). (The former follows from Eq.(7.38) since, according to Néel's theory,[4] $L = A\lambda_{100} + B\lambda_{111}$, where A and B are constants and λ_{100} and λ_{111} are longitudinal magnetostriction along the quaternary and ternary axis for the fcc lattice. The latter follows from Eq. (7.29) since $B_s(T) = M_s(T)/M_s(0)gS$.[16] Here $M_s(T)$ is the saturation at temperature T and $M_s(0)$ that at $0°K$.) The temperature range involved is too small, however, to verify the $1/T'$ dependence. For ideal solutions, Néel's theory predicts a variation of $E(T)/(T_c - T)$ proportional to $c^2(1 - c)^2$ where T_c is the Curie temperature and c is the concentration. Substantial difference between the theoretical and measured curves is attributed to other factors such as nonideal solutions, and the variation of λ_s and of the elastic constants with concentration.

The orientation superstructure in Néel's theory has no connection with the ordinary type of superstructure. In fact, the existence of an ordinary superstructure prevents the appearance of an orientation superstructure since A and B atoms then occupy completely determined positions. Néel has carried out the calculations for the uniaxial anisotropy including the effect of the ordinary superlattice formation. (See second part of Ref. 4.) In this case, $c_a^2 c_b^2 = c^2(1 - c)^2$ used in the ideal solution case should be replaced by

$$S = 4c_a^2 c_b^2 e^{-v/k_B T} \sqrt{1 + x}(1 + \sqrt{1 + x})^2 \tag{7.40}$$

where v and x are related to the energy of the superlattice formation. Chikazumi and Oomura,[8] in their experiments with bulk Permalloy have found that Eq. (7.40) is compatible with their results only when the degree of ordinary order is small. In the derivation of Eq. (7.40), the influence of the ordinary order was taken into consideration only through such variation as the total number of $A-B$ pairs. The ordinary order, however, may also have such influence as to oppose directional order when perfect order is approached. In Ferguson's experiments, however, the lowest annealing temperature used for all the alloys was above the critical temperature of long range superstructure formation. A large proportion of ordered phase would cause a decrease of the induced anisotropy, as the $A-A$, $A-B$, and $B-B$ links are then no longer free to take up an anisotropic distribution in that phase. Thus, Ferguson concluded, along with Chikazumi and Oomura, that Kaya's explanation[10] of the induced anisotropy as the precipitation of elongated particles of the ordered phase cannot therefore be valid for the Ni-Fe alloys.

(c) Comparison with Experiment for Permalloy Films

In contrast with the case of bulk Permalloy, the experimental results on the anisotropy of thin Permalloy films cannot, in general, be fully explained by the Néel-Taniguchi theory. We shall begin our discussion by summarizing the experimental results of various investigators and then proceed to see what factors, other than that of atomic pair ordering, may also contribute to the induced anisotropy.

The various sources of the induced uniaxial anisotropy in Permalloy films can be examined by determining the anisotropy field as a function of composition.[17]

---

[16] See, e.g., R. F. Soohoo, *op. cit.*, p. 39.

[17] D. O. Smith, *J. Appl. Phys.*, **30**: 264S (1959).

In Fig. 7.1, we have shown the anisotropy field of Permalloy films of various compositions deposited in a static magnetic field oriented parallel to the substrate. It is seen from the figure that the anisotropy field $2K_1/M$ decreases monotonically with increasing nickel (or decreasing iron) composition. Since the total directionally ordered iron pair energy in a nickel matrix should decrease with decreasing iron content, this dependence of H_k upon composition is qualitative consistent with the results of the Néel-Taniguchi theory. It is of particular interest to note that when a film is deposited in a rotating magnetic field, supplied by two orthogonal pairs of

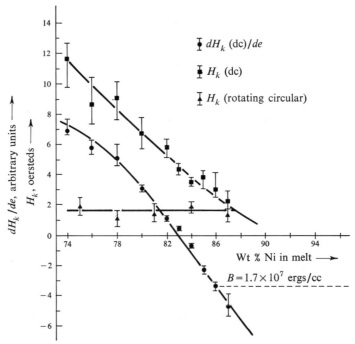

FIG. **7.1.** Anisotropy of Permalloy films as a function of composition (after D. O. Smith, Ref. 17).

Helmholtz coils supplied by 60-cycle currents in time quadrature, the resulting anisotropy field is found to be independent of composition. Furthermore, the easy axis in this rotating deposition field scheme is found to be randomly oriented. These experimental results are interpreted to imply the suppression of directed pair formation since the deposition field is not fixed in direction.

However, as also shown in Fig. 7.1, a significant amount of compositional independent anisotropy remains in this case. We therefore interpret this result to imply that the remaining anisotropy in thin Permalloy films has other than ordered pair origin. The polycrystalline films that were used in these experiments were deposited with the vapor beam normally incident upon the substrate. If the vapor beam makes a finite angle with the substrate normal, the resulting anisotropy is found to be much larger when compared to that of the normal incidence case, and has quite a different origin. It will be shown that an inclined vapor beam gives rise to a crystallite shadowing effect which in turn causes preferential crystallite elongation and consequent shape anisotropy. Since most films are normally deposited to eliminate the angle of incidence effect, this source of anisotropy is of secondary importance in our present discussion and we shall pospone its detailed treatment until a later section in this chapter.

It is naturally of interest to see whether the compositional dependence of the anisotropy field as a function of composition as depicted in Fig. 7.1 is in quantitative agreement with the Néel-Taniguchi theory. However, as we have mentioned previously in connection with the experiments of Chikazumi and Oomura, the generalized Néel theory which takes into account the influence of arbitrary concentration is probably only valid when the degree of ordinary order (superlattice formation) is small. Thus, a precise comparison between theory and experiment with regard to the compositional variation of the anisotropy would be rather difficult although this situation is alleviated somewhat by a recent calculation of Iwata.[18] In contrast to the Néel calculation, he takes into consideration the self-consistent distribution of atoms including the directional order in the fcc lattice so that the resulting theory is truly applicable to a solid solution of any concentration. However, in order to compare Iwata's theoretical results on the compositional dependence of the anisotropy with that shown in Fig. 7.1, it is necessary to know the temperature dependence of the pseudodipole coupling coefficients L_{aa}, L_{ab}, L_{bb} since the Curie temperature is a function of composition. Since such data are in general not available, we can proceed no further.

A more fruitful approach to the foregoing problem is to compare the theoretical and experimental temperature dependence of the induced anisotropy. According to Eq. (7.30), $E_u : B^2(T)B^2(T')$ where $B(T)$ and $B(T')$ are Brillouin functions corresponding to a particular temperature T and annealing temperature T', respectively. $B(T)$ is in turn proportional to $M_s(T)/M_s(0)$ where $M_s(T)$ and $M_s(0)$ are magnetizations corresponding to the saturation magnetization at temperatures T and $0°K$ respectively. Thus, we find

$$E_u = \frac{A''}{k_B T'} \frac{M_s^2(T)}{M_s^2(0)} \frac{M_s^2(T')}{M_s^2(0)} \tag{7.41}$$

where A'' is a function of both the coefficients of the pseudodipole interactions for atom pairs and the concentration of Fe-atoms. In Figs. 7.2 and 7.3, we have shown the experimental values of the uniaxial anisotropy constant as a function of temperature obtained by Takahashi for iron films and for 55% Ni-45% Fe polycrystalline Permalloy films prepared with various substrate temperatures and annealing cycles.[19] Using the expression for the magnetization of bulk material $M_s(T)$ as a function of temperature given by Bloch on the basis of spin-wave theory [see Eq. (6.8)], we can compute the theoretical E_u vs T curve normalized to the value at the observation temperature of $20°C$. The resulting curve is shown dotted in Figs. 7.2 and 7.3. It is clearly seen from these figures that there is a large discrepancy between the results of the Néel-Taniguchi theory and experiment in all cases. It is surprising that K_u is almost constant for the iron film. For the same temperature range, Graham and Lommel have obtained similar near-constancy for a nickel film.[20] For the 55–45 Permalloy films, the experimental values of K_u are roughly proportional to $M_s^{17}(T)$

[18] T. Iwata, *Trans. Japan Inst. Metals*, **2**: 92 (1961).

[19] M. Takahashi, *J. Appl. Phys.*, **33**: 1101 (1962).

[20] C. D. Graham, Jr., and J. M. Lommel, *J. Phys. Soc. Japan*, **17**: Suppl. B-1, 570 (1962).

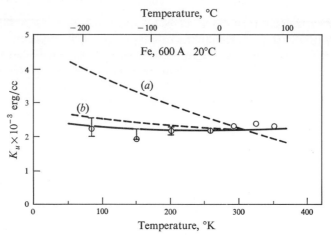

FIG. 7.2. Temperature dependence of the anisotropy energy of Fe-films. Curves (a) and (b) are plotted using, respectively, the expressions $K_u(T) = K_u(20°C)[M_s(T)/M_s(20°C)]^{10}$ and $K_u(T) = K_u(20°C)[M_s(T)/M_s(20°C)]^2$ (after M. Takahashi, Ref. 19).

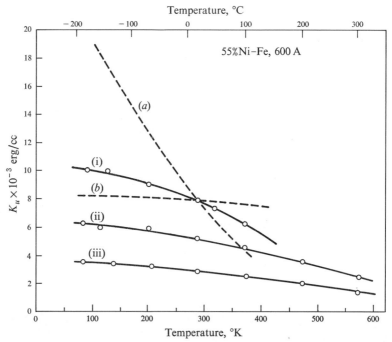

FIG. 7.3. Temperature dependence of the anisotropy energy of a 55% Ni-45% Fe film. Curves (a) and (b) are plotted using the expressions $K_u(T) = K_u(20°C)[(1 - 1.74T/T_c)/(1 - 1.74 \times 293/T_c)] \times [M_s(T)/M_s(20°C)]^{10}$ and $K_u(T) = K_u(20°C)[M_s(T)/M_s(20°C)]^2$. (i) Substrate temperature was held at 20°C during evaporation. (ii) Substrate temperature was held at 300°C during evaporation and the film was magnetically annealed at 350°C for 5 hrs immediately afterwards. (iii) Substrate temperature was held at 300°C during evaporation and the film was magnetically annealed at 450°C for 5 hrs immediately afterwards (after M. Takahashi, Ref. 19).

for curve (1) and to $M_s^{14}(T)$ for curves (2) and (3). Nevertheless, the pair orientation may be partially responsible for the origin of K_u, as, by annealing at 350°C or 450°C for several hours, the temperature dependence of K_u approaches that given by the dotted curves in Figs. 7.2 and 7.3 in accordance with the Néel-Taniguchi theory. However, a great part of K_u seems to have another origin.

(d) Possible Sources of Anisotropy

Let us now return to a more detailed discussion of the anisotropy of nickel as a function of temperature.[20] The data shown represents the "stable" uniaxial anisotropy which was obtained after the first few annealing treatments and was measured as a function of temperature for two films. The nearly linear decrease in K_u above room temperature is unlike the temperature dependence of the magneto-crystalline anisotropy, of the saturation magnetization, or of the magnetostriction. Since nickel is a pure metal, pair orientation cannot be the source of its induced anisotropy. To decide whether trapped impurity atoms are responsible for the uniaxial anisotropy, Graham and Lommel measured the anisotropy constant for films deposited in vacuums ranging from 2×10^{-10} to 10^{-5} mm of Hg and at two widely different evaporation rates. All the films tested, including those made under the best vacuum conditions, show a uniaxial anisotropy of 1 to 3×10^3 erg/cm^3 which can be reoriented by annealing in a field. Therefore, it can be concluded that trapped impurity atoms such as oxygen are not responsible for the uniaxial anisotropy in the nickel films. The residual gas in the vacuum system was probably almost all carbon monoxide;[21] the torque curves of these films were measured in vacuum before removal from the deposition system. If we assume that every CO atom which strikes the substrate during deposition is trapped in the film, then for the films deposited in the best vacuum the final CO content would be about 8 parts per million by weight. If the CO disassociates to C and O in the film, then there will be 4.5 ppm of oxygen. The presence of such minute amounts of impurities in these films would eliminate oxygen or any trapped impurity atom as the source of the induced anisotropy in nickel. The above results, however, do not necessarily imply that other defects such as vacancies, or dislocations formed during evaporation, cannot contribute to the uniaxial anisotropy. A directional ordering of these imperfections, perhaps via magnetostriction, may indeed be a very significant source of the induced anisotropy. We shall return presently to a more detailed discussion of this topic after a brief examination of other possible origins of the anisotropy.

For many materials, Evans and Wilman have reported texture axes inclined toward the incident beam.[22] Knorr and Hoffman have shown that in iron films, an easy axis forms perpendicular to an inclined beam[23] and electron diffraction shows this to be the [111] crystallograph direction. Crystalline anisotropy and magnetoelastic coupling with the isotropic strain can interact with such a texture to produce a uniaxial anisotropy. When the magnetoelastic effect is neglected, texture anisotropy is obtained by averaging the cubic anisotropy energy density expression $E_k = K_1(\alpha_1^2 \alpha_2^2 + \alpha_2^2 \alpha_3^2 + \alpha_3^2 \alpha_1^2)$ where the α_i's are directional cosines of **M** relative to the cubic crystalline axis around the [111] axis. This simple averaging results in

[21] T. W. Hickmott, *J. Appl. Phys.*, **31**: 128 (1960).

[22] D. M. Evans and H. Wilman, *Acta Cryst.*, **5**: 731 (1952).

[23] T. G. Knorr and R. W. Hoffman, *Phys. Rev.*, **113**: 1039 (1959).

$E_T = -(\tau K_1/2)(\cos^2 \theta - \dfrac{7}{6}\cos^4 \theta)$ where θ is the angle $\mathbf{M}$ makes with the [111] texture axis and $0 < \tau < 1$ describes the degree of texture.[24] Converting the above expression into a function of the angle ϕ between $\mathbf{M}$ and the projection of the fiber axis on the film plane, we find

$$E_T = -\tau \frac{K_1}{2}\left(\sin^2 \beta \cos^2 \phi - \frac{7}{6}\sin^4 \beta \cos^4 \phi\right) \tag{7.42}$$

where β is the angle that the texture [111] axis makes with the film normal. In iron, $K_1 > 0$ so that according to Eq. (7.42), the easy axis occurs at $\phi = 0$ or in the direction of the incident beam, contrary to experiment.

Calculation of the anisotropy due to the combined effect of texture, isotropic strain, and the anisotropic magnetoelastic constants is somewhat more complicated than the case of texture and crystalline anisotropy above. A specific calculation assuming complete isotropic stress has been carried out[23] which shows explicitly how anisotropic effects of these types can arise. For iron, the anisotropy direction obtained is consistent with experiment, while the theoretical value is about ⅓ of that observed. For iron films deposited with an inclined incident beam, anisotropic strain is found to occur in addition to the usual isotropic strain with the axis of greatest strain perpendicular to the incident beam. Inclusion of this effect appears to account for the remainder of the anisotropy observed by Knorr and Hoffman.[24] In this connection we may mention that for the films used by Takahashi in his experiments no appreciable fiber structure could be detected by electron diffraction.[19]

The temperature dependence of K_u due to the fiber structure should be the same as that for crystalline anisotropy. It was pointed out by Zener that throughout the ferromagnetic temperature range neighboring spins in a crystal maintain essentially parallel alignment since the short-range order disappears much more slowly with temperature than the long-range order.[25] Thus, the local environment of a given atom at a finite temperature is much the same as that at 0°K. Therefore, for short-range interactions, the anisotropy can be described by the same constant that measures the coupling in the latter case. At a finite temperature T, however, the local magnetization of an atom and its neighbors no longer is parallel to the applied field; instead it precesses about the field through a spread of angles, over which we must perform averages to obtain the observed result. Carrying out these averages within the framework of the molecular field approximation, Carr found that K_u is proportional to $M_s^{10}(T)$ for iron and to $(1 - 1.74 T/T_c)M_s^{10}(T)$ for nickel and Permalloy where T_c is the Curie temperature.[26] This dependence of K_u on T is plotted in Figs. 7.2 and 7.3. It is seen that there is a large discrepancy between this theoretical curve and the observed ones in all cases.

Collecting all the evidences discussed above, we may safely conclude that texture axis formation is not the predominant mechanism in inducing the uniaxial anisotropy in Permalloy films. This is particularly true for films deposited with the vapor beam normally incident upon the substrate. Although there is inevitably some departure from normal incidence due to the finite extent of the source and the separation between

---

[24] J. B. Goodenough and D. O. Smith in C. A. Neugebauer *et al.* (eds.), *Structure and Properties of Thin Films*, John Wiley & Sons, Inc., New York, 1959, p. 112.

[25] C. Zener, *Phys. Rev.*, **96**: 1335 (1954).

[26] W. J. Carr, Jr., *J. Appl. Phys.*, **29**: 436 (1958).

substrate and source, the angle of deviation of the beam from the normal is small in these cases. For normal incidence the texture axis is also normal to the film ($\beta = 0$), and Eq. (7.42) shows that planar anisotropy can result in this case.

7.3 MAGNETIC ANNEAL AND IMPERFECTION MODEL

In the last section, we discussed at length the theory of and experimental results on the uniaxial anisotropy in thin magnetic films deposited at normal incidence of the vapor beam. We found that whereas the Néel-Taniguchi pair-ordering theory is amply supported for bulk Permalloy, in itself it is not sufficient to account for the total induced anisotropy in iron, nickel, and Permalloy films. It is then obvious that we should ask the elementary but significant question: *In what respects are thin films different from bulk matter as far as anisotropy is concerned?* The answer to this simple question would, of course, reveal the real sources of the induced anisotropy in thin magnetic films.

In the first place, the thickness of a thin film is many orders of magnitude smaller than the linear dimensions of a bulk sample. We may thus be inclined to attribute the difference in the anisotropy between bulk matter and thin films, in part at least, to this dimensional difference per se. However, if the anisotropy is due to spin-orbit coupling, as assumed in the Néel-Taniguchi theory, the pseudodipole interaction involved is of such short range (a few lattice spacings, say) that the linear dimension of the sample is usually insignificant as far as the volume anisotropy is concerned.

Preferred orientation, such as texture axis formation, is another possible source of anisotropy. In contrast to the case of bulk matter, a texture axis may be defined by the direction of the incident beam. However, as we have discussed in the last section, this source of anisotropy is relatively insignificant especially in normal-incidence films. It then follows that anisotropic stress is also unimportant as a source of anisotropy in these films.

As we discussed in Chap. 2 on the preparation of thin films, a film is exposed to oxygen, hydrogen, and other residual gases during its formation in an imperfect vacuum. Thus, it may be reasonable that absorbed gases within the film and oxidized layers at the surface of the film may contribute to the induced anisotropy. This is particularly plausible when we recall that Neugebauer has found that nickel films deposited in vacuum less than 10^{-9} mm Hg have magnetization and Curie temperatures indistinguishable from that of bulk matter, whereas very thin films deposited at normal vacuum of 10^{-6} to 10^{-5} mm Hg have lower than bulk values of magnetization and Curie point (see Chap. 6). However, according to the experiments of Graham and Lommel,[20] the difference in pressure during evaporation of thin films has no noticeable effect upon their induced anisotropy. Thus, we may conclude on the basis of these experiments that neither oxygen nor other types of trapped atoms in or on the surface of the film could be the significant source of anisotropy.

Next, we should investigate the influence of the substrate thickness, material, and temperature during deposition upon the anisotropy of the material. Takahashi has carried out a number of rather definitive experiments in this regard.[19] As is well established, stress occurs in evaporated films.[27] Furthermore, this stress is localized

---

[27] R. W. Hoffman, R. D. Daniels, and E. C. Crittenden, Jr., *Proc. Phys. Soc.* (London), Ser. 6-B, **117**: 497 (1954).

in a surface layer of the film.[28-30] Thus, the average stress in the film γ is related to the localized stress in a surface layer γ_o by the expression $\gamma = \gamma_o t_o / T$, where t_o and T are the thicknesses of the surface layer and film respectively. If this surface layer is responsible for the induced anisotropy, then the anisotropy energy $E_u = -(3/2)\lambda(\gamma_o t_o / T)$ where λ is the isotropic magnetostrictive constant. Therefore, K_u should vary inversely as thickness, since K_u is due to a volume effect while the localized stress is a surface effect. The thickness dependence of K_u for iron and nickel films deposited at substrate temperatures of 20° and 300°C has been determined by Takahashi. It is found that the observed values of K_u vary considerably from one experiment to another for the 20°C case, while it decreases only slightly with increasing thickness for the 300°C case, inconsistent with the theoretical predictions above.

As we have discussed in Chap. 2, the coefficient of thermal expansion for microscope glass is about the same as that of Permalloy while that of quartz is practically zero. Thus, by depositing films on glass and quartz substrates and comparing their respective anisotropies, we should be able to ascertain whether the induced anisotropy is influenced by the type of substrate material. The anisotropy of films of different composition with different substrate material and temperature was found to be nearly the same so that substrate material differences giving rise to different thermal stress in the film can not account for the induced anisotropy. Note that different composition gives rise to different magnetostriction in the film.

With regard to the dependence of K_u upon the substrate temperature, the torque curves of an iron film deposited at 20°C show that the easy axis does not coincide with direction of the deposition field, but is likely to approach it as the substrate temperature increases. K_u for 50–50 Permalloy decreases from 7.5×10^3 ergs/cm³ at 20°C substrate temperature to 1.4×10^3 erg/cm³ (bulk value) beyond 500°C. For iron, K_u first decreases with increasing substrate temperature reaching a minimum at about 325°C. Thereafter, K_u increases for the available data. Although the origin of this behavior is not completely clear at this point, we may point out that it neither contradicts the localized stress model, which has been discarded previously on other grounds, nor the structural defect model to be introduced below.

We thus have arrived at the conclusion that none of the obvious sources of anisotropy in thin films could adequately account for it. However, since the film formation process is a very complicated one, it is not inconceivable that there may be a directional alignment of such imperfections as vacancies, dislocations, and perhaps other defects which would contribute to the induced anisotropy. This idea is particularly plausible when we note that all these defects are more mobile than the substitutional atoms.[31] Since these defects have relatively low activation energy, it should be possible to indirectly observe their migration or reorientation during magnetic or nonmagnetic anneal. We shall therefore discuss the results of magnetic annealing on thin magnetic films in some detail below. Then, we shall examine the possible contribution of imperfections to the induced anisotropy.

The general subject of magnetic anneal has been reviewed qualitatively by Graham,[32] who also furnishes a comprehensive reference on the subject. It turns

[28] H. P. Murbach and H. Wilman, *Proc. Phys. Soc.* (London), Ser. 11–13, **116**: 905 (1953).

[29] J. D. Finegan and R W. Hoffman, *J. Appl. Phys.*, **30**: 597 (1959).

[30] K. Kinosita and H. Kondo, *J. Phys. Soc. Japan.*, **15**: 1339 (1960).

[31] R. M. Bozorth, *Proc. Conf. Magnetism Magnetic Materials*, AIEE, Boston, 1956, p. 69.

[32] C. D. Graham, Jr., in C. A. Neugebauer *et al.* (eds.), *op. cit.*, p. 288.

out that the materials which show the largest magnetic-annealing effects are the binary and ternary alloys of the three ferromagnetic elements, iron, nickel and cobalt. We may mention here from the very beginning that materials which respond to magnetic annealing will magnetically anneal themselves even when cooled in zero field. The field which is effective in producing the new anisotropy is the local field of the magnetic material itself, and this exists within each domain at all temperatures below the Curie point whether an applied field is present or not. Indeed, in the absence of an applied field, the local field is composed of the demagnetizing field and the anisotropy field which are difficult to eliminate.

In order to see whether directional alignment of imperfections is one of the important mechanisms giving rise to uniaxial anisotropy in thin films, it is necessary to examine the changes of K_u with isothermal magnetic anneal at relatively low temperatures. Such experiments have been performed by Mitchell[33] and by Segmüller[34] for 80% nickel-iron films, which were annealed between 20° and 300°C. In Mitchell's experiments, the films were annealed from 75°C to 200°C in an inert environment consisting of a beaker filled with heated dc 550 silicone fluid and in an alternating field of 30 Oe. rms. Using a hysteresis looper, it was found that the initial magnetic properties of these films can be altered provided that the initial temperature is high enough. If a field is applied at right angles to the original preferred direction and in the plane of the film, the magnitude of the magnetic anisotropy can be reduced without changing the preferred direction. The preferred direction of the magnetization can be changed, however, if the annealing temperature is sufficiently high. Thus, Mitchell inferred from his results the existence in these films of two anisotropy energy terms whose value can be altered by annealing at relatively low temperatures. The term sensitive to the lower temperature appears to be reversible and is characterized by changing only in magnitude when the film is annealed. The term sensitive to the higher temperature does not appear to be reversible and is such that the anisotropy can be changed by altering this term. The structural phenomena which give rise to these terms were not considered by Mitchell but we may conclude from these that there are probably two sources of anisotropy with different activation energies. This fact will help us in formulating the structural defect model of anisotropy below.

In Segmüller's experiments, all annealing treatments and magnetic measurements were performed simultaneously in a vacuum of 10^{-8} to 10^{-7} mm Hg. The films were annealed from 20°C to 300°C by light radiation from outside in a Pyrex glass vacuum system. During annealing the hysteresis loop in any direction of the film was observed by means of a hysteresis looper. For a film never heated above the deposition temperature, the temperature dependence of the uniaxial anisotropy is stronger than that in bulk Permalloy, and magnetic annealing changes the anisotropy even at temperatures below 350°C. These changes are strongly dependent on whether or not the magnetization is aligned in the direction during cooling. The ability of films to anneal magnetically at low temperatures disappears irreversibly if the film is heated for some minutes above 400°C. The anisotropy can then be changed only at higher temperatures and exhibits about the same relaxation time as bulk Permalloy. Also, during annealing above 400°C, the coercive force is increased. From these experiments we may conclude that the anisotropy in evaporated Permalloy films differs from that induced by a magnetic anneal in bulk alloys, for it can be changed by magnetic annealing at temperatures much lower than those necessary in bulk alloys.

[33] E. N. Mitchell, *J. Appl. Phys.*, **29**: 286 (1958).
[34] A. Segmüller, *J. Appl. Phys.*, **32**: 89S (1961).

This may be caused by enhanced diffusion resulting from vacancies, dislocations, and impurity atoms, which are very numerous in evaporated films. Again, this conclusion will be helpful for our discussion later.

Graham and Lommel have presented data of nickel films annealed at room temperature for about 400 hrs. A field of 1000 Oe was applied in the hard direction at $t = 0$; at $t = 255$ hrs, the field was rotated back to the original easy direction. From $t = 0$ to $t = 100$ hrs, K_u continuously decreased to zero while for $t = 100$ hrs to $t = 255$ hrs, K_u was negative indicating that the easy axis had been rotated by 90° into the original hard direction. When the field was applied along the original easy axis, K_u quickly went positive and increased as the annealing temperature further increased.

Extensive measurements of the kinetics of the magnetic-annealing process have been performed by Graham and Lommel. Much of their data can be represented fairly well by an empirical equation of the form $1 - f = e^{-(t/\tau)^{1/3}}$, where f is the fraction of the annealing process completed, and τ is a relaxation time of the order of 100 hrs at 300°K.[35] Thus, the magnetic-annealing process clearly does not follow any first- or second-order kinetic law.

A systematic investigation of isothermal magnetic anneal of Permalloy and iron films over a broader range of temperatures has been undertaken by Takahashi.[19] Torque curves of an as-evaporated 50–50 Permalloy film and those following anneal are shown in Fig. 7.4. The change of K_1 obtained from these curves is in turn plotted in Fig. 7.5 as a function of the annealing time at various temperatures. The curves marked (a_1) and (b_1) in Fig. 7.4 correspond to those existing at points (a_1) and (b_1) of Fig. 7.5. It is seen from these figures that the abrupt change of the amplitude of the torque curve at the start of magnetic annealing increases gradually with the annealing temperature, while the shape of the torque curve is deformed with the lapse of time, and finally, the easy direction is almost interchanged with the hard direction [cf. (a_3), (b_3); (a_4), (b_4)]. Note that the reversed torque curve does not have a complete fourfold symmetry. Furthermore, it is seen that the original easy direction is again recovered by annealing without a magnetic field, as seen in the changes from (b_3) to (a_4) and from (b_4) to (a_5). However, the recovered torque curve, although unchanged in form, has a smaller amplitude than the original curve. The amplitude of variation of K_1 is gradually decreased with repeated cycles of annealing at a definite temperature or with the increase in annealing temperature, as exemplified by such points as (b_3), (b_4), (b_5) and (a_1), (a_2), (a_3), respectively. Curves similar to those shown in Figs. 7.4 and 7.5 have also been found for pure iron films. However, it was found that the torque curves of iron films are more easily changed than those of iron-nickel films by low-temperature magnetic anneal. Furthermore, the recovery phenomenon exhibited by Permalloy films after prolonged annealing without a magnetic field was not found in iron films. However, the original easy direction could be easily recovered if a magnetic field is applied in that direction.

The relaxation curves of Figs. 7.4 and 7.5 and, in particular, the fact that the amplitude of the K_1 variation decreases with annealing time enable us to propose the following structural-defect model of anisotropy. Let us assume that the uniaxial anisotropy in Permalloy films can be attributed to two sources, namely, atomic pair ordering and imperfection ordering. As shown in Fig. 7.6(a), these sources give rise to an anisotropy component K_a due to the orientation of pairs of atoms occupying small round regions in the figure and another component K_i due to the ordering of

---

[35] C. D. Graham, Jr., and J. M. Lommel, *J. Appl. Phys.*, **32**: 83S (1961).

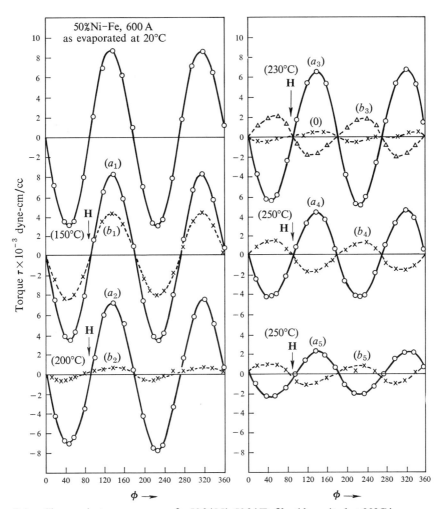

FIG. 7.4. Changes in torque curves of a 50% Ni–50% Fe film (deposited at 20°C in a magnetic field of 250 Oe) due to isothermal anneal with and without a magnetic field (after M. Takahashi, Ref. 19).

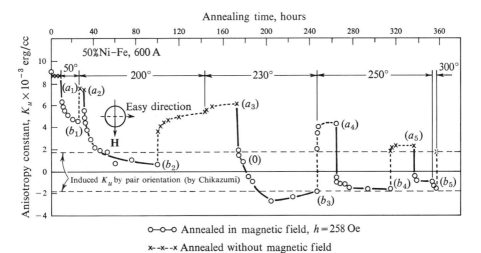

o–o–o Annealed in magnetic field, $h = 258$ Oe

x–-x–-x Annealed without magnetic field

FIG. 7.5. The anisotropy constant as a function of isothermal annealing time for a 50% Ni–50% Fe film deposited at 20°C in a magnetic field of 250 Oe (after M. Takahashi, Ref. 19).

imperfections such as vacancies, dislocations, impurities, etc., which occupy the remaining part of the film. The activation energy required for atomic pair orientation is usually thought to be about 2 eV, while this energy as obtained from the relaxation curves of Figs. 7.4 and 7.5 is only about 1 eV, a value which is almost the same as that required for vacancy displacement. Thus, for magnetic annealing below 300°C with the field applied perpendicular to the initial easy axis, the direction of the imperfection orientation can change while that of the atomic pair orientation can

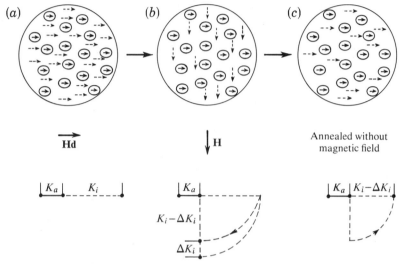

FIG. 7.6.   Structural imperfection model for the explanation of the relaxation and recovery phenomena in Permalloy films (after M. Takahashi, Ref. 19).

not. As shown in Fig. 7.6(b), the direction of easy magnetization in the imperfection region will accordingly be changed so as to align with the applied field with an accompanying decrease in the anisotropy constant K_i by an amount ΔK_i. This decrease in K_i is due to the diminishing of imperfection density with annealing, whether a magnetic field is applied or not. Thus, the directional ordering of imperfections will rotate into the direction of the applied field gradually with an anisotropy constant equal to $K_i - \Delta K_i$. In films which contain only a few lattice defects as a result of annealing at a sufficiently high temperature, the relaxation phenomena at such low temperatures will not take place.

As illustrated in Fig. 7.6(c), the direction of easy magnetization is recovered if the film after reversal is subsequently annealed in the absence of a magnetic field. The reason for this recovery is related to the existence of the atomic pair orientation and, possibly, is caused by some interaction between K_a and K_i regions which are magnetostatic or magnetoelastic in character since this recovery phenomenon was not found in iron films. It is also suggested from the experimental relation of K_1 to film composition that the origin of K_i may be closely related to magnetostriction. In this connection, MacDonald has pointed out that there are three systems of stress in Permalloy films:[36] (1) a planar system, due to a different contraction of the metal and substrate, arising from the difference in their coefficient of thermal expansion;

[36] J. R. MacDonald, *Phys. Rev.*, **106**: 890 (1957); J. D. Blades, *J. Appl. Phys.*, **30**: 260S (1959).

(2) either a compression or tension system caused by magnetostriction as induced by the depositing magnetic field; and (3) a complex stress system created by inherent impurities and imperfections. It is clear that stress systems (2) and (3) could give rise to an imperfection-ordering anisotropy K_i as postulated above.

Before we conclude our discussion of the structural-defect model of anisotropy, we may point out that this model advanced by Takahashi[19] is consistent with the experimental results of Mitchell[33] and Segmüller[34] which imply the presence of two sources of anisotropy with different activation energies.

7·4 OBLIQUE-INCIDENCE ANISOTROPY

In the last sections, we studied the uniaxial anisotropy resulting from the vapor beam impinging upon the substrate at normal incidence. Electron micrographs of such films show that the crystallites are randomly oriented so that preferential crystallite orientation can be eliminated as a source of normal-incidence anisotropy. On the other hand, if the depositing vapor beam makes a finite angle with the substrate normal, preferential growth of crystallite chains turns out to the dominant mechanism giving rise to the relatively large anisotropy observed in Permalloy films.

Knorr and Hoffmann[23] and Smith[17] have found that uniaxial anisotropy can be induced in an iron or Permalloy film even in the absence of a magnetic field if the vapor beam is allowed to impinge upon the substrate at oblique rather than normal incidence. Knorr and Hoffmann have explained this angle-of-incidence effect in terms of inclined crystallographic texture and strain in the film [see Sec. 7.2(d)]. However, according to other experimental and theoretical evidence, texture does not appear to be the chief source of the observed anisotropy.[17, 37–40]

Subsequently, Smith, Cohen, and Weiss demonstrated rather conclusively, using electron microscopy, that the anisotropy observed in oblique-incidence films is due mainly to a geometrical effect.[41] The explanation is based upon the preferential growth of crystallite chains due to a self-shadowing mechanism. It is postulated that in the initial stages of film formation, a random distribution of small crystallites is created on the substrate and each crystallite acts as a nucleus for further growth. The region of the substrate behind a growing crystallite is prevented from receiving metal vapor because it is in the shadow of the crystallite. Thus, as crystallites grow in the film they will leave vacant areas behind them. When the crystallites are sufficiently large, they will grow together and agglomerate into chains whose long axis tends to be perpendicular to the beam direction as illustrated in Fig. 7.7. For this chain growth to occur, however, we must implicitly assume that the metal atoms have low mobility on the substrate surface for otherwise the atoms would diffuse into the shadow region. This assumption is consistent with the electron microscopy observation that in high substrate temperature films the initial nucleation density is much smaller and the crystallite size is much larger than in lower substrate temperature films. Now, the demagnetizing field is smaller along the axis of the chain than in a direction perpendicular to it. Therefore, a geometrical uniaxial anisotropy is

[37] R. D. Heidenreich and F. W. Reynolds in C. A. Neugebauer *et al.* (eds.), *op. cit.*, p. 402.
[38] E. W. Pugh *et al.*, *J. Appl. Phys.*, **31**: 293S (1960).
[39] E. W. Pugh, E. L. Boyd, and J. F. Freedman, *IBM J. Res. Develop.*, **4**: 163 (1960).
[40] M. S. Cohen *et al.*, *J. Appl. Phys.*, **31**: 291S (1960).
[41] D. O. Smith, M. S. Cohen, and G. P. Weiss, *J. Appl. Phys.*, **31**: 1755 (1960).

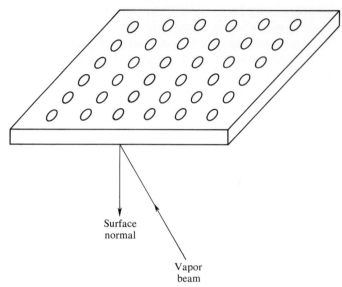

Surface
normal

Vapor
beam

FIG. 7.7. Crystallite chain formation due to the shadowing effect in oblique-incidence deposition.

developed with an easy axis in the direction of the chain and a hard axis in the orthogonal direction. Oblique-incidence anisotropy field could take on a wide range of values (a few to several hundred oersteds) dependent upon the angle of incidence and other film preparation variables.

Using a table of random numbers (i.e., the coordinates of the points appearing in a figure are taken from a table of random numbers) to locate the initial nucleation centers on a plane, we can schematically illustrate the self-shadowing effect.[41] It is reasonable to assume that due to surface tension, each crystallite maintains an approximately spherical shape as it grows. For a 60° incidence angle (with respect to the film normal), the growth of a crystallite which is behind another one will be strongly inhibited if the separation between the centers of the two is less than about two crystallite diameters $2d$. Growth inhibition in the shadow region can be illustrated by a construction using the following rule. A nucleus located by a table of random numbers is circled with a circle of diameter d only if the distance from the given nucleus to the next circled nucleus in the direction toward the source is greater than $2d$. (The beam direction is defined as the projection of the vapor beam on the surface of the film.) In this way, it can be conclusively illustrated that chain formation does occur in a direction perpendicular to the vapor beam.

Further evidence in support of the geometrical model of oblique-incidence anisotropy may be found in the results of magnetic replication experiments.[40] In these experiments 83–17 Permalloy was deposited at normal incidence on films of Al, Au, Ag, or Pt which had been previously deposited at oblique incidence. The resulting Permalloy films show magnetic anisotropy with easy axis perpendicular to the nonmagnetic metal beam direction, i.e., the anisotropy of the under layer was transmitted to the Permalloy. Similar replication behavior was found when Permalloy films were deposited onto glass substrate vacuum coated with a chromium gold film deposited at oblique incidence.[42]

[42] M. Lauriente and J. Bagrowski, *J. Appl. Phys.*, **33**: 1109 (1962).

Anisotropic resistivity, optical dichroism and birefringence, and anisotropy resonance line widths observed in oblique-incidence films are all consistent with the preferential crystal chain growth model of anisotropy.[41] For film deposited at an incident angle of 45°, Smith *et al.* found that the resistivities measured parallel and perpendicular to the long axis of the chain were approximately 0.5 for films about 30 Å thick; for 200 Å films the ratio was about 0.9. More extensive and accurate measurements by Pugh *et al.*[39] showed that resistivity difference of several percent for the two orthogonal directions exists in films up to 1500 Å thick. Since the film is essentially continuous in the axial direction of the chains and essentially discontinuous in a direction perpendicular to it, such anisotropic resistivity should indeed exist. As the film thickness increases, however, the space between chains becomes gradually filled and the resistivity should then become less anisotropic as observed.

When polarized light is passed through the oblique-incidence film at normal incidence, the absorption and phase shift were found to depend on the orientation of the electric field of the incident radiation. It was found that polarized light of 5460 Å wavelength suffers the greatest absorption on passage through an oblique-incidence film when the electric field is parallel to the long axis of the chain. Since the resistivity is smaller in the axial direction of the chains, this result should be anticipated.

The line width of normal-incidence films, according to Eq. (10.34), is the same in the easy and hard directions of magnetization. This prediction has been amply verified by experiment indicating that any crystallite shape anisotropy that may exist in normal-incidence films is too small to give an observable difference in line width in the two directions. On the other hand, the resonance line width for oblique-incidence films was found to be approximately 20% greater when the easy axis is perpendicular than when it is parallel to the static field. This result can be interpreted by noting that due to demagnetizing effects, more spatial dispersion in the direction of the magnetization M should occur when M is perpendicular to the long axis of the chains than when it is parallel to them. Therefore, different effective fields exist in different regions of the film. A broader line will therefore be expected in the former case since different spins go through resonance over a wider range of applied fields. Oblique-incidence films have been annealed in a ferromagnetic resonance apparatus.[43] After anneal, the room temperature easy axis of these films with positive magnetostriction was found to be in the original direction. However, films with negative magnetostriction developed a new room temperature easy axis orientated at 90° to the original one; at 300°C the easy axis was in the original direction. Application of a large magnetic field in any direction during anneal did not influence the final magnetic anisotropy in either case. These effects can be explained by assuming that the annealing process increases the tension along the axis of the crystallite chains, a process which converts surface energy into strain energy.

It should be pointed out in closing that oblique-incidence anisotropy has so far been solely a scientific curiosity with no pertinent technical applications. Indeed, in thin-film memory fabrication, oblique incidence of the vapor beam is avoided so as to yield a low value of anisotropy in order to minimize driving requirements.

---

[43] G. P. Weiss and D. O. Smith, *J. Appl. Phys.*, **32**: 85S (1961).

7.5 ANOMALOUS ANISOTROPIES

In the foregoing sections of this chapter, we have studied, aside from the oblique-incidence effect, mainly the anisotropy of typical films. These films are usually deposited in a vacuum of 10^{-7} to 10^{-6} mm Hg on microscope slides kept at 200–400°C during deposition at a rate of about 1000 Å/min. These films usually have an anisotropy field H_k and coercive force H_c of a few oersteds with $H_k > H_c$. Furthermore, the angular deviation of the easy-axis orientation of these films is in general quite small, say about a degree or so. These films possess many of the desirable properties from the application standpoint so that studies of films with anomalous properties would have essentially only a physical import. However, it must be emphasized that the study of the behavior of anomalous films, aside from its own scientific merit, may yield information of consequence to the understanding of the behavior of normal films themselves. Consequently, in what follows, we shall study such anomalous anisotropic phenomena as rotatable anisotropy, inversion, that is, $H_k < H_c$, negative H_k, and the associated phenomena of high coercivity and anisotropy, rotatable initial susceptibility, and mottled Bitter patterns, etc.

Films with anomalous properties can be produced by various techniques. These methods include evaporation at slow rates and at high substrate temperatures, evaporation on aggregated metal deposits, electroplating on annealed gold films, and annealing ordinary typical films.[44] In general, for a given technique, a mild treatment yielded high coercivity and high anisotropy films, a moderate treatment gave rotatable initial susceptibility films and a drastic treatment produced mottled films. Following Cohen, we shall discuss each of these phenomena in turn and relate them to the subject of rotatable anisotropy, inversion and negative H_k below.

(a) High Coercivity and High Anisotropy

The coercive force and anisotropy of anomalous films, like those of ordinary films, can be measured with a hysteresisgraph as described in Secs. 8.3(a) and 7.9(a), respectively. However, in contrast to the case of normal films, H_k as obtained from a hysteresisgraph for high coercivity and high anisotropy films (H_c and H_k many times those of ordinary films) may differ widely from the value $2K_1/M$ measured by a torque magnetometer. For these films, $2K_1/M$ values as obtained from a torque magnetometer were many times lower than the H_k values measured by a hysteresisgraph; the $2K_1/M$ values were similar to H_k of ordinary films. In addition, torque-magnetometer curves of these films often show considerable rotational hysteresis at fields much higher than H_k. However, this effect was much weaker than that in rotatable initial susceptibility and mottled films. Furthermore, Bitter patterns of high coercivity and high anisotropy films often showed "locking," i.e., when a reversing field was applied the magnetization did not reverse, but an unusual configuration of domain walls appeared. However, such locking was much more pronounced in rotatable initial susceptibility films. Inverted films ($H_c > H_k$), to be discussed below, were often found among these films, but their occurrence was unpredictable.

(b) Rotatable Initial-Susceptibility Films

For a class of films, the high field hysteresis loops remained almost the same when measured in any azimuth, while the remanent magnetization was almost equal to

----
[44] M. S. Cohen, *J. Appl. Phys.*, **33**: 2968 (1962).

the saturated value. The Bitter patterns of such films presented a spotted or mottled appearance, but this mottling was much less pronounced than in the patterns of mottled films. Cohen[44] has designated these films "rotatable-initial-susceptibility" (RIS) films to distinguish them from low-remanence films, i.e., from mottled films, for which the initial susceptibility can also be rotated, and from rotatable-anisotropy films whose high field loops are similar to those of mottled films.

Two different types of RIS films could be distinguished by hysteresisgraph initial-susceptibility measurements made after the film was subjected to a high ac field. For a type I film, the initial susceptibility as measured by a low drive field was zero in the arbitrary direction in which a high ac field had been previously applied, but attained a maximum 90° away. For a type II film, however, the converse was true. On the other hand, if a high dc field was applied in an arbitrary direction to either type of film, the initial susceptibility behavior was like that of a type I film after it had been subjected to an ac field. For some films the application of a high ac field in an arbitrary direction did not establish a maximum or zero initial susceptibility in that direction, but merely changed its magnitude. Presumably, in these cases, the rotatable initial susceptibility effect was not strong enough to overcome the field induced anisotropy.

When an RIS film, particularly a type II RIS film, was subjected to an ac field applied in the zero initial susceptibility direction, the hysteresis loop slowly expanded with time if the field exceeded a certain threshold value. This effect, known as creep, first observed in mottled films by Huber and Smith,[45] has been attributed to interaction effects between domains.[46]

Rotational hysteresis in an ordinary film has been studied by Doyle et al.[47] They found that beyond a threshold field, the rotational hysteresis integral W_r, increased with the applied field H to a maximum and then decreased. It was found that W_r/K_1 for these films was about 1.3 and that W_r decreases to zero when $H/H_k > 1$. In contrast, for RIS films, Cohen found that $W_r/K_1 \simeq 60$ and W_r did not vanish until $H/H_k \simeq 425$.

If the magnetization of an RIS film was first saturated in the plane of the film by a high dc field in an arbitrary direction and this field was then reversed, a locking pattern consisting of Néel walls perpendicular to the field direction was seen. When the magnitude of the reversed field exceeds a certain critical value, the locking pattern was swept away and the film became saturated in the reverse direction.

(c) Mottled Films

Huber and Smith[45] have observed low remanence, creep, rotatable initial susceptibility, and mottled-looking Bitter patterns in some films. These are Permalloy films having negative magnetostriction and whose thickness is above a certain critical value. The mottled character of the Bitter patterns and the low-remanence hysteresis loop both disappeared when the films were stripped from the substrate. This is interpreted to mean that the negative magnetostriction makes the film normal an easy axis, and that the disappearance of the film's mottled properties upon its detachment from the substrate is due to the consequent release of the isotropic stress involved

[45] E. E. Huber, Jr., and D. O. Smith, *J. Appl. Phys.*, **30**: 267S (1959).
[46] L. Néel, *J. Phys. Radium*, **20**: 215 (1959).
[47] W. D. Doyle, J. E. Rudisill, and S. Shtrikman, *J. Appl. Phys.*, **32**: 1785 (1961).

[see Sec. 3.1(b)]. In practice, it was found that a direct indication of a mottled film was the low-remanence hysteresis loop. Torque magnetometer studies showed that considerable rotational hysteresis at high fields was associated with mottled films.

(d) Anisotropy Model for Anomalous Films

The wide variety of experimental results for the different types of anomalous films produced by various techniques can be correlated by the assumption of a simple qualitative model.[44] According to this model, the various techniques for production of anomalous films cause the embedding in a matrix of normal uniaxial material of small scattered regions having high values of randomly oriented magnetic anisotropy. When the film is mildly treated the anisotropy-center density and values of the anisotropy are low, and high coercive force and high anisotropy films result. As the treatment becomes more drastic, the center density and values of the anisotropy rise and first RIS then mottled films appear. How this model can be used to explain the observed hysteresisgraph and torque magnetometer data and Bitter patterns has been considered in detail by Cohen.[44] We shall summarize some of the highlights here.

The switching of embedded single-domain anisotropy centers could cause high rotational hysteresis. Thus, in accord with the anisotropy-center model, the magnitude of the rotational hysteresis of a film has been found to increase as the film acquires more anomalous properties. As the center density and values of the anisotropies rise, higher fields are necessary to overcome the coercive forces of the centers and reverse the film, in accord with experiment. Also, the dispersion of the film monotonically increases as the center density and center anisotropy increase, since a smaller and smaller portion of the film remains strictly uniaxial. This prediction is also in accord with experiment. As films become more anomalous, the density of mottling gradually increases. These results are due to the large directional variations of the magnetization as a consequence of the influence of the anisotropy centers. In addition, the hysteresis behavior of the RIS films can be understood by considering the Bitter patterns after an ac field is applied and then removed. The different hysteresisgraph behavior of the two types of RIS films can thus be explained in terms of different magnetization configurations observed after application of high ac field. The origin of the difference in the ac magnetization configuration may be explained in turn by considering the dc states of the two types of films.

The high anisotropy centers may be generated by various sources or combinations of sources. These sources include crystalline anisotropy, geometric anisotropy of agglomerates of crystals, antiferromagnetic exchange anisotropy caused by the presence of islands of NiO, or inhomogeneous strain on the microscale in conjunction with magnetostriction.[44] Since anomalous films can be made by such a variety of techniques, it is possible that the origins of the anisotropy centers vary with the condition of film preparation. However, there are indications that the predominant effect is inhomogeneous strain in conjunction with magnetostriction.

Crystalline anisotropy is probably not the main source of the anisotropy center since the largest crystalline anisotropy field is about 200 Oe whereas much larger fields were often necessary to reduce the rotation hysteresis to zero. Geometric anisotropy of crystal agglomerates is also unlikely to be the origin of anisotropy centers. In this case, the temperature dependence of the hysteresis should follow the temperature dependence of the magnetization, inconsistent with experiment. Since anomalous properties are absent in Permalloy films deposited at pressures of 10^{-3} mm Hg of oxygen, it may be argued also that antiferromagnetic exchange cannot be the source of the anisotropy centers.

On the other hand, arguments can be cited in favor of the strain-magnetostriction mechanism. The monotonical decrease of rotation hysteresis with increasing temperature may be explained by the strain and magnetostriction temperature dependencies. Furthermore, the fact that mottled films stripped from their substrates have become normal can be explained by a strain relief mechanism although a similar behavior was not found in RIS films. The strain inhomogeneities may be associated with the microscopic inhomogeneities in structure created by the method of producing anomalous films. This is probably in turn related to an increase in crystallite size and to the microscopically roughened substrates in these procedures.

7·6 ROTATABLE ANISOTROPY

Rotatable anisotropy has been studied by various investigators since its first observation.[48-51] A rotatable anisotropy is one whose easy axis can be rotated by application of a field, and the time required for the change of state is dependent upon both the magnetic field and annealing temperature. It differs from the usual anisotropy in thin films in that with the latter, the easy axis can be rotated only by heating and cooling in a magnetic field.

Rotatable anisotropy films can be made by various means. Prosen et al. prepared these films by a special process involving the introduction of oxygen into the vacuum system before evaporation. Lommel and Graham produced these films by evaporating Ni on Mo-covered substrates and by oxidizing nickel films. On the other hand, Matcovich et al. produced rotatable anisotropy films by thermal decomposition of nickel and iron carbonyls. Whereas Matcovich et al. suggested that the rotatable phenomena are due to the presence of carbon in their films, Prosen et al. and Lommel and Graham try to account for it by invoking the NiO antiferromagnetic exchange hypothesis. However, since Permalloy films deposited in 10^{-3} mm of oxygen showed no rotatable properties, Cohen[44] concluded that the presence of NiO cannot be the source of the anisotropy.

Cohen observed that the rotatable anisotropy films, although also having a mottled Bitter pattern, differ in some respects from the anomalous films discussed above. In contrast to the case of mottled films, the rotatable anisotropy films retain their low-remanence hysteresis loop upon stripping from their substrates. However, the rotational hysteresis of these films was found to fall to about half its original value after being stripped from its substrate. Thus, Cohen concluded that stripping does relieve some strain in these films and again proposed that his anisotropy-center hypothesis should be invoked for the rotatable anisotropy films also. However, it is far from clear how the introduction of oxygen could create these anisotropy centers.

Lehrer has also studied rotatable anisotropy in negative magnetostriction Ni-Fe films.[51] He found that the rotatable anisotropy effect occurs under the same conditions

[48] R. J. Prosen, J. O. Holmen, and B. E. Gran, *J. Appl. Phys.*, **32**: 91S (1961); R. J. Prosen, *et al.*, *J. Appl. Phys.*, **33**: 1150S (1962).

[49] T. Matcovich, E. Korostoff, and A. Schmeckenbecher, *J. Appl. Phys.*, **32**: 93S (1961).

[50] J. M. Lommel and C. D. Graham, Jr., *J. Appl. Phys.*, **33**: 1160S (1962).

[51] S. S. Lehrer, *J. Appl. Phys.*, Pt. 2, **34**: 1207 (1963).

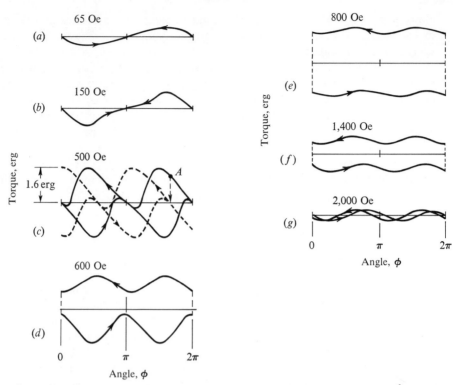

FIG. 7.8.   Room-temperature torque vs angle at various static fields for a 1500 Å nickel film deposited at a rate of 500 Å/min onto a substrate at 50°C. The dashed curve 1(c) ($H = 500$ Oe) is obtained by saturating at point A and then continuing the measurement at 500 Oe (after S. S. Lehrer, Ref. 51).

of film thickness and composition as the mottling effect previously reported by Huber and Smith.[45] In both cases the effects only occur for compositions with negative magnetostriction λ and for thicknesses greater than a critical thickness t_c which is nearly inversely proportional to λ. These thickness and compositional dependencies suggest that magnetostriction and strain are responsible for both effects.

Rotatable anisotropy is illustrated in Fig. 7.8 for a nickel film which shows room temperature torque vs the angle α between the measuring field and the direction of last saturation. The low-level torque [Fig. 7.8(a) and (b)] is reversible and varies $\sim$ as $\sin \alpha$, which implies $H < H_k'/2$, where H_k' is the uniaxial anisotropy field. At higher fields [Fig. 7.8(c)] a typical uniaxial switching torque is obtained, indicating that $H_k'/2 \leq H \leq H_k'$. At point A a saturating field is applied at an angle to the easy axis and then reduced to the previous measuring valve. Continuing the measurement at 500 Oe gives the dotted curve, which shows that the easy axis has been rotated without changing the magnitude of the anisotropy. At higher fields the dependence of the torque on angle begins to disappear [Fig. 7.8(d) and (e)], but the rotational hysteresis continues to increase. Finally, the rotational hysteresis approaches zero [Fig. 7.8(f) and (g)] and a nonrotatable uniaxial torque remains which is an order of magnitude smaller than the rotatable component. When the rotational hysteresis for nickel films of different thicknesses are plotted vs field, two maxima are seen to occur for a given film. The first maximum is associated with the switching of aligned uniaxial material [cf. Fig. 7.8(c)] while the second is associated with the torque which is independent of α but which changes sign with the direction of rotation [Fig. 7.8(e)]. These data can be qualitatively explained by assuming two kinds of high anisotropy regions.[51]

7·7 INVERTED FILMS

By inverted films, we mean that the coercive force for the film H_c is larger than its anisotropy field H_k. In principle, then, if a reversing field is applied along the easy axis, the magnetization should reverse by the fast rotation rather than the slow domain wall motion mode. However, experimentally, it has been observed that the magnetization reversal is prevented by the resulting presence of "locking" in the Bitter patterns; the locking walls are observed to be perpendicular to the easy axis. Cohen[44] again proposed that the anisotropy-center model should explain the inversion behavior. Thus, in the range of center density and anisotropy value giving high coercivity and anisotropy films, H_c may be sometimes raised more than H_k and inversion results.

Inverted films may be prepared in various ways, e.g., by slow evaporation onto normally cleaned glass substrate, fast or slow evaporation onto specially cleaned substrates, and electrodeposition onto glass substrates which have an underlayer of sputtered Au when the sputtering voltage and pressure are held within certain limits.[52] However, no method has yet been found which can, with certainty, produce inverted films.

7·8 NEGATIVE H_k

In certain films, it has been suggested that the easy axis of small regions of the film is perpendicular to the deposition field; i.e., negative H_k regions are present.[53] This suggestion was based upon the observed dependence of wall coercive force on the anisotropy field in composite films and high-angle locking in low-dispersion films. Doyle *et al.* also presented data in support of this suggestion based upon the unidirectional rotational hysteresis centered around the easy axis.[47]

This experimental evidence, however, has not been completely unambiguous. Smith, in a recent note,[54] has presented experimental evidence considerably more convincing of the existence of these regions in some films by using the technique of transversed biased permeability introduced by Torok *et al.*[55] In this method, the film is biased with a dc field of the order of H_k along the hard axis and the permeability along the easy axis measured with a small ac field $\ll H_k$. If the dc field corresponds in magnitude and direction to the tip of a switching asteroid for any region of the film, irreversible switching occurs in that region and the permeability contains a loss component of flux which is in time quadrature with the ac field; i.e., quadrature flux is observed. For a typical film containing only positive anisotropy regions, quadrature flux occurs only when the dc field is within a small range of angles around

[52] D. O. Smith *et al.*, *J. Appl. Phys.*, **31**: 295S (1960).
[53] D. O. Smith, *J. Appl. Phys.*, **32**: 70S (1961); D. O. Smith and K. J. Harte, *J. Appl. Phys.*, **33**: 1399 (1962); D. O. Smith, *J. Phys. Soc. Japan Suppl. B-1*, **17**: 550 (1962).
[54] D. O. Smith, *Appl. Phys. Letters*, **2**: 191 (1963).
[55] E. J. Torok *et al.*, *J. Appl. Phys.*, **33**: 3037 (1962).

the hard axis and for small angle of dc field magnitudes around the average H_k. In a film in which negative anisotropy regions are present, the hard axis of such regions is along the easy axis of the rest of the film, so that in the linear-superposition approximation, quadrature flux should occur when the dc field is along both the macroscopic easy and hard axes. Accordingly, the presence of peaks in the maximum quadrature flux at both $\phi = 0$ and $\phi = \pi/2$ can be interpreted to mean that both positive and negative anisotropy regions exist in the film, ϕ being the angle between the dc field and the macroscopic easy axis. Such peaks at $\phi = 0$ and $\pi/2$ have indeed been found by Smith in support of the negative H_k hypothesis.

Since the measured quadrature flux is proportional only to the volume V and not to the K of the region, the relative amplitude of the quadrature flux at $\phi = 0$, $\pi/2$ can be used to determine the relative volume of the positive and negative H_k regions. In this way, it is surprising to find that the ratio of the two volumes for the film investigated is nearly unity.

The origin of the negative anisotropy in these films has not been resolved. However, since these films were obtained using slow evaporation rates (~ 50 Å/min) and alloy composition having negative magnetostriction, we may surmise that strain energy is involved at some stage of the phenomenon.

It may be tempting to attribute the formation of negative anisotropy centers and negative H_k regions to the same underlying phenomena since they both seem to be related to the magnetostriction and strain in the film. However, it must be pointed out that H_k in the anisotropy centers has to be very high (up to several hundred oersteds) while that in the negative H_k regions is very low; since the macroscopic K is positive and the volume of the positive and negative H_k regions may be about equal, K in these negative anisotropy regions may be smaller than that of the positive regions. We may also mention in passing that the intermediate state after magnetic anneal in normal films as proposed by Takahashi and shown in Fig. 7.6(b) represents a state with positive and negative H_k regions.

7·9 MEASUREMENT OF ANISOTROPY

In this section, we shall discuss the various methods of anisotropy measurement. These methods include the use of the torque magnetometer, the hysteresis looper and the ferromagnetic resonance spectrometer. In addition, the related measurements of magnetostriction, stress and strain in thin films and their relationship to the anisotropy is also discussed.

(a) Hysteresis-Looper Method

According to Eq. (8.10), the hysteresis loop of a thin film in the hard direction is given by

$$M \sin \phi = M \, \frac{H_\perp}{2K_1/M} \tag{8.10}$$

where ϕ is the angle between the magnetization and the easy axis at a given transverse field $H_\perp$. It is seen from this equation that the transverse loop is a straight line without hysteresis and saturates at $H_\perp = 2K_1/M$. Thus, the transverse loop can be used to determine both M and the anisotropy field $H_k = 2K_1/M$. In practice, however, the closed loop exists only at $H_\perp \ll 2K_1/M$. At high drives, the loop opens up and encloses a finite area as shown by the dotted curve in Fig. 8.5. Therefore, H_k is usually determined by the hysteresis looper method in the following way. The easy-axis rectangular hysteresis loop is first displayed on the face of the oscilloscope and the saturation level of the loop is noted. Next, the low level transverse loop is displayed. If the straight line so exhibited is extended until it intersects with the horizontal saturation line determined by the easy-axis loop, H_k may be determined. This procedure is illustrated in Fig. 7.9.

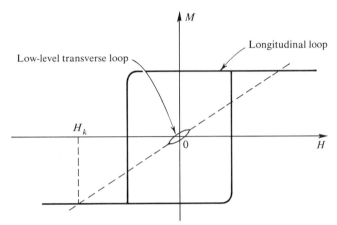

FIG. 7.9.   Procedure for determining H_k using the hysteresis looper.

(b) Torque-Magnetometer Method

One of the more dependable methods of measuring anisotropy is to measure the torque on a specimen as a function of the direction of the saturation magnetization relative to the easy axes. The usual scheme employed in this torque measurement[56] consists of supporting, from a vertical torsion fiber, a test specimen in an applied field and recording, point by point, the angular deflection of the fiber for various directions of the field relative to the specimen orientation. In addition to being time consuming, this method has several disadvantages which include the necessity of judicious fiber selection for a given type of specimen to maximize deflection and ensure stability.

A continuous reading magnetometer with the conventional fibre replaced by a system which instantaneously produces a torque just equal and opposite to that produced by the test specimen and which emits an electrical signal proportional to this torque would overcome the disadvantages of the conventional torsion-fiber magnetometer. Such an apparatus is being widely used.[57, 58] The operation of this balance can be described as follows: a torque produced by the specimen tends to rotate the suspension, balancing coil and mirror. The mirror rotation causes an unbalance in the amount of reflected light which falls on each phototube. This unbalance is amplified and converted to a current which is passed through the balancing coil in a direction such that the suspension returns to its equilibrium

[56] R. M. Bozorth, *Ferromagnetism*, D. Van Nostrand Company, Inc., Princeton, N.J., 1951, p. 556.

[57] R. F. Penoyer, *Rev. Sci. Instr.*, **30**: 711 (1959).

[58] G. T. Craft, F. J. Donahoe, and W. F. Love, *Rev. Sci. Instr.*, **26**: 360 (1955).

position. Such an automatic balancing magnetometer has a sensitivity of about 10^2 dyne-cm. Boyd[59] subsequently improved the sensitivity of the Penoyer's instrument to 0.5×10^{-3} dyne-cm, chiefly by changing the support of the sample from a bearing to a fiber, and applied it to thin-film measurement as did Doyle et al.[47] Recently, Humphrey and Johnson,[60] using a unique fused-silica suspension and servo system, increased the sensitivity of the torque magnetometer by about three orders of magnitude to 10^{-5} dyne-cm with a resolving time of a fraction of a second. This instrument, as designed, is a low field apparatus which can measure the magnetization, anisotropy, coercive force, and rotational hysteresis. If measurements in vacuum are desired, a vacuum torsion magnetometer may be constructed as shown in Fig. 6.7 in connection with the measurement of thin-film magnetization.

We now turn to a brief discussion of the use of the torque magnetometer for the determination of the anisotropy constant K_1. The free energy of the system composed of a thin film with a uniaxial anisotropy and a field H applied in the film plane is

$$E = K_1 \sin^2 \theta - MH \sin(\phi - \theta) \tag{7.43}$$

where θ and ϕ are angles between the easy axis and the magnetization $\mathbf{M}$ and field $\mathbf{H}$ respectively. Setting $\partial E/\partial \theta = 0$, we easily find the equilibrium position of the magnetization as

$$\sin(\phi - \theta) = \frac{K_1 \sin 2\theta}{MH} \tag{7.44}$$

It is seen from Eq. (7.44) that if $K_1 \sin 2\theta \ll MH$, $\phi \simeq \theta$ for high field (> 300 or 400 Oe, say), $\phi - \theta$ is typically less than $1°$ for Permalloy. Thus, under these circumstances, measurement of the magnetic torque as a function of θ, where θ is now taken as the angle between the field and the easy axis, will yield a sinusoidal torque curve equal to the anisotropy torque $K_1 \sin 2\theta$. Thus, the amplitude of the torque curve is proportional to K_1 while its periodicity is dependent upon the symmetry of the anisotropy.

(c) Ferromagnetic-Resonance Method

As we shall discuss in detail in Sec. 10.3, the anisotropy field H_k can be determined by measuring the resonance field separation between the cases where the applied field H_s is in the direction of and perpendicular to the easy axis. Indeed, this separation is simply equal to $2H_k$ as the resonance condition is given by

$$\omega_{o\pm} = |\gamma|\sqrt{4\pi M(H_s \pm H_k)} \tag{10.22}$$

where the $+$ and $-$ signs refer to the cases where H_s is applied parallel and perpendicular to the easy axis respectively. Since the ferromagnetic resonance spectrometers used for H_k determination will be discussed in detail in Sec. 10.3, we shall not further elaborate upon the subject here. We only wish to mention in passing that the accuracy of the method is dependent upon the accuracy with which H_s can

[59] E. L. Boyd, *IBM J. Res. Develop.*, **4**: 116 (1960).
[60] F. B. Humphrey and A. R. Johnson, *Rev. Sci. Instr.*, **34**: 348 (1963).

be measured. Since most field-measuring instruments can only measure accurately to a certain percentage of the field values in question, it is advantageous to use comparatively low frequencies, several hundred megacycles per second, say. However, there is a minimum frequency which is permissible for such measurements due to the finite value of H_k as can be seen from Eq. (10.22).

(d) Measurement of Angular Dispersion of Anisotropy

As we have already mentioned in Sec. 7.9(a), the transverse loop opens slightly at high fields and in some cases may be almost square, suggesting a poorly defined easy axis. Experimentally, it has been found that films do exhibit an apparent dispersion of the easy axis.[61-63] In the method used by Alexander to measure the easy-axis dispersion, a noncoherent rotational process was utilized. After the thin film has been saturated in the hard direction, the magnetization is allowed to relax toward a minimal-energy condition. In Crowther's method, the first step in making the measurement is to align the film in a hysteresisgraph as shown in Fig. 7.10 with $H_s = 0$. An ac transverse field $H_\perp > H_k$ will cause the magnetic vector of those regions with hard axes in quadrants II and IV to rotate in a counterclockwise direction. For those regions with their hard axes in quadrants I and III, rotation will be clockwise. When the two rotating components are equal, $\phi_L = 0$, and a null is obtained. For zero dispersion, the application of an infinitesimal positive H_L dc field will cause the magnetization of the entire film to oscillate back and forth only in quadrants I and IV. For finite dispersion, the field required to keep all the flux in quadrants I and IV can be used to calculate the dispersion. For a single region with skew α, the dc field required will be given by

$$H_s = H_k \sin \alpha \qquad (7.45)$$

In other words, the dc field must be larger than the longitudinal component of the ac field when it has the value H_k.

In addition, it is often found that there is a gross skew of the easy axis upon which the dispersion is superposed. The consequence of both effects is an equivalent rotation of the threshold switching curve of Fig. 9.2 which will be different for different parts of the film. This causes incoherent rotation and reduces the maximum allowable field for reversible switching.[63]

From the results of ferromagnetic resonance line-width measurements at the uhf and vhf range, Rossing[64] was able to determine the dispersion in the magnitude of the anisotropy in Permalloy films. Furthermore, the results of his experiments indicate that the increase in the damping constant with decreasing frequency in these frequency ranges is due to anisotropy dispersion (see further discussion in Sec. 11.2).

(e) Measurement of Compositional Dependence of H_k

The dependence of H_k upon melt composition for normal-incidence films has been studied by Smith and is shown in Fig. 7.1.[17] One curve represents the anisotropy resulting from deposition in an oriented dc field. It is seen that H_k decreases monotonically with composition, in qualitative agreement with the Fe-pair orientation

[61] R. G. Alexander, *J. Appl. Phys.*, **30**: 266S (1959).

[62] T. S. Crowther, *MIT Lincoln Lab. Group Rept. 51–2*, February, 1959.

[63] J. A. Raffel *et al.*, *Proc. IRE*, **49**: 155 (1961).

[64] T. D. Rossing, *J. Appl. Phys.*, **34**: 995 (1963).

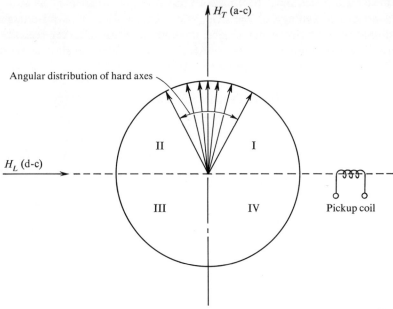

FIG. 7.10.   Diagram for the measurement of easy-axis dispersion in magnetic films (after Raffel, Crowther, Anderson, and Herndon, Ref. 63).

theory. Another represents the anisotropy which results from deposition in a circular rotating field. As anticipated, preferentially oriented pair formation is suppressed but a uniaxial anisotropy of considerable nonuniformity still remains. Compositional dependence of the H_k for oblique-incidence films has been given by Smith *et al.*[41] and Pugh *et al.*[39]

(f) Magnetoelastic Measurements

We shall briefly discuss here the measurement of the magnetoelastic constant B and the magnetoelastic parameter η and their relationship to the anisotropy. According to the discussion in Sec. 2.4(b), the magnetoelastic constant can be determined by the rate of change of the anisotropy constant K_1 with respect to a small applied strain e, that is, by dK_1/de since $B = dK_1/de = (M/2)\,dH_k/de$. The compositional dependence of B for vapor deposited films has been studied by Smith[17] and his result is shown in Fig. 7.1 along with the curves for H_k. It is seen from the figure that $B = 0$ at a melt composition of about 83% nickel (film composition of 81% nickel). At this composition, H_k is seen to be reasonably low, an important fact for memory applications. Wolf and Crowther have found that B was significantly less for plated than for evaporated films of the same composition.[65]

It is clear from the above discussion and from Eq. (2.6) that H_k could be increased or decreased depending upon whether strain is tensile or compressive, on the direction in which stress is applied, and on the sign of the magnetoelastic constant. For memory applications, it is important to produce films with very low magnetoelastic sensitivity.

[65] I. W. Wolf and T. S. Crowther, *J. Appl. Phys.*, **34**: 1205 (1963).
[66] E. N. Mitchell, G. I. Lykken, and G. D. Babcock, *J. Appl. Phys.*, **34**: 715 (1963).

In this sense, the results cited above indicate that electrodeposited films are more desirable than evaporated ones.

Mitchell et al.[66] have derived an expression which relates the magnetoelastic parameter η to the magnetostriction λ_s of the film; η being equal to $\Delta H_k/(\Delta l/l)$. Here ΔH_k is the change in H_k upon the application of a stress sufficient to strain the film an amount $\Delta l/l (\sim 4 \times 10^{-5}$ typically). η has been measured as a function of composition,[66, 67] and the predicted value of λ_s agrees within limits of precision to that observed for bulk material. If we assume the film to be isotropic in the film plane, a relation between applied stress and change in the anisotropy field is developed and within limits experimentally verified.

Isotropic stress in Permalloy films has been measured as a function of thickness, deposition rate, and substrate temperature.[68] This is done by clamping one end of a substrate consisting of a thin strip of glass or mica and observing the deflection of the free end during deposition. Results indicate that the stress is independent of thickness in the 100–2000 Å thickness range. However, tensile, compressive, or zero stress may be observed.

Strains may be determined using the Tolansky multiple-beam interferometry method to measure the bending of the substrate.[24] If the strain is isotropic, the interference rings are well-known Newton's rings. If the strain is anisotropic, these rings will be elliptical. Quantitative results are readily obtained by applying linear strain theory.[69, 70]

[67] E. N. Mitchell and G. I. Lykken, *J. Appl. Phys.*, **33**: 1170 (1962).

[68] G. P. Weiss and D. O. Smith, *J. Appl. Phys.*, **33**: 1166 (1962).

[69] A. Brenner and F. Sanderhoff, *Bur. Std. J. Res.*, **42**: 105 (1949).

[70] A. E. Love, *Treatise on the Mathematical Theory of Elasticity*, Dover Publications, Inc., New York, 1944, p. 133.

CHAPTER 8

HYSTERESIS AND EDDY CURRENTS

The losses that occur in a ferromagnetic material arise from two causes: (1) the tendency of the material to oppose the change in the magnetic state, often referred to as magnetic hysteresis and (2) the Joule heating which appears in the material as a result of the voltages and consequent circulatory currents induced in it by the time-varying flux. Here we are interested mainly in the quasistatic characteristics so that residual losses due to domain rotation resonance, domain wall relaxation and dimensional resonance are not included. The first of these contributions to the energy dissipation is known as hysteresis loss and the second as eddy-current loss. Because of the presence of a uniaxial anisotropy in magnetic thin films, the hysteresis loop in the easy direction, unlike that of ordinary bulk ferromagnetic materials, is highly rectangular and possesses two bistable remanent states. These states may be used to represent "0" and "1" of a binary system; thus, the film could function as a magnetic memory. In the hard direction, the hysteresis loop is essentially a straight line with slope M/H_k where M is the magnetization and H_k is the anisotropy field. For the quasistatic loops, the magnetization changes are accomplished by two distinct processes when the field is applied in the easy and hard directions. The easy-axis magnetization reversal is accomplished by domain wall motion while the hard-axis magnetization change is accomplished mainly by uniform rotation of the magnetization.

From the context of the above discussion, it is clearly of interest to inquire into the origin of hysteresis in thin film and to relate quantities such as the remanent magnetization and coercive force to the magnetization reversal process. Furthermore, since thin films may have high conductivity, it is also pertinent to study the eddy-current effects in thin films and to ascertain the influence of eddy currents upon the shape of the hysteresis loops.

In this chapter, we shall begin with a brief review of the general theory of hysteresis and eddy-current effects. Then, starting with the expression for the free energy of a thin film in a magnetic field, we derive the mathematical description for the hysteresis loops of a thin film. Furthermore, we shall study the dependence of the coercive force of a thin film upon its thickness, composition, etc., and correlate the theoretical results with experiment. Methods for measuring the hysteresis loop and conductivity of thin films will also be examined in some detail.

8·1 GENERAL THEORY

A typical hysteresis loop of an ordinary bulk ferromagnetic material is shown in Fig. 8.1. Hysteresis results from the tendency of a ferromagnetic material to oppose a change in the magnetic state under external stimulus so that the flux density is not a single-valued function of the magnetic field. For example, if a magnetic field $\mathbf{H}$ is applied to a ferromagnetic material so that the magnetic induction in the direction of $\mathbf{H}$ is changed from B_1 to B_2, decreasing H to zero will in general decrease B_2 to B_1' which is larger than B_1. The energy E per unit volume absorbed by the material in changing its magnetization from B_1 to B_2 is given by

$$E(B_1 \rightarrow B_2) = \frac{1}{8\pi} \int_{B_1}^{B_2} H\,dB = \text{area II} \tag{8.1}$$

If H is decreased to zero, energy is given up by the material and the sign of E is negative. Thus,

$$E(B_2 \rightarrow B_1') = \frac{1}{8\pi} \int_{B_2}^{B_1'} H\,dB = -\text{area I} \tag{8.2}$$

Therefore, the hysteresis loss in this example is simply the sum of the energies given by Eqs. (8.1) and (8.2) or area II–area I.

As shown in Fig. 8.1, H is varied cyclically between the values $-H_{\max}$ and $H_{\max}$ with the ferromagnetic material initially at the demagnetized state. Since the values of B on the falling curve are greater than those on the rising curve due to the tendency of a ferromagnetic material to oppose a change in the flux density, the hysteresis loop is not closed. However, as the number of cyclic variations of H between $-H_{\max}$ and

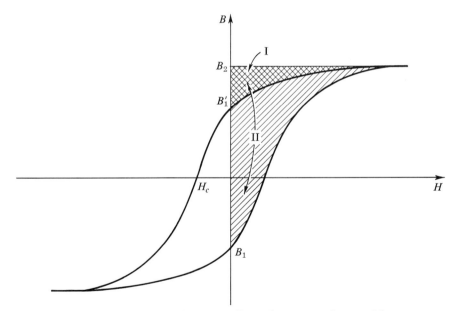

FIG. 8.1.   Hysteresis loop of ordinary ferromagnetic materials.

$H_{\max}$ approaches infinity, the path becomes a closed hysteresis loop. If the loop is not symmetrical even for a symmetrical excitation, the material is said to exhibit unidirectional hysteresis. If the material is subjected to a cyclic excitation involving smaller values of H and B, a smaller hysteresis loop is obtained. If magnetizing the force is not varied continuously in one direction between the maximum values of H, small internal loops, called minor hysteresis loops, are introduced. From the above discussion and from Fig. 8.1, we see that the hysteresis loss per cycle for a cyclic magnetization of the material can be defined only after an infinite number of cycles of magnetization and is given by the area of the closed loop.

It is instructive to inquire into the physical origin of hysteresis. Consider the energy of a specimen as a function of the position of the domain wall x. This energy E_w may vary in some manner as shown in Fig. 8.2 due to local variations in internal strains, impurities, crystallite dimensions, etc. The energy minima are usually located at points of imperfections such as vacancies, dislocations, nonmagnetic impurities, and voids. Suppose a domain wall is initially located at point A. Consider an applied magnetic field H of a magnitude such that the domain wall moves from A to B. When H is subsequently reduced to zero, the domain wall will move reversibly back to A.

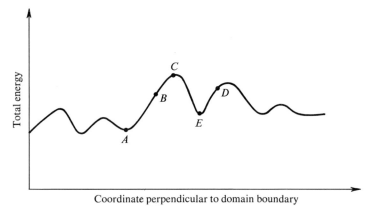

FIG. 8.2. Total energy of a ferromagnetic specimen as a function of the position of the domain wall.

On the other hand, if H is sufficiently large so that the domain wall could surmount the energy peak C so that it moves from A to D, decreasing H to zero will cause the domain wall to move from D to E instead of back to A. This irreversible process occurs because there is insufficient energy stored in the domain wall to overcome the energy peak C. In this example, the energy absorbed by the sample in going from A to D may be likened to area II of Fig. 8.1, while the energy given up in going from D to E may be likened to area I. The difference in these two energies is just the hysteresis loss and accounts for the energy dissipated in moving a domain wall from an energy minimum over energy maxima. Since the magnetization in the direction H must increase in going from A to the right along x, the magnetization at E is smaller than that at D but larger than that at A in accord with Fig. 8.1. Indeed, the field required to reduce M to zero is defined as the coercive force H_c.

Next, we should like to consider the case of eddy-current losses in a ferromagnetic material. Whenever the flux in a medium is changing, there will be an associated electric field according to the Maxwell equation:

$$\nabla x\mathbf{E} = -\frac{1}{c}\frac{\partial \mathbf{B}}{\partial t} \tag{8.3}$$

Integrating both sides of Eq. (8.3) over some surface S and using Stoke's theorem

$$\oint_C \mathbf{E \cdot dl} = \int_S \nabla\mathbf{XE \cdot dS}$$

we have

$$\oint_C \mathbf{E \cdot dl} = -\frac{1}{c}\frac{\partial}{\partial t}\int_S \mathbf{B \cdot dS} \tag{8.4}$$

If the medium is conducting, a current is set up around the contour C by the induced voltage $\oint_c \mathbf{E \cdot dl}$. These currents are called eddy currents and the energy loss in the medium, which is proportional to $i^2\rho$, where i is the eddy-current density and ρ, the resistivity, is called eddy-current loss.

We shall now calculate the eddy-current loss in a thin film of thickness T as shown in Fig. 8.3. Consider a rectangular parallelpiped of unit height and thickness T. Integration of Eq. (8.4) yields

$$2E_z = -\frac{1}{c}\frac{d}{dt}(2Bx) \tag{8.5}$$

where E_z is the electric field at x and B has been assumed constant for simplicity.

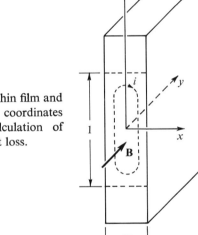

FIG. 8.3.   Thin film and associated   coordinates for   the   calculation   of eddy-current loss.

Since the current density j_z for a material with resistivity ρ is E_z/ρ we have from Eq. (8.5) that the instantaneous power loss in the differential slab dx thick is

$$j_z^2 \rho\, dx = \frac{1}{c^2\rho}\left(\frac{dB}{dt}\right)^2 x^2\, dx \tag{8.6}$$

Integrating Eq. (8.6) over the volume of unit height and unit width and thickness T, we get

$$2\int_0^{T/2} j_z^2 \rho\, dx = \frac{2(T/2)^3}{3c^2\rho}\left(\frac{dB}{dt}\right)^2 \tag{8.7}$$

For a sinusoidal variation of B, we easily find the average value of the eddy-current power loss per unit film surface area at a frequency f as

$$p_e = \frac{\pi^2}{c^2} \frac{f^2 T^3 B_{max}^2}{6\rho} \tag{8.8}$$

Although ρ is small for a conductor, p_e is usually negligible at switching frequencies of thin-film memories since thickness T is extremely small for thin films. However, at microwave frequencies, eddy-current damping of the magnetization precession may play a very dominant role in the relaxation process and cannot usually be neglected.

8·2 HYSTERESIS LOOP OF THIN FILMS

Due to the presence of the uniaxial anisotropy, the shape of the hysteresis loop of thin films, unlike that of ordinary ferromagnetic materials, is dependent upon the direction of the applied field. As we shall show below, for the case where the measuring field is applied in the direction of the easy axis, the hysteresis loop is highly rectangular while if the field is applied perpendicular to the easy axis, it is essentially a straight line without hysteresis. If the applied field is applied at angles intermediate between the easy and hard axes, the loop resembles a parallelogram, somewhat more akin to the loop of ordinary ferromagnetic materials shown in Fig. 8.1.

(a) Hard-Axis Loop

The free energy E of the single-domain system shown in Fig. 8.4 is given by[1]

$$E = K_1 \sin^2(\phi - \alpha) - H_s M \sin \theta \cos \phi - H_\perp M \sin \theta \sin \phi + 2\pi M \cos^2 \theta \tag{8.9}$$

The first term represents the anisotropy energy with K_1 being the first-order anisotropy constant, while the second and third terms represent the Zeeman energies associated with the x- and y-oriented magnetic fields H_s and $H_\perp$, respectively. The last term represents the demagnetizing energy; since it is zero when the magnetization is parallel to the film ($\theta = \pi/2$), an infinitely thin sample has been implicitly assumed.

Let us first consider two special cases of interest, namely $\alpha = 0$ and H_s or $H_\perp$ equals zero. For the case where $\alpha = 0$ and $H_s = 0$, the switching magnetic field $H_\perp$ is applied perpendicular to the easy axis and the resultant $M \sin \phi$ vs H hysteresis loop is termed the transverse loop. For simplicity, let $\theta = \pi/2$. The torque τ acting on the magnetization is equal to $\mathbf{r} \times \mathbf{F}$ where $\mathbf{r}$ is the radial coordinate and $\mathbf{F}$ is a generalized force. Since $\mathbf{F}$ is conservative, it could be represented by $-\nabla E$. Noting that E has only a ϕ dependence, we find that $\tau = \hat{\phi}(1/\sin\theta)(\partial E/\phi)$, where $\hat{\phi}$ is a unit vector in the ϕ direction. Thus, the equilibrium position of $\mathbf{M}$ is given by $\partial E/\partial \phi = 0$. Using Eq. (8.9), we easily find

$$\cos \phi = 0$$

$$M \sin \phi = M \frac{H_\perp}{2K_1/M} \tag{8.10}$$

---

[1] D. O. Smith, *J. Appl. Phys.*, **29**: 274 (1958).

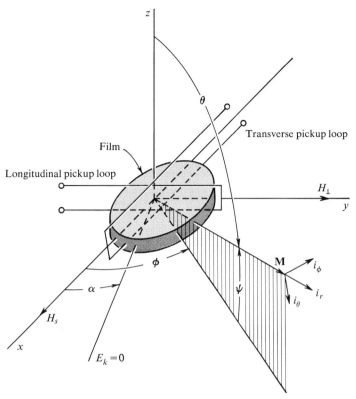

FIG. 8.4.   Anisotropic thin film and associated coordinates (after D. O. Smith, Ref. 1).

where $2K_1/M$, having the dimension of $H_\perp$, is known as the anisotropy field. The transverse loop as determined by Eq. (8.10) is plotted in Fig. 8.5. It is seen that the loop has no hysteresis and that it saturates at $H_\perp = 2K_1/M_1$. Therefore, the transverse loop may be used to determine both M and $2K_1/M$. In practice, the closed loop exists only at $H \ll 2K_1/M$. At high drives, the loop opens up

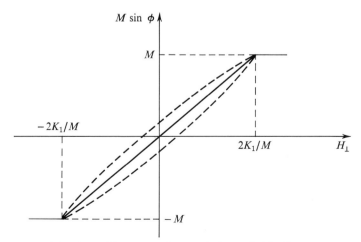

FIG. 8.5.   Transverse hysteresis loop of thin films.

and encloses a finite area as shown by the dotted curves shown in Fig. 8.5. From the above discussion, we see that a transverse field of the value $2K/M$ is required to rotate the magnetization **M** completely to the applied field axis and that the magnetization along the field axis increases linearly with H up to the saturated value M.

(b) Easy-Axis Loop

For the longitudinal loop, we set $\theta = \pi/2$, $\alpha = 0$, $H_\perp = 0$ in Eq. (8.9) and find $M \cos \phi$ by equating $\partial E/\partial \phi$ to zero giving

$$\sin \phi = 0$$

$$M \cos \phi = -M \frac{H_s}{2K_1/M} \tag{8.11}$$

Since there is always an extrema at $\phi = 0$, we must further require that $\partial^2 E/\partial \phi^2 = 0$ giving

$$\cos 2\phi = \left(\frac{H_s}{2K_1/M}\right)^2 \tag{8.12}$$

where we have made use of Eq. (8.11). From Eq. (8.12), we see that when $H_s = 2K_1/M$, $\phi = 0$ or π. Thus, when $\partial^2 E/\partial \phi^2 = 0$ we pass from the case where the extrema is a minimum to where it is a maximum. In this case an irreversible magnetization change of $2M$ occurs when $H_s = 2K_1/M$ as shown in Fig. 8.6.

It is seen from Fig. 8.6 that there are two stable states of the system with the magnetization making an angle ϕ of 0 or π with the x axis. These two states may then represent the binary states "0" and "1" of a computer memory. For example, if the magnetization is initially along the $\phi = \pi$ direction and a field H_s equal to $2K_1/M$ is applied in the $\phi = 0$ direction, according to Fig. 8.6, the magnetization will reverse irreversibly to the $\phi = 0$ direction of the applied field. If H_s is now reduced to zero, the magnetization along the $\phi = 0$ direction remains unchanged due to the perfect

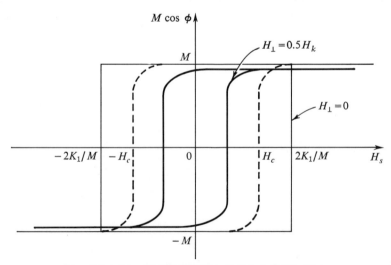

FIG. 8.6.   Longitudinal hysteresis loop of thin films.

rectangularity of the loop. If a pickup loop is placed with its plane perpendicular to the x axis as shown in Fig. 8.1, a voltage proportional to $\dot{M}$ will appear across its terminals indicating a change of state. On the other hand, if $\mathbf{M}$ were initially along the direction $\phi = 0$, a field H_s applied in this direction would not cause a realignment of the magnetization so that $\dot{M} = 0$ and there will be no voltage appearing across the terminals of the pickup loop. Thus, according to whether or not a voltage is generated in the pickup loop when H_s is applied, we can determine the initial state of the system.

According to the foregoing discussion, the energy required to switch a film from one stable state to another is dependent upon H_k. However, in practice, the film begins to reverse its state of magnetization at a value of field usually below that of H_k. This is because films usually reverse by domain wall motion rather than by coherent rotation in the easy direction. The field at which the magnetization component $M\cos\phi$ is actually zero is the coercive force H_c as shown in Fig. 8.6. If $H_c/H_k < 1$, the film is termed normal and if $H_c/H_k > 1$, it is termed inverted. Most films are of the normal type and it is not quite certain as to how inverted films could be consistently produced.[2]

To analyze the effect of the application of $H_\perp$ upon the shape of the longitudinal loop, we return to Eq. (8.9) and set $\partial E/\partial\phi = 0$ and $\partial^2 E/\partial\phi^2 = 0$ for finite values of $H_\perp$ and H_s. The result is

$$\frac{H_\perp}{H_k} = \sin^3\phi$$

$$\frac{H_s}{H_k} = \cos^3\phi$$

(8.13)

which is equivalent to $H_s/H_k = \pm[1 - (H_\perp/H_k)^{2/3}]^{3/2}$. Denoting the threshold field H_s by H_{cr}, we may plot the switching threshold H_{cr}/H_k as a function of $H_\perp/H_k$ as shown in Fig. 9.2. We see that the field at which the magnetization reverses is continuously decreased from H_k at $H_\perp = 0$ to 0 at $H_\perp = H_k$. The corresponding hysteresis loop gradually changes from the highly rectangular shape to a collapsed S shape. A typical hysteresis loop with $H_\perp/H_k \neq 0$ (=0.5) is also shown in Fig. 8.6 along with the $H_\perp = 0$ loop for comparison. Since the switching speed should decrease with increasing values of H_s above the effective coercive force H_{cr}, application of a transverse field would decrease the switching time τ for a given drive. Conversely, for a given τ, the drive field required is correspondingly decreased. This is an important conclusion for fast switching conditions. It must be noted, however, that according to Fig. 8.6, the loop becomes less rectangular as $H_\perp$ increases, which is undesirable for computer memory applications. This problem will be discussed further in Chap. 12.

(c) Coercive Force and Anisotropy

As we briefly discussed in Chap. 4, magnetization reversal in the easy direction starts with the motion of the domain walls associated with small regions of reversed magnetization at the edge of the film. As the switching field applied opposite to $\mathbf{M}$ increases, these reversed domains grow over the whole film, forming long walls parallel to the easy direction, and the reversal is completed by a parallel shift of these walls. The field range in which this wall motion process takes place is very small so

---

[2] D. O. Smith, *J. Appl. Phys.*, **32**: 74S (1961).

that the corresponding easy-axis loop is highly rectangular. The field at which domain wall motion begins, denoted by H_w, is called the wall motion coercive force or, in computer-technology notation, the H_{cd}. When the field is increased slightly above H_w, half of the magnetization has been reversed. The field corresponding to this point, denoted by H_c, is known simply as the coercive force of the film.

In the above discussion, we have implicitly assumed that the field required for edge domain wall motion ($=H_w$) is smaller than the wall nucleation field H_n. This is usually the case although it is possible to prepare films whereby the opposite is true. Furthermore, for inverted films ($H_c > H_k$), the magnetization would be expected to reverse in the easy direction by coherent rotation rather than by wall motion when $H_k < H < H_c$. However, results of switching experiments indicate that, due to the dispersion of the easy axis, the reversal process is still predominantly one of domain wall motion preceded by incoherent rotation which divides the film into many long domains oriented parallel to the easy axis.

Both the coercive force H_c and the anisotropy field H_k may take on a large range of values, from a fraction of an oersted to several hundred oersteds, depending upon the thickness, composition, deposition rate and substrate temperature, and angle of incidence of the vapor beam, etc. For films close to the 80% Ni–20% Fe composition, however, H_c and H_k are in the order of an oersted. In Chap. 7, we discussed in some detail the origin of the uniaxial anisotropy in thin films and the results of related experiments. Here, we shall investigate the possible dependence of the coercive force H_c upon the composition and thickness of the film. In particular, we shall attempt to correlate between theory and experiment in this regard.

As we have already briefly discussed in Sec. 8.1, the coercive force is related to the energy required for a wall to overcome certain potential barriers in its motion through the film. Thus, it is logical to surmise that the coercive force should be a function of film imperfections such as surface roughness due to finite crystallite size and substrate imperfection. For films whose thickness is in the range where cross-tie walls exist, we can expect a dependence of the total transition wall energy upon the magnetostrictive constant and hence the composition of the film due to the swirling of the magnetization in the region of these walls.[3]

It is therefore instructive to construct a mathematical theory for the coercive force of thin films, taking into account as many of the pertinent factors involved as possible.[4] Referring to Fig. 8.7, let us assume that the film is reversed by the parallel shift of a wall parallel to the easy axis so that the energy of the wall is a function of x only. For a small shift Δx of the wall parallel to itself, the increase of the free energy of the system must be equal to the work done on it, or

$$2H_c M_s l T \Delta x = \Delta(e_w l T) \tag{8.14}$$

where l is the length of the domain wall, T the thickness of the film, and e_w the surface energy density of the domain wall. Thus, it follows from Eq. (8.14) that for an infinitesimal wall displacement dx, the coercive force is given by

$$H_c = \frac{1}{2M_s} \left(\frac{de_w}{dx} + \frac{e_w}{T}\frac{dT}{dx} + \frac{e_w}{l}\frac{dl}{dx} \right) \tag{8.15}$$

---

[3] J. B. Goodenough and D. O. Smith in C. A. Neugebauer *et al.* (eds.), *Structure and Properties of Thin Films*, John Wiley & Sons, Inc., New York, 1959, p. 112.

[4] S. Middelhoek, *Ferromagnetic Domains in Thin Ni-Fe Films*, Drukkerij Wed. G. Van Soest, N.V., Amsterdam, 1961, p. 127. (We follow closely his treatment here.)

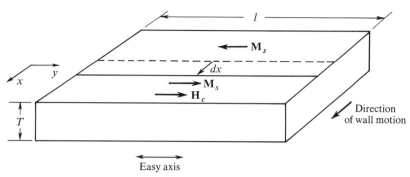

FIG. 8.7.   Parallel displacement of a domain wall due to the application of a magnetic field.

The first term is related directly to the change of wall energy. The wall energy e_w may be decomposed into three components, exchange e_{ex}, anisotropy e_{an}, and magneto-static e_m. The contribution to the coercive force as expressed by the second term is due to possible film-thickness variations first proposed by Néel.[5] The third term represents the contribution due to the change of the domain wall length as it propagates and can usually be neglected in comparison to the other contributions.[4]

Let us now return to a discussion of the contribution of H_c due to the $e_w = e_{ex} + e_{an} + e_m$ term. The contribution to the coercive force of a bulk material due to spatial exchange energy variations has been given by Bloch.[6] Since we do not know whether there is a significant spatial dependence of the exchange energy in thin films, we shall not pursue this topic further. Due to the presence of residual crystal anisotropy and magnetostriction, the anisotropy energy may vary from crystallite to crystallite so that for the one-dimensional case considered here, $de_{an}/dx = (\partial e_{an}/\partial K_1)(dK_1/dx)$ where K_1 is the first-order anisotropy constant. The magnetostatic energy consists of two terms. The first is due to poles formed at the intersection of wall with the surface. Since the thickness T determines the magnitude of this energy,[5] we have $de_{m1}/dx = (\partial e_{m1}/\partial T)(dT/dx)$. The second contribution to the magnetostatic energy is due to the angular dispersion of the easy axis along the wall. Since the wall is not at all places exactly parallel to the local easy axis, poles and associated magnetostatic energy would occur. Thus, we have $de_{m2}/dx = (\partial e_{m2}/\partial \phi) \times (d\phi/dx)$, where ϕ is a measure of the deviation of the wall direction from the average easy direction.

It now follows from Eq. (8.15) and the discussion above that the anisotropy contribution to the coercive force, H_{ck} is given by

$$H_{ck} = \frac{1}{2M_s} \left(\frac{\partial e_{an}}{\partial K_1} \frac{dK_1}{dx} + \frac{\partial e_{m2}}{\partial \phi} \frac{d\phi}{dx} \right) \tag{8.16}$$

Likewise, the thickness variation contribution to the coercive force H_{cT} is given by

$$H_{cT} = \frac{1}{2M_s} \left(\frac{\partial e_{m1}}{\partial T} \frac{dT}{dx} + \frac{e_w}{T} \frac{dT}{dx} \right) \tag{8.17}$$

Let us first consider the contribution due to the variation of the magnitude and easy direction of the anisotropy as expressed by Eq. (8.16). First, the contribution of the

[5] L. Néel, *J. Phys. Radium*, **17**: 250 (1956).
[6] F. Bloch, *Z. Physik*, **74**: 295 (1932).

anisotropy energy to the total wall energy is, according to the results of Sec. 4.2, equal to $\frac{1}{2}DK_1$ where D is the wall width. Assuming that K_1 changes by ΔK_1 from crystallite to crystallite of size L, this source of contribution to the coercive force $(1/2M_s)(\partial e_{an}/\partial K_1)(dK_1/dx)$ is given by $D\Delta K_1/4M_sL$ if the wall width is not dependent on K_1. Secondly, the total anisotropy energy consists of the induced uniaxial anisotropy energy K_1 and the stray anisotropy energies K_s. Assuming that the K_s is biaxial and K_1 is independent of crystallite orientations, we find

$$E_k = K_1 \sin^2 \phi_r + K_s \sin^2 2(\phi_r + \alpha) \tag{8.18}$$

where α is the angle between the easy axes. The resulting easy direction orientation ϕ_r may be obtained by setting $\partial E_k/\partial \phi_r = 0$ and assuming ϕ_r small, giving

$$\phi_r \simeq - \frac{K_s}{2K_1 + 4K_s \cos 4\alpha} \sin 4\alpha \tag{8.19}$$

The angle ϕ_r is also a function of the magnetostatic coupling according to the discussion in Sec. 3.3. To account for this, we assume that a $K_e \ll K_1$ may be used in place of K_s so that the $4K_s \cos 4\alpha$ term in Eq. (8.19) can be neglected compared to $2K_1$. The magnetostatic surface energy of the wall is proportional to the square of the magnetization component normal to the wall or equal to $e_m \phi_r^2$ for ϕ_r small. Using only the maximum deviation of ϕ_r, we find from the discussion above that

$$H_{ck} = \frac{D}{4} \frac{\Delta K_1}{M_sL} + \frac{e_m}{4M_sL} \left(\frac{K_e}{K_1}\right)^2 \tag{8.20}$$

We conclude from Eq. (8.20) that H_{ck} is a function of, among other things, composition since ΔK_1, M_s, K_e, and K_1 are likely to be functions of composition. Indeed, such compositional dependence of H_c as a function of composition of a Permalloy film of 150 Å thickness has been observed.[3] It has been found that the coercive force has a rather broad minimum in a range of composition centered about that corresponding to zero magnetostriction (83–17 Permalloy). Quantitative checks between theory as represented by Eq. (8.20) and experiment are difficult as quantities such as e_m, ΔK_1, K_e, are not well known.

We now proceed to discuss the contribution to the coercive force due to film-thickness variations as represented by Eq. (8.17). The first term in Eq. (8.17) represents the dependence of wall energy on film thickness, while the second term results from the fact that the force on the wall at a certain field is proportional to the thickness of the film. For a Bloch wall, the surface energy, according to Sec. 4.2, is given by

$$E_B = \frac{\pi^2 A}{D^2} D + \frac{1}{2} DK_1 + \frac{1}{2} \frac{2\pi D^2}{D+T} M_s^2 \tag{4.15}$$

Minimizing E_B with respect to D for a thick film ($D \ll T$) and substituting the resulting expression for E_B into Eq. (8.17), we find

$$H_{cT} = 4.2 \sqrt[3]{\frac{A^2}{M_s}} \frac{1}{T^{4/3}} \frac{dT}{dx} \tag{8.21}$$

which gives the well-known $T^{-4/3}$ dependence of H_c calculated by Néel.[5] In this calculation, the wall has been approximated by a cylinder of elliptical cross section. However, it has been shown that the 4/3 law given by Eq. (8.21) is also valid for a more sophisticated model of the Bloch wall.[7] For the Néel wall ($T \ll D$), using the results of Sec. 4.2, we similarly found that

$$H_{cT} = \pi M_s \frac{dT}{dx} \qquad (8.22)$$

which is independent of thickness.

It is now pertinent to see how the theoretical results of Eqs. (8.21) and (8.22) correlate with experiment. Tiller and Clark[8] have measured the variation of H_c of vapor-deposited thin Permalloy films with thickness ranging from tens of angstroms up to about 3000 Å as shown in Fig. 8.8. They found that for thickness below a few hundred angstroms, H_c varies more like D^{-1} rather than $D^{-4/3}$ according to Néel. This departure from the 4/3 law is probably not surprising as in the thickness range below a few hundred angstroms, Néel and cross-tie walls rather than Bloch walls exist, according to the discussion in Sec. 4.2. It may then be noted that, according to Eq. (8.22), H_c is independent of thickness for a Néel wall so that the inverse T dependence of H_c found by Tiller and Clark is not too unreasonable. Behrndt and Maddocks[9] found that for evaporated films in the 500 Å to 4000 Å range the exponential of the T dependence depends sensitively on the substrate cleaning process. For a series of films evaporated on a thick SiO film, they found an exponent of 1.24 as shown in Fig. 8.8. Middelhoek,[4] on the other hand, found that H_c of evaporated films has a

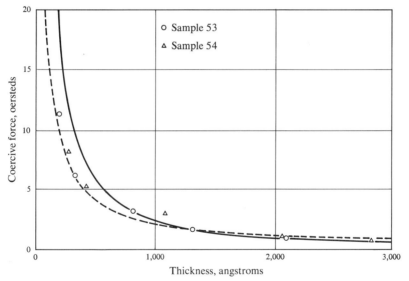

FIG. 8.8.   Coercive force vs thickness for 81% Ni–19% Fe films. The Néel theoretical curve, calculated with $H_c = 3.1$ Oe at a thickness of 809 Å, is shown by the solid line. The dashed curve is a plot of H_c as an inverse function of thickness while circles and rectangles represent experimental points (after Tiller and Clark, Ref. 8).

[7] R. E. Behringer and R. S. Smith, *J. Franklin Inst.*, **272**: 14 (1961).
[8] C. O. Tiller and G. W. Clark, *Phys. Rev.*, **110**: 583 (1958).
[9] K. H. Behrndt and F. S. Maddocks, *J. Appl. Phys.*, **30**: 276S (1959).

minimum at $T \simeq 500\,\text{Å}$ and a maximum at $750\,\text{Å}$. It is believed that the transition from Bloch to cross-tie wall at $750\,\text{Å}$ accounts for the maximum in H_c there. One may conclude from these various results that the deviation from the 4/3 law is probably due to the fact that Bloch walls do not exist in films thinner than a few hundred angstroms and that dT/dx may be a function of the thickness T itself.

For electrodeposited films from about 15 to 20,000 Å thick, Lloyd and Smith[10] found that the exponent for T in Eq. (8.21) ranges from 1.4 to 0 as shown in Fig. 8.9. They account for this deviation from the 4/3 power law by invoking three types of roughness. They are (1) periodic roughness with a wavelength large compared to a domain wall width and an amplitude small compared with the film thickness; (2)

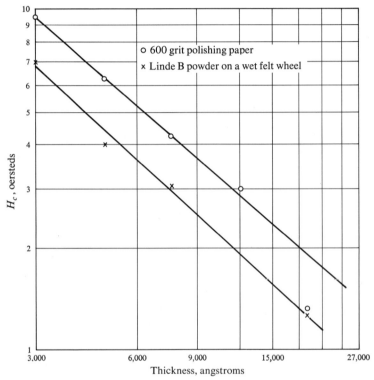

FIG. 8.9.   Wall motion coercive force vs film thickness for two substrate roughnesses, corresponding to 600 polishing paper and Linde B polishing compound. The value of n for both curves is about -0.93 (after Lloyd and Smith, Ref. 10).

roughness of the order of size of a domain wall; and (3) substrate roughness that is large compared to the film thickness. Accordingly, since the evaporated films used by Tiller and Clark have rather smooth surfaces, only roughness of the first kind exists and their data should show the approximate 4/3 dependence of H_c on T. The various thicknesses of these films were obtained by uniformly etching an initially thick film and electron micrographs shows that the surface roughness is small.

For electroplated films, however, Lloyd and Smith found from electron micrographs that roughness of the second kind increases with film thickness, indicating that

[10] J. C. Lloyd and R. S. Smith, *J. Appl. Phys.*, **30**: 274S (1959).

n depends on this factor. Here H_c is represented by $CT^n(dT/dx)$ where C is a constant. Roughness of the third kind, as introduced by unidirectional polishing, results in an increase of $C(dT/dx)$ while n is not affected. The third type of roughness was observed to orient the magnetic axis parallel to the polishing grooves. In our theoretical discussion above, we have implicitly assumed that the wavelength L of the wall-energy variations was greater than the wall width. This assumption is probably valid for Bloch walls in thick films but not for Néel walls in thin films as the width of a Néel

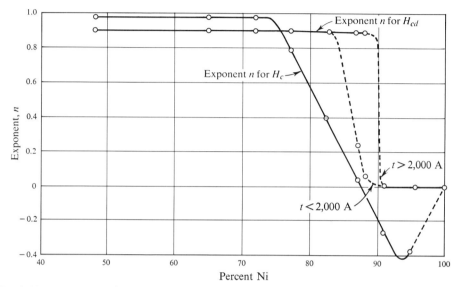

FIG. 8.10. Exponent n in the T^{-n} thickness dependence of the coercive force H_c and easy-axis disturbed field H_{cd} vs nickel composition in Ni–Fe films (after I. W. Wolf, Ref. 11).

wall is of the order of a few thousand angstroms. Similar calculations[4] show that when $L < D$, H_c increases as the wavelength of large-scale energy variation is decreased, or as the wavelength of small-scale energy variations is increased. It is plausible that H_c will have a maximum when D and L are of the same order of magnitude.

Wolf,[11] in investigating the thickness dependence of H_c for electrodeposited films of thickness between 500 and 5000 Å, found that even the signs of the exponent change as shown in Fig. 8.10. The T exponent for H_c and the easy-axis disturbed field $H_{cd}(T^{-n})$ is plotted vs composition in Fig. 8.10 for electroplated films for different thicknesses.

8·3   MEASUREMENT OF HYSTERESIS LOOP

According to the discussion in the previous section, it is evident that it is pertinent to measure the values of the saturation magnetization M_s, the remanent magnetization M_r, the coercive force H_c, and the anisotropy field H_k. These quantities may be measured by one of three methods, the hysteresis-looper method, the torque-magnetometer method, or the ferromagnetic-resonance method. In what follows, we shall discuss these methods in some detail.

[11] I. W. Wolf, J. Appl. Phys., 33: 1152 (1962); J. Electrochem. Soc., 108: 959 (1961).

(a) Hysteresis-Looper Method[12, 13]

The hysteresis looper is an instrument which plots the magnetization of a sample vs the magnetic field applied to it, usually on the face of an oscilloscope. Due to the nonlinear multivalued characteristics of a hysteresis loop, flux density in the sample is in general nonsinusoidal although the driving field varies sinusoidally. Thus, distortions in the shape of the hysteresis loop would occur if over-all performance of the looper is not independent of frequency. In particular, in the case of thin films whose loops are highly rectangular, the amplifiers used must be able to amplify equally well signals of very low to very high frequencies; the steep sides of the loop imply the presence of high frequencies while the flat tops imply the presence of low-frequency components. For a typical thin-film loop, amplifiers with a constant gain from a fraction of a cycle to 10 kc/sec at a driving frequency of 60 cycles/sec are adequate.

Fig. 8.11 shows the schematic diagram of a hysteresis looper. If the gain $A \gg 1$ and C is large compared to the grid-cathode capacitance, then the integrated output or the voltage applied to the vertical plates of the oscilloscope E_o is simply[14]

$$E_o = \frac{1}{RC} \int_0^t E_i \, dt \tag{8.23}$$

where E_i is the input voltage due to the sample. The vertical scale may be calibrated by inserting a sample of known magnetization and geometry and observing the resulting scope deflection. The horizontal drive, as indicated in Fig. 8.11 is derived from the resistor R_1 in series with the driving coil. The magnetic field H for a given current may be calculated since the driving coils are formed by a Helmholtz pair whose

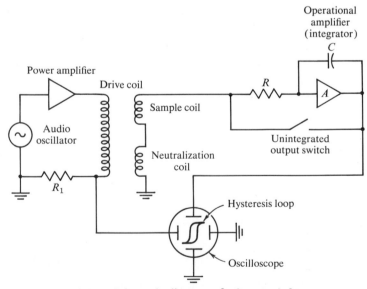

FIG. 8.11.   Schematic diagram of a hysteresis looper.

[12] E. C. Crittenden, Jr., A. A. Hudimac, and R. I. Strough, *Rev. Sci. Inst.*, **22**: 872 (1951).

[13] D. D. Strassberg, *MIT Lincoln Lab. Group Rept.*, 51–10 (1959).

[14] See, e.g., F. E. Terman, *Electronic and Radio Engineering*, 4th ed., McGraw-Hill Book Company, New York, 1955, pp. 623–624.

separation is equal to their common radii. This type of field configuration produced extremely uniform fields near the center of gravity of the coil pair.[15]

The various coil arrangements of the looper are shown in Fig. 8.12. Whereas the driving coils surround the sample, the pickup coil is placed adjacent to the sample. This entails a slight loss of sensitivity but greatly facilitates the design of the thin-film holder and the easiness with which samples may be changed. Since a voltage is induced in the pickup coil even if the film is not switched, this voltage must be subtracted out so that the switching voltage only will appear at the amplifier input. This cancellation could be easily accomplished by introducing a bucking coil, similar in construction to the pickup coil, connecting the two series opposing and placing them more or less symmetrically about the center of the coil configuration. Various adjustments of the pickup and bucking coil positions and orientations are provided as shown in Fig. 8.12 to facilitate initial cancellation of undesirable voltages. Movable aluminum compensation blocks are also used sometimes for perfect cancellation by means of eddy currents induced in them.

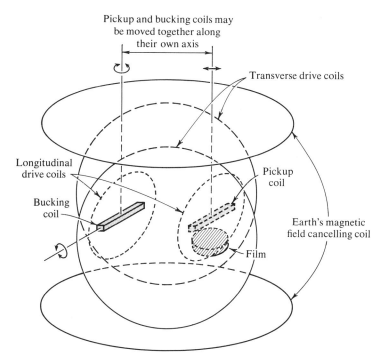

Pickup and bucking coils may be moved together along their own axis

Transverse drive coils

Longitudinal drive coils

Pickup coil

Bucking coil

Earth's magnetic field cancelling coil

Film

FIG. 8.12.   Arrangement of coils for a thin-film hysteresis looper.

Since the magnetization M is more of a direct fundamental interest than B in the study of magnetic thin films as indicated in Sec. 8.2, the thin-film looper usually gives the M–H rather than the B–H plot. This is done by subtracting a quantity proportional to H, using the voltage across R_1 which is proportional to the driving current i or H, say, from the voltage applied to the vertical plates of the oscilloscope. However, since $B = H + 4\pi M$ and $4\pi M \gg H_c$, the B–H and M–H loops differ negligibly from

[15] See, e.g., M. W. Garrett, *J. Appl. Phys.*, **22**: 1091 (1951) and W. Franzen, *Rev. Sci. Instr.*, **33**: 933 (1962).

each other below saturation. Beyond saturation, the B–H curve has a slope of unity while the M–H loop has a slope of zero.

Since the coercive force may be as low as 0.2 Oe, it is necessary to cancel out the horizontal component of the earth's magnetic field by means of a Helmholtz pair of bucking coils as shown in Fig. 8.12.

In Sec. 8.1 we indicated that the eddy-current loss is negligible for a thin film at ordinary frequencies. It is now of interest to examine this question in more detail with regard to the degree of distortion of the hysteresis loop due to eddy currents in thin films. Let the driving field H be of the form $H_m \sin \omega t$. Then, according to Eq. (8.7), we have for the power loss per unit height and unit width and thickness T for the general case of nonsinusoidal B

$$p_e = \frac{T^3}{12c^2\rho} \int_0^{2\pi} \left(\frac{dB}{dt}\right)^2 d(\omega t) \tag{8.24}$$

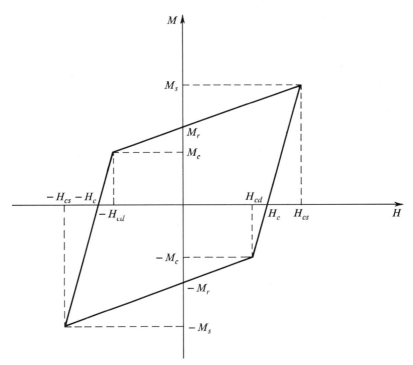

FIG. 8.13. Approximate hysteresis loop of a thin film.

Let us approximate the hysteresis loop of a thin film by that shown in Fig. 8.13. Accordingly, the expression for $B(t)$ is

$$B(t) = -4\pi M_s + \frac{4\pi M_s - 4\pi M_r}{H_{cs}}(H + H_{cs}) \tag{8.25}$$

for the region where $-H_{cs} < H < H_{cd}$ where we have neglected the contribution of H to B. Similarly, we find

$$B(t) = -4\pi M_s + \frac{4\pi M_s - 4\pi M_r}{H_{cs}}(H_{cd} + H_{cs})$$

$$+ \frac{4\pi M_s + 4\pi M_c}{H_{cs} - H_{cd}}(H - H_{cd}) \qquad (8.26)$$

for the region where $H_{cd} < H < 2H_{cs}$. Combining Eqs. (8.24) to (8.26), we have for p_e

$$p_e = \frac{8\pi^2 T^3 \omega^2 H_{cs}^2}{3c^2 \rho} \left[\int_{-\pi/2}^{\sin^{-1}(H_{cd}/H_{cs})} \left(\frac{M_s - M_r}{H_{cs}} \right)^2 \cos^2 \omega t\, d(\omega t) \right.$$

$$+ \int_{\sin^{-1}(H_{cd}/H_{cs})}^{\sin^{-1}(H_c/H_{cs})} \left(\frac{M_s + M_c}{H_{cs} - H_{cd}} \right)^2 \cos^2 \omega t\, d(\omega t)$$

$$\left. - \int_{\sin^{-1}(H_c/H_{cs})}^{\pi/2} \left(\frac{M_s + M_c}{H_{cs} - H_{cd}} \right)^2 \cos^2 \omega t\, d(\omega t) \right] \qquad (8.27)$$

Integrating Eq. (8.27), we easily find

$$p_e = \frac{8\pi^2 T^3 \omega^2 H_{cs}^2}{3c^2 \rho} \left\{ \left(\frac{M_s - M_r}{H_{cs}} \right)^2 \left[\frac{\sin^{-1}(H_{cd}/H_{cs})}{2} + \frac{\pi}{4} + \frac{\sin 2(\sin^{-1} H_{cd}/H_{cs})}{4} \right] \right.$$

$$+ \left(\frac{M_s + M_c}{H_{cs} - H_{cd}} \right)^2 \left[\sin^{-1}\left(\frac{H_{cd}}{H_{cs}} \right) - \frac{\sin^{-1}(H_{cd}/H_{cs})}{2} + \frac{\sin 2(\sin^{-1} H_c/H_{cs})}{2} \right.$$

$$\left. \left. - \frac{\sin 2(\sin^{-1} H_{cd}/H_{cs})}{4} - \frac{\pi}{4} \right] \right\} \qquad (8.28)$$

It should be pointed out here that Eq. (8.24) was derived by assuming that the eddy currents have negligible effect in crowding the flux away from the central plane of film toward its surface so that the flux density B is uniform throughout the sample. If this assumption of uniform B is removed, a more accurate calculation would show that the field amplitude decreases with distance below the surface of the film for the case of constant permeability.[16] However, because of the extreme thinness of the film, calculations indicate that the field in the interior of the film is only about 0.1% lower than that at the surface even at microwave frequencies.[17] In any event, the nonuniform distribution of B should lead to a decrease in the eddy-current power loss compared to that of the uniform case. Thus, Eq. (8.28) should give the upper bound for the value of p_e.

Next, we must compute the hysteresis power loss per unit area in order to compare it with the eddy-current power loss given by Eq. (8.28). Using Eqs. (8.1) and (8.2) in conjunction with Fig. 8.13, we find the hysteresis loss per unit area of the film with thickness T as

$$p_h = \frac{\omega}{\pi} H_{cd}\left(1 + \frac{H_{cs}}{H_{cd}}\right)4\pi M_s T \qquad (8.29)$$

[16] R. M. Bozorth, *Ferromagnetism*, D. Van Nostrand Company, Inc., Princeton, N.J., 1951, p. 770.
[17] R. F. Soohoo, *J. Appl. Phys.*, **31**: 218S (1960).

For a typical film, $4\pi M_s = 10^4$ gauss, $M_r/M = 0.99$, $T = 10^{-5}$ cm, $\rho = 21 \times 10^{-6}$ ohm–cm, $H_c = 5$ Oe, and $H_{cd}/H_{cs} = 0.9$. Using these values p_e/p_h may be plotted as a function of frequency using Eqs. (8.28) and (8.29) as shown in Fig. 8.14. It is seen from the figure that p_e/p_h is quite negligible up to frequencies of the order of a Mc/sec. Thus, the change in shape of the hysteresis loop of thin films as a function of the driving frequency of a hysteresis looper (usually <1 kc/sec) cannot be attributed to eddy-current effects. The more likely explanation is based upon the domain-wall

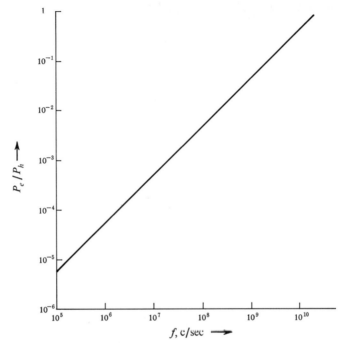

FIG. 8.14.   Ratio of eddy current to hysteresis power loss in thin films as a function of frequency.

relaxation mechanism involved during magnetization reversal. As we shall show in Chap. 9, the domain-wall relaxation frequency, which may be in the order of a Mc/sec or less could correspond roughly to the frequency components of consequence represented by the steep sides of the hysteresis loop of Fig. 8.13.

(b) Torque-Magnetometer Method

The construction of the low-field torque magnetometer has already been discussed in detail in Sec. 7.9 in conjunction with the measurement of the magnitude and symmetry of the anisotropy. Here, we shall consider the application of the low-field torque magnetometer to the measurement of other quantities of interest.[18] These quantities, as identified in Fig. 8.13 are remanent magnetization M_r, saturation magnetization M_s, coercive force H_c, and the rotational hysteresis.

Let us first consider the measurement of the remanent magnetization M_r. If a field H is applied at an angle α to the easy axis, we find the expression for the torque τ

────────

[18] F. B. Humphrey and A. R. Johnston, *Rev. Sci. Instr.*, **34**: 348 (1963).

from the free energy expression given by Eq. (8.9) as

$$\tau = -\hat{\phi}MH\sin(\alpha - \phi) = -\hat{\phi}K_1\sin 2\phi \tag{8.30}$$

where K_1 is the first-order anisotropy constant and ϕ is the angle between the equilibrium magnetization direction and the easy axis. If $H \ll H_k/2$, where $H_k = 2K_1/M$, we find from Eq. (8.30) that the magnetization will initially be pulled away from the easy axis and then fall back toward it again as α is increased. Since ϕ remains small in this case, there will be no magnetization reversal and τ will be essentially proportional to $\sin \alpha$. However, as H increases, we find that at some angle α such that $\alpha - \phi = \pi/2$

$$-\tau_{\max} = \frac{\tau_\alpha}{V} = HM \tag{8.31}$$

where the total torque τ_α is a measure of M. If $H \ll H_c$ and the loop is highly rectangular, $M \simeq M_r$ so that according to Eq. (8.31), $M_r = \tau_\alpha/VH$.

If the film is rotated through 2π radians in the presence of the field H applied parallel to the surface of the film, we find that the torque curve in general enclosed a finite net area. The energy loss represented by this area is termed the rotation hysteresis loss and is given by

$$E_r = -\int_0^{2\pi} \tau\,d\alpha \tag{8.32}$$

Thus, E_r can be measured by graphically obtaining the net area enclosed by a τ vs α curve.

For the measurement of the magnetization and coercive force, we need to consider the case where **H** makes an angle β with the plane of the substrate. With the easy axis perpendicular to the torsion axis, the free energy, according to Eq. (8.9), is

$$E = -MH\cos(\beta - \psi) + 2\pi M^2\sin^2\psi \tag{8.33}$$

where ψ is the angle between the magnetization and the substrate and is in general very small due to the demagnetizing energy perpendicular to the film plane. Thus, since $\tau = \hat{\psi}\,\partial E/\partial\psi$, we have

$$\tau \simeq -\hat{\psi}MH\sin\beta \tag{8.34}$$

According to Eq. (8.33), the approximations leading to Eq. (8.34) are particularly good when the angle β is small. According to Eq. (8.34), the saturation magnetization M_s is given by

$$M_s = \frac{T_\beta}{HV\sin\beta} \tag{8.35}$$

for $H_k \ll H \ll 4\pi M_s$.

Again, according to Eq. (8.34), the torque becomes positive if the field is reversed so that it and the magnetization is oppositely directed. As **H** is increased, τ would remain positive until it equals $H_c/\cos\beta$. If we denote the field at the point where the torque is zero and going negative by H'_c, we find

$$H_c = H'_c \cos \beta \qquad (8.36)$$

Thus, a measurement of H'_c and β suffices in determining the coercive force H_c.

(c) Ferromagnetic-Resonance Method

In Sec. 7.9, we discussed the subject of the determination of the anisotropy constant by means of ferromagnetic resonance. In Sec. 10.3 we shall describe the micro-wave spectrometer used for such purposes in detail. Here, we wish to study the method of determining H_c by ferromagnetic resonance.

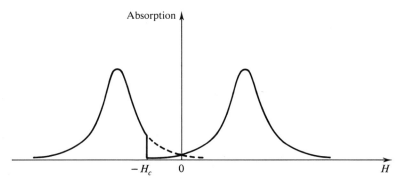

FIG. 8.15.   Determination of the coercive force H_c using resonance techniques.

As is shown in Sec. 10.2, the ferromagnetic-resonance equation applicable to the uniform mode is given by

$$\omega_{r\parallel} = \gamma\sqrt{4\pi M(H_{o\parallel} + H_k)} \qquad (8.37)$$

where $\omega_{r\parallel}$ is the resonance frequency, γ the gyromagnetic ratio, $H_{o\parallel}$ the applied magnetostatic field, and H_k the anisotropy field $2K_1/M$. Eq. (8.37) is the resonance condition for the case where H_o is applied parallel to the easy axis providing M is saturated in the direction of H_o. If H_o is reversed in direction until it is numerically equal to H_c, the ferromagnetic resonance absorption intensity suddenly increases as shown in Fig. 8.15. In the range when $0 < |H_o| < H_c$, M is opposite to H_o, while in the range $|H_o| > H_c$, the magnetization has reversed so that M is parallel to H_o. For a perfectly rectangular loop, the absorption curve is multivalued at H_c, so that H_c can be easily measured using the ferromagnetic-resonance method.

8·4 ELECTRICAL PROPERTIES

The electrical conductivity of thin metallic films has been extensively studied by many investigators although most of these studies were carried out with nonmagnetic films. In this section we shall study the resistivity of thin magnetic films with particular reference to its dependence upon temperature, thickness, electric field strength, etc.

The electrical properties of thin evaporated nickel films ranging in thickness from 30 Å to 1300 Å were studied from 2 to 300°K by Kondorsky, Galkina, Chernikova, and Chsian.[19] They measured both the electrical resistivity and the Hall electromotive force. To avoid complications due to oxidation, these films were deposited in vacuums of 10^{-9}–10^{-7} mm Hg with the evaporation apparatus submerged in a helium bath to freeze the residual gas to obtain high-purity films. For as-evaporated films, they found that their resistance in vacuo decreases with increasing temperature from 4.2°K to 300°K. However, when the films were then cooled from 300°K to 4.2°K after being at room temperature for 18 hr, they found instead a positive temperature coefficient. Furthermore, they found that the thinner the film the smaller the relative change in resistance as the temperature is increased. At 300°K, the film resistance was found to decrease with increasing thickness in the 0 to 500 Å range while the resistance is independent of thickness above 500 Å thickness. However, at 4.2°K, resistance continuously decreased until 900 Å. Thus, resistivity drops 2–2.5 fold in the transition from room temperature to helium temperature in thicker films ($T > 1000$ Å) and only by 4–5% in thin films ($T < 100$ Å).

At room temperature, the Hall field for 835 Å–1300 Å thick films with the applied field perpendicular to the film plane is approximately the same as for bulk specimens. For films down to 50 Å thick, the Hall field increases with the applied field and this increase is apparently associated with the increase in resistivity. They conclude, therefore, that both the resistance and Hall field of a nickel film are close to the bulk value when deposited with both the substrate and evaporator in a helium bath.

Belser and Hicklin have measured in vacuo the electrical resistance of many types of sputtered films in the thickness range of 75–2000 Å.[20] They found that the resistance of a sputtered nickel film increases with temperature and that oxidation of a nickel film heated in air becomes rather rapid at approximately 250°C. Also, for nickel, they found the ratio of the temperature coefficient of a nickel film to that of bulk nickel is about 0.78.

The electrical conduction mechanism in ultrathin films tens of angstroms thick are considerably more complicated than that in thicker films. This is so because these films consist of a planar array of many small discrete islands. Neugebauer and Webb proposed that the conduction process consists of, first, charge carrier creation which is thermally activated and involves charge transfer between initially neutral particles, and, second, the drift velocity of these charges in an applied field.[21] Charge transfers between particles are thought to occur by tunneling. According to this theory, the conductivity σ in ohm^{-1} cm^{-1} is given by the expression

$$\sigma : \frac{1}{r} R^2 e^2 D e^{-(e^2/r)/k_B T} \tag{8.38}$$

where D is the transmission coefficient, r the radius of the island, and R the distance between the islands. As usual, e is the electron charge, k_B the Boltzmann constant and T the absolute temperature. Thus, according to Eq. (8.38), the conductivity depends exponentially on reciprocal temperature and should be independent of field at low fields. These predictions have been experimentally verified by the results of their experiments. Deviations from these dependences were also experimentally found. They proposed that deviations from the exponential temperature dependence can be understood in terms of a spectrum of activation energies, while deviations from Ohm's law at high fields can be explained readily in terms of a field-dependent activation energy.

[19] E. I. Kondorsky et al., J. Phys. Soc. Japan, Suppl. B-1, **17**: 588 (1962).
[20] R. B. Belser and W. H. Hicklin, J. Appl. Phys., **30**: 313 (1959).
[21] C. A. Neugebauer and M. B. Webb, J. Appl. Phys., **33**: 74 (1962).

Hartman, in a recent calculation, showed that tunneling is the predominant conduction mechanism, and electrons are not thermally activated over the barrier, as assumed by Neugebauer and Webb, but penetrate through this barrier (i.e. tunnel emission) along a constant energy surface.[22] The electrical conduction mechanism of tunneling is dominated by transitions from the first excited level of one particle to the corresponding level in the next. The electrical conductivity derived in this way has an exponential dependence on reciprocal temperature in the zero field limit, consistent with experiment. The activation energy depends on the particle size and is the difference in energy between the ground and first excited electronic levels in the particle, again in good agreement with experimental results.

For more details on the subject of thin-film conductivity see Refs. 20–22 of this section.

8·5 MAGNETORESISTANCE AND HALL EFFECT

Magnetoresistance is the resistance of a ferromagnet in the presence of a magnetic field. Its value is dependent upon the relative direction of the measuring current and the applied field. In low saturating magnetic fields, the magnetoresistive effect in a polycrystalline ferromagnet is described by the relation $\Delta\rho/\Delta\rho_o = \cos^2\alpha$ where $\Delta\rho$ is the resistivity change which occurs when the saturation magnetization M_s is oriented first normal then at an angle α to the current i. The maximum change $\Delta\rho_o$ for $\alpha = 0$ is characteristic of the material. The uniform rotation model of a uniaxially anisotropic film in a transverse magnetic field $H_\perp$ leads to a dependence of $\Delta\rho$ on $H_\perp$ of the form $\Delta\rho/\Delta\rho_o = (H_\perp/H_k)^2$ when i is normal to the easy axis, and of the form $\Delta\rho/\Delta\rho_o = 1 - (H_\perp/H_k)^2$ when i is parallel to it.[23] If the anisotropy of the film has angular dispersion β then $\Delta\rho/\Delta\rho_o = (H_\perp/H_k + \beta)^2$ when i is normal to the average easy axis, and $\Delta\rho/\Delta\rho_o = 1 - (H_\perp/H_k + \beta)^2$ when i is parallel to it. On the basis of this simple dispersion model, West investigated the transverse magnetization process in Permalloy films.[24]

Magnetoresistance measurements have been used to study the magnetic properties of Permalloy films by Coren and Juretschke.[25] Resistivities parallel and transverse to the current were measured simultaneously as the applied magnetic field was varied in magnitude and direction in the film plane. The statistical domain-wall switching model of Conger and Essig discussed in Sec. 9.3 is extended to include the situation in which the field and easy axis are not parallel. It is also shown that the magnetoresistance curves may be understood in terms of magnetic changes.

In an electrically isotropic single-domain film, magnetized in the film plane, the components of the electric field per unit current density in the plane, parallel and normal to the current, can be easily shown to be[26]

$$e_\| = \rho + \Delta\rho \cos 2\phi$$
$$e_\perp = \Delta\rho \sin 2\phi$$

(8.39)

[22] T. E. Hartman, *J. Appl. Phys.*, **34**: 943 (1963).
[23] F. G. West, *Nature*, **188**: 129 (1960).
[24] F. G. West, *J. Appl. Phys.*, **32**: 290S (1961).
[25] R. L. Coren and H. J. Juretschke, *J. Appl. Phys.*, **32**: 292S (1961).
[26] J. P. Jan, F. Seitz, and D. Turnbull (eds.), in *Solid State Physics*, Academic Press Inc., New York, 1957, Vol. 5.

where $\rho = \frac{1}{2}(\rho_{\parallel} + \rho_{\perp})$, $\Delta\rho = \frac{1}{2}(\rho_{\parallel} - \rho_{\perp})$ and ϕ is the angle between the current and magnetization. $\rho_{\parallel}$ and $\rho_{\perp}$ are the longitudinal resistivities for $\phi = 0$, $\pi/2$. The measurements of Coren and Juretschke show that $\Delta\rho/\rho$ is typically about 1 percent for Permalloy films.

Hall effect measurements on a ferromagnetic film can be used to examine the normal anisotropy and the distribution of stresses in the plane of the film.[27] The measured Hall voltage exhibits a smooth transition from low to high field regions rather than the sharp cross-over, at technical saturation, which is characteristic of a single domain. Since the ferromagnetic Hall effect depends upon the component of magnetization perpendicular to the film plane, one can attribute this difference of behavior to the domain structure described by a distribution of normal anisotropies.

In a single-domain film, the magnetization dependent Hall resistivity (electric field/current density) may be written as[28]

$$\rho_H = \frac{E}{J} = R_o M \sin\theta \qquad (8.40)$$

where E and J are mutually perpendicular in the film plane, θ is the angle the magnetization $\mathbf{M}$ makes with the plane while R_o is the ferromagnetic Hall coefficient. In addition, there is also an extraordinary Hall effect which we shall discuss below in another connection.

It is possible under certain conditions to detect a dc voltage in the film plane at ferromagnetic resonance. The origin of this effect has been attributed to galvanomagnetic interactions by Egan and Juretschke.[29]

From the galvanomagnetic theory, we obtain the following equation for the electric field:[30]

$$\mathbf{E} = \rho_{\perp}\mathbf{J} + (\rho_{\parallel} - \rho_{\perp})\frac{\mathbf{J}\cdot\mathbf{B}}{\mathbf{B}^2}\mathbf{B} + R_o\mathbf{B}\times\mathbf{J} + 4\pi R_o(\alpha - 1)\mathbf{M}\times\mathbf{J} \qquad (8.41)$$

The first two terms on the right-hand side of Eq. (8.41) are magnetoresistance terms, the third is the ordinary Hall term and the last is the extraordinary Hall effect term. $\rho_{\perp}$ and $\rho_{\parallel}$ are the sample resistivities perpendicular and parallel to the magnetic induction $\mathbf{B}$, R_o is the ordinary Hall coefficient, α is the extraordinary Hall "field parameter," $\mathbf{M}$ is the magnetization vector, and J is the current density. When, as in a resonance experiment, $\mathbf{B}$, $\mathbf{M}$ and $\mathbf{J}$ have microwave components, product terms appear which, in general, have nonzero average values. Thus, a dc voltage is generated which exhibits a resonance behavior.

In the case of a thin film, the geometry can be arranged so that the dc voltage is developed in the film plane[31] if the usual condition for resonance is met and the microwave eddy current is parallel to $\mathbf{H}$ (z-directed). As the magnetization precesses, a component of magnetization appears normal to the film plane (y-directed). The product of this component and the current gives an extraordinary Hall voltage in the x direction

[27] R. L. Coren, *J. Appl. Phys.*, **33**: 1168 (1962).

[28] E. M. Pugh, *Phys. Rev.*, **36**: 1503 (1960); E. M. Pugh and T. W. Lippert, *Phys. Rev.*, **42**: 709 (1962).

[29] W. G. Egan and H. J. Juretschke, *Bull. Am. Phys. Soc.*, Ser. II, **3**: 194 (1958).

[30] J. P. Jan, *op. cit.*, pp. 15, 75.

[31] M. H. Seavey, *J. Appl. Phys.*, **31**: 216S (1960).

in the film plane. The ordinary Hall term does not contribute since, due to demagnetization effects, the microwave magnetic induction normal to the film is very small. Seavey's calculation shows that an extraordinary Hall voltage should be developed when **H** is applied in the plane of the film. On the other hand, if **H** is normal to the film, the extraordinary Hall voltage is found to be zero. These predictions are consistent with experiment. Thus, there is good evidence for the interpretation of the observed dc voltage as due to the extraordinary Hall effect.

CHAPTER 9

MAGNETIZATION REVERSAL

From an application standpoint, the time required for the magnetization to reverse from one stable state to another at a given drive is of utmost significance. It is clear that in order to liberalize the requirement on the driving circuitry, minimum switching time for a given drive or minimum drive for a specified switching time is required. This optimum condition could only be achieved by a clear understanding of the magnetization reversal process. In the realm of physics, magnetization changes in thin films induced by external fields afford us a unique opportunity in the study of the fundamental processes involved in the collective dynamic behavior of ferromagnetic spins in a solid. Because of the low coercive force and anisotropy field in Permalloy films relative to other materials it is not difficult to obtain switching-field pulses of large enough amplitude with sufficiently short rise time to achieve coherent rotation of the magnetization from one stable state to another. Thus, the switching processes could be determined or inferred over a wide range of values of the switching time by merely changing the pulse amplitude. This fact is significant from a fundamental standpoint as for ferrite cores, for example, the easily available driving fields are usually insufficient to enable us to study the pure rotation mode.

It has been found experimentally that the reversal processes in thin films are threefold: domain wall motion, "incoherent rotation," and rotation in unison, depending upon the value of the switching and biasing fields. We shall discuss in this chapter the theoretical and experimental facts regarding these reversal processes in some detail. The role of imperfections and edge and surface effects in switching of thin films will also be discussed.

9·1 MAGNETIZATION REVERSAL PROCESSES

Experimentally, it has been found that there are three distinct regions of magnetization reversal depending upon the values of the switching field H_s and the biasing field $H_\perp$ applied along and perpendicular to the easy axis respectively as shown in Fig. 9.1.[1] Aside from the occurrence of the breaks in the $1/\tau$ vs H_s curves shown, the existence of the three distinct reversal processes can be verified directly by monitoring the voltage induced in the longitudinal and transverse pickup loops schematically represented in Fig. 8.4. When τ is large (~ 1 μsec or more), there is no voltage induced in the transverse loop indicating the reversal process is one of domain wall motion with the

---

[1] C. D. Olson and A. V. Pohm, *J. Appl. Phys.*, **29**: 274 (1958); F. M. Humphrey and E. M. Gyorgy, *J. Appl. Phys.*, **30**: 935 (1959).

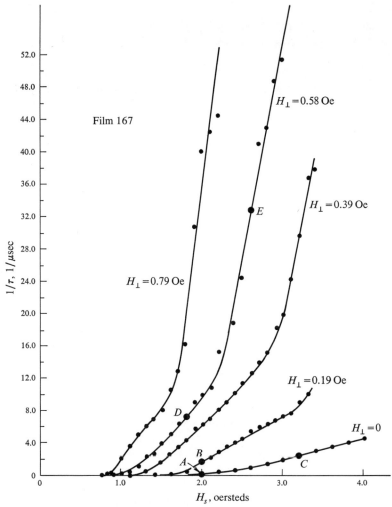

FIG. 9.1. Experimental inverse switching time of Permalloy films vs switching field for various transverse biasing fields (after Olson and Pohm, Ref. 1).

magnetization always in the direction of the easy axis. When the values of H_s and $H_\perp$ are such that τ has intermediate value (0.1 μsec $< \tau < 1$ μsec), it has been found that zero induced voltage in the transverse loop does not occur when the film is half switched.[2] This result can be interpreted to mean that the magnetization is neither reversed by coherent rotation, in which case the zero induced voltage in the transverse loop should occur at the same time as the half-switched point as indicated by the longitudinal loop, nor by domain wall motion in which case the transverse loop voltage is zero for all times. We may term this mechanism "incoherent rotation." When H_s is sufficiently large compared with H_c ($H_\perp \neq 0$) so that τ is quite small (<0.1 μsec), the transverse loop has zero induced voltage in it when the film is half switched. Thus, the reversal mechanism in this region is evidently one of coherent or nearly coherent rotation.

[2] F. B. Humphrey, *J. Appl. Phys.*, **29**: 286 (1958).

For $H_s > H_c$, we would expect the film to reverse. Indeed, since the switching time τ should approach zero as $H_s \to \infty$, τ should be a monotonically decreasing function of $H_s - H_c$. It is seen from Fig. 9.1 that the switching time for $H_\perp = 0$, and with $H_s \leq H_k = 2.4$ Oe, is ≥ 1 μsec, not particularly impressive compared to the switching time of ferrite cores. However, if a transverse biasing field $H_\perp$ is applied, the effective coercive force may be lower than the case where $H_\perp = 0$. This situation arises because for a finite $H_\perp$, the equilibrium position of $\mathbf{M}$ would be away from the easy axis, the position of minimum anisotropy energy. Thus, lower longitudinal Zeeman energy or small H_s is required to overcome the energy maximum at $\phi = \pi/2$.

To analyze the effect of $H_\perp$ upon the longitudinal switching time, we utilize the free energy expression given by Eq. (8.9) and obtain $\partial E/\partial \phi = 0$ and $\partial^2 E/\partial \phi^2 = 0$ giving

$$h_{sc} = \cos^3 \phi$$
$$h_\perp = \sin^3 \phi \qquad (9.1)$$

where h_{sc} and $h_\perp$ are the rotation coercive force and transverse biasing field normalized to the anisotropy field H_k. The parametric equations (9.1) are plotted in Fig. 9.2

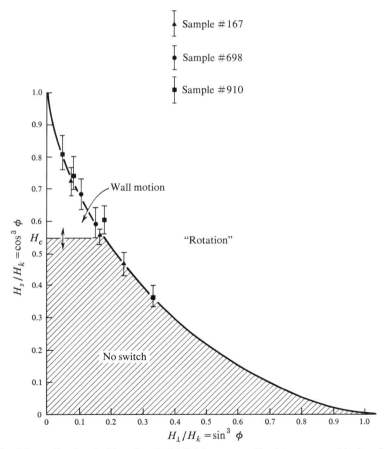

FIG. 9.2.   Normalized switching threshold field vs normalized transverse biasing field (after Olson and Pohm, Ref. 1).

along with the experimental values of the threshold fields, i.e., values of H_s and $H_\perp$ at which rotational switching begins to occur. It is seen that the experimental points follow reasonably well the theoretical rotational threshold curve. As indicated in Fig. 9.2, for a combination of H_s and $H_\perp$ falling into the area bounded by the threshold curve, a horizontal line intersecting h_{sc} axis at H_c/H_k where H_c is the wall coercive force, and the h_{sc} and $h_\perp$ axes, there will be no switching possible. If the values of H_s and $H_\perp$ are such that the points fall into the area bounded by the threshold curve, the horizontal line intersecting the h_{sc} axis at H_c/H_k, and the h_{sc} axis, the magnetization reversal proceeds by domain wall motion. If the points fall above the threshold curve, the reversal process is one of rotation. It should be mentioned here that in the experimental determination of the critical field, it was found that the transverse signal vs time area is considerably smaller than that expected. This implies that the threshold reversal process is not one of complete coherent rotation, consistent with the hypothesis of the existence of an "incoherent rotation" region intermediate between the domain wall region and the coherent rotation region as discussed in the introduction. In high-speed nanosecond switching, the agreement between theory and experiment is more impressive. In this region, switching should proceed by coherent rotation.[3]

In the following sections, we shall study the coherent rotation, domain wall motion, and incoherent rotation processes in that order. This order of discussion has been chosen so that we can proceed from the simplest to the most difficult subject. It may be mentioned here that not all the questions involved in these topics have been completely resolved. However, as we shall presently show, the gross features of thin-film switching theory are reasonably well understood.

9·2 COHERENT ROTATION THEORY

If magnetization changes proceed by coherent rotation from a single-domain state, the dynamic as well as the static distribution of the magnetization is independent of position in the material. Since thin films of interest are essentially single-domain ferromagnets in the remanent state due to the existence of the uniaxial anisotropy, the magnetization of the film during switching should not be a function of position if the reversal is one of coherent rotation. This fact considerably simplifies the mathematical analysis so that meaningful analytical and numerical results for this process could be easily obtained.

The dynamic behavior of the magnetization, as given by its spatial orientation angles ϕ and ψ shown in Figs. 8.4 and 10.2, can be obtained by solving Eqs. (10.18) and (10.19) or alternatively, Eq. (10.20). The solution in the general case is sufficiently complicated that numerical computation has to be employed. However, for cases where the switching speed is sufficiently small, the $\dot{\phi}$ terms in Eqs. (10.18) and (10.19) could be neglected in comparison. Accordingly, we have

$$4\pi\lambda\dot{\phi} + 4\pi\gamma^2 \frac{\partial E}{\partial \phi} = 0 \tag{9.2}$$

$$\dot{\psi} = 0 \tag{9.3}$$

---

[3] D. O. Smith and G. P. Weiss, *J. Appl. Phys.*, **29**: 290 (1958).

Since ψ starts from zero in a switching experiment due to the shape anisotropy of the film, the magnetization will be constrained to move in the plane of the film as $\dot{\psi} = 0$ according to Eq. (9.3). As we shall show below, setting $\ddot{\phi} = 0$ would by necessity underestimate the switching time since we thereby implicitly exclude the time required for the magnetization to move in the ψ direction.

(a) Theory

Thin-film switching by coherent rotation has been studied by many investigators. In particular, the case where $\ddot{\phi}$ is assumed zero has been studied theoretically by Conger and Essig[4] and by Smith[5] while the more general case ($\ddot{\phi} \neq 0$) has also been studied by Smith[5] by numerical solution of Eqs. (10.18) and (10.19). A similar problem has also been solved by Kikuchi.[6] However, he did not include the biasing transverse field or anisotropy, so that his results cannot be directly applied to thin-film switching experiments. An even more general set of equations applicable to a single-domain ferromagnetic body of any type of anisotropy, with an applied field in an arbitrary direction, has also been derived by Gillette and Oshima,[7] using also the Landau-Lifshitz equation. Since such generalization is unnecessary for the thin-film switching experiment envisaged, we shall restrict our analyses to those given by Conger and Essig and by Smith.

The solution of Eq. (9.2) for the switching time $(\Delta t)_\phi$ is seen to be

$$(\Delta t)_\phi = \frac{\lambda}{\gamma^2} \int_{\phi_1}^{\phi_2} \frac{d\phi}{\partial E / \partial \phi} \tag{9.4}$$

where the limits ϕ_1 and ϕ_2 are initial and final equilibrium angles determined by the magnitudes of the biasing field $\mathbf{H}_\perp$ and the switching field $\mathbf{H}_s$. Noting that E is given by Eq. (10.11), we can evaluate the integral Eq. (9.4) for the case where $h_\perp$ is a static field and h_s is a step function. The result is shown in Fig. 9.3.

A simple physical interpretation of the switching behavior of thin films in the $\ddot{\phi} = 0$ approximation can be obtained by noting that $(\Delta t)_\phi$ is a function of the torque $\partial E / \partial \phi$ according to Eq. (9.4). Thus, the switching time is determined by the damping constant λ and the time-dependent torque acting on the magnetization $\mathbf{M}$ during its entire excursion. In particular, if $h_\perp$ is zero, $\mathbf{M}$ and $\mathbf{H}_s$ are antiparallel giving rise to zero torque and infinite switching time. As $h_\perp$ increases, the switching time rapidly decreases and is accurately given by Eq. (9.4) down to the 5–10 nanosecond range as can be verified by numerical solution of Eqs. (10.18) and (10.19).

It is of interest to inquire further into the nature of the $\ddot{\phi} = 0$ approximation. This can best be done by physically examining the path of the tip of the magnetization vector during the course of magnetization reversal. Referring to Fig. 9.4(a), at $t = 0$, the torque acting on the magnetization $\mathbf{M}$, that is, $\mathbf{M} \times \mathbf{H}_s$ is in the negative z direction perpendicular to the plane of the film. Now, since $\dot{\mathbf{M}} = \gamma \mathbf{M} \times \mathbf{H}$ where the gyromagnetic ratio γ is negative, $\dot{\mathbf{M}}$ is initially in the $+z$ direction. Thus, $\mathbf{M}$ tips slightly out of the plane so that $M_z = \Delta M$, say, with the attendant demagnetizing

[4] R. L. Conger and F. C. Essig, *Phys. Rev.*, **104**: 915 (1956); *J. Appl. Phys.*, **28**: 855 (1957).
[5] D. O. Smith, *J. Appl. Phys.*, **29**: 265 (1958).
[6] R. K. Kikuchi, *J. Appl. Phys.*, **27**: 1352 (1956).
[7] P. R. Gillette and K. Oshima, *J. Appl. Phys.*, **29**: 529 (1958).

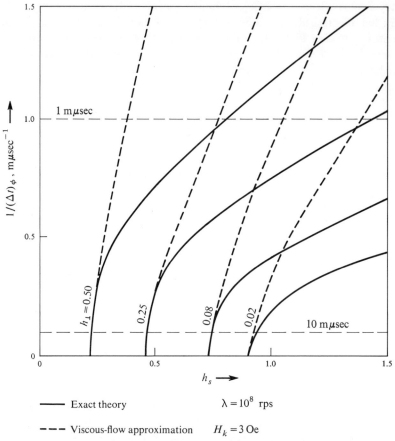

FIG. 9.3.   Theoretical inverse switching time of Permalloy films vs normalized switching field for various normalized transverse biasing fields (after D. O. Smith, Ref. 5).

field $4\pi\Delta M$ in the negative z direction. Similarly, this demagnetizing field acting on the component of the magnetization in the plane of the film will in turn produce a torque in the plane of the film in such a direction as to rotate it toward the positive x axis. A little reasoning along this line will show that ψ will depend on the angle β in the approximate manner illustrated by Fig. 9.4(b). In a typical switching experiment, the maximum value of ψ is about 2 or 3 deg. Thus, we can infer from the above discussion that the $\ddot{\phi} = 0$ approximation will give too short a switching time, since the time to move in the ψ direction is not taken into account, and that this error will become progressively greater with increasing ϕ.

An estimate of the time required for the ψ motion can be obtained by putting $(\partial E/\partial\phi) = $ constant in Eq. (10.18) and solving for ψ. With the initial conditions $\psi = \phi = 0$ at $t = 0$, we find

$$\psi = \frac{\gamma(\partial E/\partial\phi)|_\phi}{4\pi M}(1 - e^{-4\pi\lambda t}) \tag{9.5}$$

If the change in ϕ and therefore $\partial E/\partial\phi$ is small in the time $1/4\pi\lambda$ required for ψ to approach the limiting value of Eq. (9.5), we can disregard the second term in the

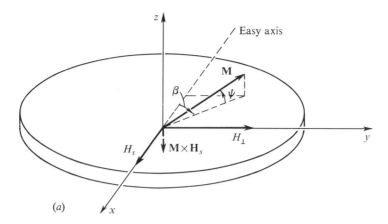

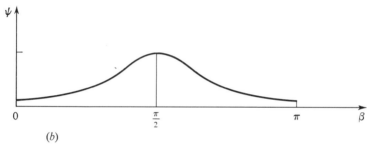

FIG. 9.4.   Path taken by the tip of the magnetization vector during magnetization reversal. For simplicity, $H_\perp \ll H_k \ll H_s$ has been assumed for (b).

equation. Therefore, we have

$$\dot{\psi} = \frac{\gamma(\partial E/\partial\phi)|_\phi}{4\pi M} \tag{9.6}$$

Substituting Eq. (9.6) into Eq. (10.18), we readily obtain the result, Eq. (9.4), based on the $\ddot{\phi} = 0$ approximation. From Eq. (9.6), ψ will reach an equilibrium value consistent with a given torque in a time approximately given by $(\Delta t)_\psi = 1/4\pi\lambda \sim 1$ nanosecond. Thus, we may expect the result, Eq. (9.4), would be quite accurate for the switching time $(\Delta t)_\phi \gtrsim 5$ nanoseconds, as can be verified by results obtained from numerical solution of Eqs. (10.18) and (10.19). The results of this exact solution are shown in Fig. 9.3 along with those from the approximate solution for the case where $H_\perp$ is a static biasing field and H_s is a step function switching field. It is seen from Fig. 9.3 that there is considerable discrepancy between the results of the two theories when $(\Delta t)_\phi < 5$ nanoseconds. In this connection, it is of interest to note that Conger and Essig, in comparing results obtained from ferromagnetic resonance and switching experiments, concluded that the damping measured in a high field (~ 5000 Oe) resonance experiment is of the order of 250 times less than that effective in a low field (~ 2 Oe) switching experiment.[4] Smith[5] has pointed out that the reason for this discrepancy is at least twofold. Use of the $\ddot{\phi} = 0$ approximation underestimates the time for switching with small damping; if a reversing field $\mathbf{H}_s$ is applied directly opposite to M, the torque

$M \times H$ is identically zero and the switching time is infinite. If the reversing field makes an angle other than $180°$ with M, the switching time will have an angular dependence as has been observed by Olson, Pohm, and Rubins,[8] and Smith.[9] Thus, it appears that in comparing λ obtained from ferromagnetic resonance and switching experiments, one should use the results of the exact theory.

The calculation of the switching response from the exact theory, i.e., from Eqs. (10.18) and (10.19), shows that following the application of a drive pulse, the film response is delayed by an amount dependent upon h_k.[5] This effect is due to the very small starting torque acting when M and H_s are nearly antiparallel and is accentuated by the time taken to move in the ψ direction before motion in the ϕ direction can start. It is interesting to note that a relatively small change in λ, e.g., from 1 to 2×10^8 rad/sec changes the solution from under- to over-damped. The calculations also show that H_k, $h_\perp$, and h_s do not affect the degree of damping appreciably.

(b) Comparison with Experiment

We now turn to a brief discussion of the comparison between the above theoretical results with experiment. As we have seen in Fig. 9.1, the uniform rotation model is only applicable to cases where the switching field is substantially larger than the critical field for domain wall motion or the apparent coercive force H_{cr}. Furthermore, in this mode of rotation, the switching time is very short, in the order of nanoseconds. Thus, the rise time of the switching field, usually in the form of a step function, must be no larger than a nanosecond or so if meaningful measurement of the switching time is to be obtained.

A step function magnetic field having a rise time of the order of 1 nanosecond can be generated by discharging 500 ft of coaxial line through a coaxial mercury relay into a 50 ohm rectangular coaxial section in which the film is placed as shown in Fig. 9.5.[3]

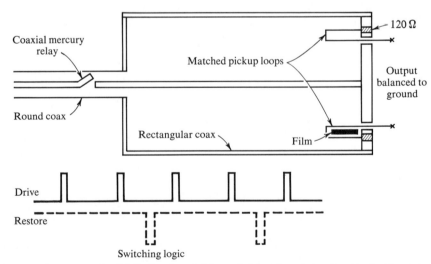

FIG. 9.5. Apparatus for high-speed switching of thin films (after D. O. Smith and G. P. Weiss, Ref. 3).

[8] C. D. Olson, A. V. Pohm, and S. M. Rubens, *Armour Symposium and Relaxation of Ferromagnetic Materials*, April, 1956, Armour Research Foundation of Illinois Institute of Technology, unpublished.

[9] D. O. Smith, *Phys. Rev.*, **104**: 1280 (1956); *Conference on Magnetism and Magnetic Materials*, Boston, October, 1956, AIEE, February, 1957, p. 625.

An original magnetization-direction restoring field is provided by external coils, also pulsed by a mercury relay. Switching is detected by using a very-wide-band traveling-wave oscilloscope with ungrounded deflection plates or by alternate wide-band methods. Pulse field amplitude calibration is accomplished as follows: The switching threshold is measured as a function of a pulsed switching and dc perpendicular field; subsequently the film is rotated 90°, resulting in a dc switching and pulsed perpendicular field. The two threshold curves must be brought into superposition by means of a single scale factor, which will then calibrate the pulse field. For a 2500 Å Permalloy film, the switching time is about 3 nanoseconds at a drive field of 3 Oe. It is of importance to note that this switching time is several orders of magnitude smaller than that of ferrite cores.

For the cases where the biasing dc field $H_\perp$ is small compared to the anisotropy field H_k ($h_\perp = 0.08, 0.11$), a definite delay in the film response after the initial application of the switching pulse H_s was observed in several films although such delay was absent in one film.[5] For high $h_\perp$ ($=0.29$), there is no observable delay in the switching response. To check the observed response with that predicted by the above theory, it is necessary to assume a value for the damping constant λ. If λ is chosen to fit the switching response for the $h_\perp = 0.29$ case as closely as possible, its value turns out to be about 3×10^8 rad/sec as compared to about 1.5×10^8 for λ determined from the line width measurements at microwave frequencies. Since, as mentioned previously, the system changes from one of underdamped to one of overdamped when λ changes from 1 to 2×10^8 rad/sec, no oscillatory behavior in the film response was observed by Smith.

When $h_\perp = 0.29$, the monitored switching voltage indicates that the entire film was switched. On the other hand, for the $h_\perp = 0.11$ and 0.08, the percentage of the film being switched is 60 and 31 respectively. In these cases, the rest of the film either remains unswitched or it switches by some slower combination of rotational and domain wall motion; in the former case, the unswitching portion of the film may interact with the switching part in such a way as to retard its motion. It is likely that the easy-axis dispersion and anisotropy variation in the film may be the basic reason for the nonconservation of total flux observed for the small $h_\perp$ cases.

A somewhat different experimental arrangement for high-speed flux reversal measurements was used by Olson and Pohm.[1] In their case, the pulse power was supplied by connecting a charged capacitor to the coaxial line through a mercury relay. The 90-ohm coaxial cable is in turn connected to a matched flat solenoid with distributed capacitance used to provide the pulse field for making high-speed reversal measurements; the coil is in turn terminated by a series combination of an 87 ohm resistive load and a 3 ohm field-monitoring resistor. It was found that the application of a transverse field causes an abrupt increase in the slope of the switching curves when the switching field H_s exceeds a certain threshold value. Below this value of H_s, the inverse switching time $1/\tau$ vs H_s curves with a transverse field $H_\perp$ approximates those with no transverse field. The threshold field for the break in the switching curve is operationally defined by the "projected cutoff" method. Let a straight line be drawn through the points on the switching curve which lie just above the break and nearly in a straight line; the point at which this projected line crosses the field axis is defined as the threshold for the onset of the rotation reversal mechanism. The experimental results indicate that below the threshold field, e.g., point A of Fig. 9.1, no signal is induced in the transverse pickup loop indicating that magnetization reversal below this field probably proceeds by domain wall motion with the magnetization in the direction of the easy axis. When the threshold is exceeded, a voltage is induced in the transverse loop signifying magnetization rotation in the plane of the film. As we shall discuss in the next section, this rotational threshold need not be the threshold corresponding to rotation of the magnetization in unison. It turns out that points B, C, and D correspond to states of nonuniform rotation wherein the instantaneous direction of the magnetization has a spatial dependence. On the other hand, point E of Fig. 9.1 truly corresponds to a state of uniform rotation.

Experimentally, the transverse-signal-time integral (α flux) is found to be only $67 \pm 16\%$ of the expected value for the case of point B of Fig. 9.1 if the magnetization is assumed to rotate in unison. This nonconservation of flux, similar to that observed by Smith,[5] may be attributed to the easy-axis dispersion and anisotropy inhomogeneity of the film.

The switching time τ in Olson and Pohm's experiments[1] is defined as the time interval which begins when the switching field has increased to the coercive force and ends when the output voltage has diminished to 10% of its peak value. It is to be noted that this definition of τ is different from the two used by Smith already discussed above. Furthermore, there are several other definitions in use which contribute further to confuse the issue. For example, Humphrey and Gyorgy,[1] who also obtained curves similar to those of Fig. 9.1 given by Olson and Pohm, define the switching time as the interval between the time when 10% of the flux has reversed and the time when 90% of the total flux has reversed. In this case, the flux vs time curve is obtained by integrating the longitudinal pickup voltage vs time curve. The choice of the definition to be used for τ is predicated mainly upon convenience and taste, although esthetically, the definitions based upon the percentage of total flux switched are more satisfying as magnetization is the most fundamental quantity for the case in point.

Before we conclude our discussion on the uniform rotational model of film-magnetization reversal, we might hasten to point out that according to Fig. 9.1, an application of a transverse static field $H_\perp$ greatly reduces the switching time τ. Indeed, τ changes from the order of a microsecond to the order of a nanosecond if sufficiently large H_s and $H_\perp$ are used. Correspondingly, the mode of reversal changes from that of domain wall motion to one of uniform rotation. In the competitive ferrite core memories, for reasonable drives, the magnetization reversal process is one of domain wall motion ($\tau \sim 1 \ \mu sec$). Thus, the switching time of these memories are some several orders of magnitude slower than the potentially very fast switching times of thin films operating in the uniform rotational mode. Thus, the role of the transverse field in a thin-film memory is very significant indeed.

By using a special pulse equipment including a pulse-sampling oscilloscope with an over-all response time of 0.35 nanosecond, switching times as short as 1 nanosecond have been measured by Dietrich and Proebster.[10] This value of τ may be compared to 3 nanoseconds measured by Smith using the traveling-wave oscilloscope[5] and 10 nanoseconds obtained by Olson and Pohm by means of an oscilloscope with distributed amplifiers.[1] The inverse switching time vs driving field curves was found to have a slope of about 10^8/Oe-sec consistent with the largest value obtained by Olson and Pohm as can be found from Fig. 9.1. The pulsing apparatus is essentially similar to that shown in Fig. 9.5. Again, the occurrence of the coherent rotational mode at high h_s and $h_\perp$ was verified by monitoring the transverse flux. In addition, oscillation of the magnetization has also been clearly detected by picking up the flux changes transverse to the driving field.

---

[10] W. Dietrich and W. E. Proebster, *J. Appl. Phys.*, **31**: 281S (1960).

(c) Free Oscillation and Hard-Axis Switching

Free oscillation of the magnetization in Permalloy films has been studied in more detail by Wolf.[11] The experimental apparatus in this case is the same as that used by Dietrich and Proebster in high-speed switching experiments.[10] In this free oscillation experiment, the magnetization vector is aligned by a dc field H_x in the plane of the film. A small step pulse field H_y is suddenly applied perpendicular to H_x also in the plane of the film. Thus, the magnetization vector starts to rotate away from its equilibrium position parallel to H_x and execute damped oscillations about its new equilibrium direction which forms an angle of $H_y/(H_x \pm H_k)$ radians with the direction of H_x. Here H_k is the anisotropy field and the $\pm$ signs are associated with the parallel or perpendicular direction of the easy axis with respect to H_x. It is evident that in order to keep the relevant angle small, H_y must be much smaller than $H_x \pm H_k$. It can be easily shown from the Landau-Lifshitz equation that the natural frequency of oscillation f_F is given by[11]

$$f_F^2 = \frac{\gamma^2 M}{\pi} (H_x \pm H_k) - \lambda^2 \tag{9.7}$$

where M is the saturation magnetization, γ the gyromagnetic ratio, and λ the damping constant of the Landau-Lifshitz equation. These free oscillations decay with a time constant τ given by

$$\tau = \frac{1}{2\pi\lambda} \tag{9.8}$$

If H_y is a weak continuous-wave microwave field and not a step pulse dc field, then forced oscillations are excited leading to ferromagnetic resonance. Thus, these small amplitude free oscillation experiments afford a direct comparison between their results and those obtained from ferromagnetic resonance. The relations for the forced resonance frequency f_R and the line width ΔH_x of the resonance curve are given by[5]

$$f_R^2 = \frac{\gamma^2 M}{\pi} (H_x \pm H_k) \tag{9.9}$$

$$\Delta H_x = \frac{4\pi f_R \lambda}{\gamma^2 M} \tag{9.10}$$

These equations are applicable for cases where H_x, H_y and $H_k \ll 4\pi M$. Since the second term of Eq. (9.7) is very small compared to the first in these experiments, we would expect the free oscillation frequency and the ferromagnetic resonance frequency to be nearly the same. This prediction was verified by the results of the free oscillation experiments described above and ferromagnetic resonance experiments performed with a wide-band microwave bridge.[3] Within experimental error, it has also been found that λ is the same for both the free oscillation and ferromagnetic resonance cases. Further λ was found to increase with decreasing frequency in the range of 0.3 to 1.3 kMc/sec.

---

[11] P. Wolf, *J. Appl. Phys.*, **32**: 95S (1961).

The identity of λ for free oscillation and force oscillation experiments does not necessarily imply that the effective damping for an arbitrary mode of large-angle magnetization reversal is given by the λ of ferromagnetic resonance. Nevertheless, for the uniform rotation model, this fact does lend additional evidence to the plausibility of using the value of λ obtained from ferromagnetic resonance in the case of uniform rotation switching.

Schwenker and Long have attributed the nonuniform rotational modes of magnetization changes to the formation of small domains.[12] They observed that the observed hysteresis loop of Permalloy films has a slightly open region instead of the closed one in the hard-axis hysteresis loop as predicted by the single-domain Stoner and Wohlfarth model.[5,13] This is presumed to be primarily due to the formation of many domains with subsequent losses. However, if we simultaneously applied a small field in the easy direction (a few percent of the anisotropy field), we can avoid the formation of these domain walls and, as a result, can observe a hysteresis loop which corresponds to the rotational model. Experiments show that the bias field required to cause completely rotational behavior is dependent upon the particular material used. A slight modification of the Stoner-Wohlfarth model enables us to account for this observed variation. The observations were, of course, made by a hysteresis looper. Reversible rotation in the hard direction has also been observed by Sanders and Rossing.[14] By reversible rotation is meant a change in the direction of the magnetization vector due to the application of a transverse field with a return to the original direction and magnitude when the field is removed. The output signal, proportional to the rate of change of the flux component in the film parallel to the easy axis of magnetization, was monitored. The actual quantity measured was the peak amplitude of the output signal corresponding to rotation of the magnetization vector through the largest angle θ_{max} at which the rotation remained reversible. As the driving field was increased, the output signal increased until the reversible limit was reached; then it dropped sharply to some smaller value. The drop indicated a partial loss of remanent magnetization after a few rotations. Although there is large scattering in the data obtained, the limiting reversible rotational angle appeared to increase with the ratio of the coercive force H_c to anisotropy field H_k. Reversible rotation of up to $60°$ has been obtained in this way and it was found that films giving a large rotation tended to have open hysteresis loops in the hard direction.

9·3 DOMAIN WALL MOTION THEORY

In Sec. 8.2(c) we investigated the possible origin of the coercive force H_c by taking into account the possible contribution to H_c due to spatial variation of the exchange, anisotropy, and magnetostatic energies of the film. The results of the calculation showed that easy-axis dispersion and surface roughness are the two most important sources of the coercive force in thin films. We were then mainly interested in the threshold field value for commencement of wall motion in connection with our study of the easy-axis rectangular hysteresis loop. Since the driving frequency of the hysteresis loop is usually low (≤ 1000 cycles/sec), such quasistatic analysis was sufficient to explain the observed rectangularity of the easy-axis loop as well as the value of coercive

----

[12] J. E. Schwenker and T. R. Long, *J. Appl. Phys.*, **33**: 1099 (1962).
[13] E. C. Stoner and E. P. Wohlfarth, *Phil. Trans. Roy. Soc. London*, **240A**: 599 (1948).
[14] R. M. Sanders and T. D. Rossing, *J. Appl. Phys.*, **29**: 288 (1958).

force as a function of various film parameters. In this section we must generalize such analysis to include a study of the dynamics of wall motion. We shall begin with a general consideration of wall motion theory and later apply its results to the study of domain wall motion in thin films. The role of imperfections and surface and edge effects of a film in the magnetization reversal process via domain wall motion will also be briefly examined. Further, the phenomenon of domain wall creeping will also be discussed.

(a) Dynamics of Wall Motion

As can be seen from domain observations, the domain wall motion in thin films is usually composed of two stages. First, the 180° walls associated with demagnetizing domains at the edges of film move in the direction of the easy axis, thus forming long domains parallel to the easy axis as shown in Fig. 9.6(a). In the second stage, the

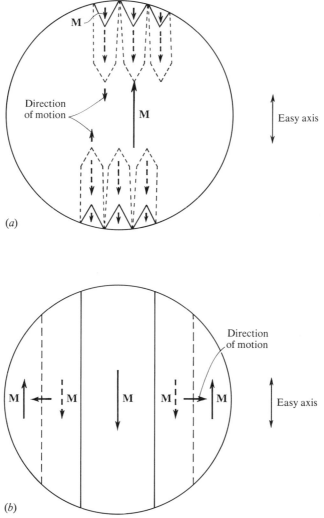

FIG. 9.6.   Two stages of domain wall motion in thin films. (a) Demagnetizing domains expand in the direction of the easy axis and (b) expansion of elongated domains by parallel shift in the hard direction.

magnetization reversal is completed by essentially parallel shift of the elongated domains in the hard direction as shown in Fig. 9.6(b). It may be recalled that in the calculation of the coercive force in Sec. 8.2(c), we explicitly assumed that the wall energy is a function of x only. In that case, the increase of wall length as a result of the motion of a domain tip in stage I was found to make a negligible contribution to the coercive force of the film. Consequently, it was sufficient to consider only parallel displacement of the domain wall in the direction of the easy axis. Admittedly, this situation is highly simplified as easy-axis dispersion and surface roughness, the two factors which are mainly responsible for the coercive force, could be expected to have a y as well as an x dependence. Nevertheless, such simplified calculation did enable us to estimate the relative significance of the various possible contributions to the coercive force. In the dynamic situation, presumably, we should take into account the spatial dependence of the various parameters of the film such as its anisotropy, thickness, etc., in the calculation of the switching time. We shall therefore start our calculation with the formulation of the problem and then examine the mathematical difficulties involved in the solution of the resulting equation of motion. In contrast to the case of the coercive force calculation, we shall determine the wall motion time for both stages of magnetization reversal.

The equation of motion of a 180° wall separating two oppositely magnetized domains can be derived from the Lagrangian and dissipation function.[15] If m is the mass per unit area of the wall, the kinetic energy T' is equal to $\frac{1}{2}m(2\sqrt{h^2 + (b/2)^2}$ $T + 2yT)\dot{y}^2$. To expand the domain, work must be done to create a larger area of wall with surface energy e_w. Work must also be done against an elastic force per unit area $\alpha'y$. Thus, the potential energy of the system V is given by

$$V = e_w\left[2\sqrt{h^2 + \left(\frac{b}{2}\right)^2} + 2y\right]T + \left(\frac{bh}{2} + by\right)T\alpha'y - 2\mathbf{H}_s\cdot\mathbf{M}\left(\frac{bh}{2}\, by\right)T \qquad (9.11)$$

Here, we have assumed that the dimensions of the wedge remain unchanged while the reverse domain elongates in the y direction; the rectangular portion of the domain is assumed to have a width b, also independent of time as the domain expands. The Lagrangian $L = T' - V$ is therefore given by

$$L = \left[2\sqrt{h^2 + \left(\frac{b}{2}\right)^2} + 2y\right]T(\tfrac{1}{2}m\dot{y}^2 - e_w) + \left(\frac{bh}{2} + by\right)2T(\mathbf{H}_s\cdot\mathbf{M} - \tfrac{1}{2}\alpha'y) \qquad (9.12)$$

and the dissipation function E_D is

$$E_D = \left[2\sqrt{h^2 + \left(\frac{b}{2}\right)^2} + 2y\right]T\tfrac{1}{2}\beta\dot{y}^2 \qquad (9.13)$$

where the viscous damping parameter has contributions due to relaxation and eddy currents, that is $\beta = \beta_r + \beta_e$.

The Lagrangian equations are[16]

$$\frac{d}{dt}\left(\frac{\partial L}{\partial \dot{q}_i}\right) - \frac{\partial L}{\partial q_i} = Q'_i \qquad (9.14)$$

[15] N. Menyuk and J. B. Goodenough, *J. Appl. Phys.*, **26**: 8 (1955).

[16] See, e.g., J. C. Slater and N. H. Frank, *Mechanics*, McGraw-Hill Book Company, Inc., New York, 1947, p. 74.

where q_i is the ith component of the coordinate $\mathbf{q}$ and $\dot{q}_i$ is the ith component of $\mathbf{q}$ Q'_i are forces which are not derivable from a potential. For the viscous damping forces under consideration,

$$Q'_i = -\frac{\partial E_D}{\partial \dot{y}} = -2\beta T\left[\sqrt{h^2 + \left(\frac{b}{2}\right)^2} + y\right]\dot{y} \qquad (9.15)$$

Combining Eqs. (9.12) and (9.15) with Eq. (9.14), we find the equation of motion for the domain wall as

$$m\left[y + \sqrt{h^2 + \left(\frac{b}{2}\right)^2}\right]\ddot{y} + \frac{m}{2}\dot{y}^2 + \beta\left[y + \sqrt{h^2 + \left(\frac{b}{2}\right)^2}\right]\dot{y}$$

$$+ \alpha'by + \frac{bh}{4}\alpha' + e_w = b\mathbf{H}_s\cdot\mathbf{M} \qquad (9.16)$$

After the step field H_s is applied, the domain wall will be accelerated to some mean velocity. If this accelerating time is small compared to the switching time of the film, we may neglect the inertial terms, i.e. terms proportional to $\ddot{y}$. The omission of these terms could be justified in general if the inertial terms are negligible compared to the others in Eq. (9.16). For nickel ferrite and magnetite, for example, it has been found that $m\ddot{r} \ll \beta r$, where r is the radial coordinate in the case of a cylindrically expanding domain.[17] Under these circumstances, Eq. (9.16) reduced to

$$\frac{m}{2}\dot{y}^2 + \beta\left[y + \sqrt{h^2 + \left(\frac{b}{2}\right)^2}\right]\dot{y} + \alpha'by + \frac{bh}{4}\alpha' + e_w = b\mathbf{H}_s\cdot\mathbf{M} \qquad (9.17)$$

Let us now define $\mathbf{H}_o$ as the field required to just overcome the retarding forces of the wall. In other words, $\mathbf{H}_o$ is defined as the threshold field for which $\dot{y} = 0$. Thus,

$$\alpha'by_i + \frac{bh}{4}\alpha' + e_w = b\mathbf{H}_o\cdot\mathbf{M} \qquad (9.18)$$

where y_i is the value of y at which $\dot{y} = 0$; for the case under consideration $y_i = 0$, that is, the base of the wedge domain is initially at the film edge. It is of interest to note that α' and e_w in this formation have been implicitly assumed to be independent of y for simplicity. It should be recalled, however, that according to the derivation in Sec. 8.2(c), the coercive force H_c, which is synonymous with the threshold field H_o, arises from the spatial dependence of the wall energy e_w. This discrepancy does not necessarily represent a contradiction; it reflects a difference in objective in the two cases concerned. In the H_c derivation, we were interested in the possible origin of H_c, not in the dynamic behavior of domain walls. In the present derivation, we are interested in the velocity of the wall once sufficient field has been supplied to at least overcome the retarding forces. Of course, the possible spatial dependence of α' and e_w could be included in our derivation above but this additional complication is probably not warranted. This is so because the spatial variation of α' and e_w, being related to the largely unknown imperfection distribution, can be expected to be very complicated.

[17] J. K. Galt, J. Andrus, and H. G. Hopper, *Rev. Mod. Phys.*, **25**: 93 (1953).

Combining Eqs. (9.17) and (9.18), we readily find

$$\frac{m}{2}\dot{y}^2 + \beta\left[y + \sqrt{h^2 + \left(\frac{b}{2}\right)^2}\right]\dot{y} - b(\mathbf{H}_s - \mathbf{H}_o)\cdot\mathbf{M} = 0 \tag{9.19}$$

Solving for $\dot{y}$ in terms of y, we immediately find

$$\dot{y} = \frac{-\beta\left[y + \sqrt{h^2 + \left(\frac{b}{2}\right)^2}\right] + \sqrt{\left[\beta\left(y + \sqrt{h^2 + \left(\frac{b}{2}\right)^2}\right)\right]^2 + 2mb(\mathbf{H}_s - \mathbf{H}_o)\cdot\mathbf{M}}}{m} \tag{9.20}$$

For the purpose of calculating the switching time, let us define an average value of $\dot{y}$ as

$$\bar{\dot{y}} = \frac{1}{y_o}\int_0^{y_o}\dot{y}\,dy \tag{9.21}$$

where y_o is the final value of y. For the case in point y_o is nearly equal to half the film height l if h/l is sufficiently small. Carrying out the integration indicated by Eq. (9.21) with the help of Eq. (9.20), we find

$$\tau_1 = \frac{y_o}{\bar{\dot{y}}} = y_o\left\{-\frac{\beta}{m}\left[\frac{y_o}{2} + \sqrt{h^2 + \left(\frac{b}{2}\right)^2}\right] + \frac{1}{2my_o}\left[y_o + \sqrt{h^2 + \left(\frac{b}{2}\right)^2}\,f(y)|_{y=y_o}\right.\right.$$

$$\left.\left. - \sqrt{h^2 + \left(\frac{b}{2}\right)^2}\,f(y)|_{y=0}\right] + \frac{b}{\beta y_o}(\mathbf{H}_s - \mathbf{H}_o)\cdot\mathbf{M}\ln\frac{g(y)|_{y=y_o}}{g(y)|_{y=0}}\right\}^{-1} \tag{9.22}$$

where
$$f(y) = \left\{\beta^2\left[y + \sqrt{h^2 + \left(\frac{b}{2}\right)^2}\right]^2 + 2mb(\mathbf{H}_s - \mathbf{H}_o)\cdot\mathbf{M}\right\}^{1/2}$$

$$g(y) = 2\beta\left[\beta y + \beta\sqrt{h^2 + \left(\frac{b}{2}\right)^2} + f(y)\right]$$

To recapitulate, we have just succeeded in deriving the expression for the time τ_1 within which a reverse domain at the film edge elongated in the easy direction to reach the center of the film. It may be recalled that this process represents the first stage of magnetization reversal via domain wall motion.

We now proceed to calculate the switching time τ_2 for the second stage of the magnetization reversal process wherein the elongated domain displaces parallel to itself in the hard direction to reach the film edge. To begin with, the potential energy for this second state is given by

$$V = e_w Dl + (lDx)\alpha'x - 2\mathbf{H}_s\cdot\mathbf{M}(lDx) \tag{9.23}$$

and the dissipation function is

$$E_D = (Dl)\tfrac{1}{2}\beta\dot{x}^2 \tag{9.24}$$

The kinetic energy T is similarly given by $Dl(\frac{1}{2}m\dot{x}^2)$. In an entirely analogous fashion as that used for the derivation of Eq. (9.16), we find the equation of motion for the domain wall as

$$m\ddot{x} + \beta\dot{x} + 2\alpha'x = 2\mathbf{H}_s \cdot \mathbf{M} \qquad (9.25)$$

Again, we shall neglect the inertial term $m\ddot{x}$ as before and then define a threshold field H_o when $\dot{x} = 0$. Thus, from Eq. (9.25), we have $2\alpha'x = 2\alpha'(b/2) = 2\mathbf{H}_o \cdot \mathbf{M}$. It follows that the switching time for the second stage of magnetization reversal τ_2 is simply given by

$$\tau_2 = \frac{(l-b)/2}{\dot{x}} = \frac{(l-b)\beta}{4(\mathbf{H}_s - \mathbf{H}_o) \cdot \mathbf{M}} \qquad (9.26)$$

The total magnetization reversal time τ is, of course, equal to $\tau_1 + \tau_2$ given by Eqs. (9.22) and (9.26). We can easily estimate the switching time τ_2 for a typical Permalloy film for which $l - b \simeq 1$ cm, $4\pi M = 10^4$ gauss, $H_s - H_o \simeq 1$ Oe, and $\beta = 4\pi\lambda m \simeq 4\pi(10^8)(10^{-10}) = 0.04\pi$; as we shall show below, we find $\tau_2 \simeq 40$ μsec. Since τ_1 is of the same order of magnitude as τ_2 according to experimental observations, we can state without carrying out complicated calculations using Eq. (9.22) that τ is in the order of tens of microseconds for a unit increment field above the threshold. This estimate is in reasonable agreement with τ corresponding to point A of Fig. 9.1 which is a plot of $1/\tau$ vs H_s.

We must now proceed to calculate the viscous damping parameter β and the mass m in terms of the fundamental quantities of ferromagnetism such as the damping frequency λ, magnetization M, exchange constant A, and gyromagnetic ratio γ, etc. The essential features in the calculation of β_r, the relaxation contribution to β, has been given by Kittel.[18] Because of the small thickness of thin films, eddy-current contribution to domain wall relaxation can be neglected. The effective mass m of a moving Bloch wall was first calculated by Doring,[19] and Becker has given a simplified treatment leading to the same result.[20] Kittel[18] then generalized the Doring equation in order to include the case where the intrinsic relaxation frequency of the substance is high.

Becker noticed that the rotational motion of the local magnetization which accompanies the uniform motion of a Bloch wall (with velocity v in the x direction normal to the wall) may be described as caused by an effective field $H_e(x)$ such that the resulting precessional velocity $d\phi(x)/dt$ is equal to the rotational velocity required by the motion. Thus,

$$\frac{d\phi}{dt} = -v\frac{d\phi}{dz} = \gamma^*H_e \qquad (9.27)$$

and

$$(\gamma^*)^2 = \gamma^2 + \frac{\lambda^2}{M^2} \qquad (9.28)$$

where γ is the gyromagnetic ratio and λ is the damping constant. The kinetic energy of

---

[18] C. Kittel, *Phys. Rev.*, **80**: 918 (1950).

[19] W. Doring, *Z. Naturforsch.*, **3**: 373 (1948).

[20] R. Becker, *Proc. Grenoble Conference*, July, 1950.

the wall is given by the field energy so that per unit area,

$$\delta e_B = e_B - e_{Bo} = \frac{1}{8\pi} \int H_e^2 \, dx = \frac{v^2}{8\pi\gamma^{*2}} \int_{-\infty}^{\infty} \left(\frac{d\phi}{dx}\right)^2 dx \qquad (9.29)$$

where e_{Bo} is the surface energy of the wall at rest. From the results of the elementary theory of the Bloch wall given in Chap. 3, we easily find that the integral $\int_{-\infty}^{\infty}(d\phi/dx)^2 \, dx$ for a very thin film or bulk matter is just equal to $e_{Bo}/2A$ where A is the exchange constant. Thus, equating Eq. (9.29) to the kinetic energy $\frac{1}{2}mv^2$, we readily find the effective mass m as

$$m = \frac{e_{Bo}}{8\pi\gamma^{*2}A} \qquad (9.30)$$

Typically, $e_{Bo} \leq 1$ erg/cm^2, $\gamma^{*2} \simeq 4 \times 10^{14}$ and $A = 10^{-6}$ so that $m \sim 10^{-10}$ gram/cm^2 as mentioned previously.

To determine the relaxation contribution to the viscous damping parameter, we start from the Landau-Lifshitz equation of motion of the magnetization:

$$\frac{d\mathbf{M}}{dt} = \gamma \mathbf{M} \times \mathbf{H} - \lambda\left[\frac{(\mathbf{H}\cdot\mathbf{M})\mathbf{M}}{M^2} - \mathbf{H}\right] \qquad (9.31)$$

where λ is the relaxation frequency. [See Sec. 10.2. The second terms of Eqs. (9.31) and (10.10) are equal via a vector identity.] The power dissipated per unit volume is $\mathbf{H}\cdot(\dot{\mathbf{M}}) \simeq \lambda H_e^2$, so that the power per unit area which must be supplied to keep the spins in uniform motion is

$$\int_{-\infty}^{\infty} \mathbf{H}\cdot\frac{d\mathbf{M}}{dt} \, dx - \lambda \int_{-\infty}^{\infty} H_e^2 \, dx = 8\pi\lambda(\delta e_B) - \frac{v^2\lambda e_{Bo}}{2\gamma^{*2}A} \qquad (9.32)$$

The power supplied by the constant external field $\mathbf{H}_s$ which drives the wall along is $2\mathbf{H}_s'\cdot\mathbf{M}v$ per unit area; we equate this to the dissipation, and find the result:

$$v = 4(\gamma^2 M^2 + \lambda^2)\frac{AH_s'}{\lambda Me_{Bo}} \qquad (9.33)$$

Comparing this result with the expression for $\dot{x} = v$ in Eq. (9.26) and observing that $H_s' = H_s - H_o$, we find the expression for β as

$$\beta = 4\pi\lambda m = \frac{\lambda e_{Bo}}{2\gamma^{*2}A} \qquad (9.34)$$

The typical value for λ is in the order of 10^8 rad/sec, and since $m \sim 10^{-10}$ gram/cm^2, β has the value of the order of 0.1 as we have assumed in the estimate of τ_2 using Eq. (9.26).

If the moving wall was of the Néel instead of the Bloch type, the spins would rotate in the film plane about the film normal z. Thus, we would have an effective field H_z instead of H_x. However, for very thin films or for bulk matter, $\int_{-\infty}^{\infty}(d\phi/dx)^2 \, dx = e_{No}/2A$

analogous to the Bloch wall case so that formally m and β are given by the same expressions as Eqs. (9.30) and (9.34) except that e_{B_o} should be replaced by e_{N_o} for the Néel wall case. It should be noted, however, that e_{B_o} and e_{N_o} are in general unequal. For example, for very thin films, according to Eqs. (4.22) and (4.32), $e_{B_o} = \pi\sqrt{2}\sqrt{2\pi AM^2}$ and $e_{N_o} = \pi\sqrt{2}\sqrt{AK_1}$ where K_1 is the first-order anisotropy constant.

We shall now turn to a brief discussion of the experimental measurement on the domain wall velocities in Permalloy films. Domain wall velocities in Permalloy films have been observed utilizing the magneto-optic effect by several investigators. Olmen and Mitchell[21] found that the general expression obtained for slow domain wall velocity as a function of applied field H_s and temperature T for a contained wall is $v = v_o(T)e^{8\cdot8(H_s-H_o)}$ expressed in Gaussian units. It was also found that the domain wall velocity increases with increasing temperature at a fixed value of the applied magnetic field. Observations were made over a range of wall velocities from 3.4×10^{-4} cm/sec to 7.6×10^{-2} cm/sec. A plot of the displacement of the point of a spike domain as a function of time reveals that initially the spike velocity is high; it becomes nearly constant over the central region of the film, and increases again as it approaches the edge of the film opposite its nucleation point. This mode of reversal is not the common one for most films but is analogous to the first stage reversal described above wherein wedge domains elongate toward the film center in the direction of the easy axis. This behavior of wall velocity is in qualitative accord with that given by Eq. (9.22).

On the other hand, Ford[22] and Copeland and Humphrey[23] have found that wall velocities are well described by the equation $v = G(H_s - H_o)$ where G is the wall mobility. This result would be in accord with our theory if the reversal time τ_2 of stage II is much larger than that of stage I, τ_1. In Ford's experiments, the wall mobility was found to be inversely proportional to $B\sigma T$ where B is the saturation flux density, σ the electrical conductivity, and T the film thickness. This is the dependence that is predicted on the basis of a simple eddy-current model[15,24] indicating that, even in films as thin as 700 Å, the dominant loss mechanism in wall motion is caused by eddy currents rather than intrinsic relaxation damping. On the other hand, Copeland and Humphrey found that for films whose thickness is 500 Å or smaller, eddy-current damping was found to be negligible and the damping mechanism is one of intrinsic relaxation. It is not clear why the transition from intrinsic to eddy-current relaxation should occur in such a small thickness range. Furthermore, it has been found that even in $\frac{1}{8}$ mil (3×10^4 Å) metal tapes, eddy-current damping is still negligible.[15]

(b) Nucleation Processes

As we have discussed above, wall motion in thin Permalloy films usually starts from nuclei of reversed magnetization at the edges of the film, which are created by the demagnetizing field. Therefore, for the investigation of nucleation processes inside the film, the edge effects have to be suppressed. This has been done by two methods. The first is based on the use of inhomogeneous driving fields, and the second on the formation of a high coercive force barrier between the edges and the central area of the film.[25] This barrier prevents the edge domains from moving into the central area.

[21] R. W. Olmen and E. N. Mitchell, *J. Appl. Phys.*, **30**: 258S (1959).
[22] N. C. Ford, Jr., *J. Appl. Phys.*, **31**: 300S (1960).
[23] J. A. Copeland and F. B. Humphrey, *J. Appl. Phys.*, **34**: 1211 (1963).
[24] H. J. Williams, W. Shockley, and C. Kittel, *Phys. Rev.*, **80**: 1090 (1950).
[25] S. Methfessel and S. Middelhoek, *J. Appl. Phys*, **32**: 294S (1961).

Depending on the maximum amplitude of the driving field, different modes of nucleation are possible, leading to different hysteresis loops.

The effect of the edge domains can be avoided by using an inhomogeneous driving field which has a much smaller value at the edges than in the central area of the film. This method is useful for the investigation of nucleation at local inhomogeneities, such as holes and scratches in the film. The effect of the edge domains could also be avoided by using a barrier with a critical field for wall motion $H_b > H_o$ between the edges and the central portion of the film. This barrier prevents the edge domains from growing into the central area. Such a barrier can be obtained by using the dependence of the coercive force upon thickness, composition, or substrate roughness. For example, barrier films can be obtained by evaporating the film through a mask aperture placed at some distance from the substrate. The thickness of such a film will slowly decrease toward the edges. As the wall motion coercive force generally passes through a maximum as the film thickness decreases, the center of the film is protected by a band of higher wall motion coercive force H_b. Moreover, the stray fields are smaller as a result of the thin edges, thus further reducing the tendency for edge domain formation.

Since the domain nucleation must be attributed to a rotational process, the starting field should be related to the rotational threshold field H_k. The change of H_k in the same sample can be obtained by superimposing a uniaxial magnetostrictive stress anisotropy to the induced anisotropy by bending the film.[26] In this way, it was found that the starting field is an increasing function while the critical field for wall motion H_o is a decreasing function of H_k.

We now wish to turn to a brief discussion of the statistical theory of magnetization reversal in thin films for reversing fields less than the anisotropy field in which it is assumed that reversal takes place by domain wall motion.[27] The number of moving domains is determined by a simple statistical model which allows for the random nucleation of walls as the reversing field increases. In any ferromagnetic film there will be many nuclei for the formation of domain walls such as crystal boundaries, lattice defects and imperfections in the films, and substrate irregularities. For fields less than the coercive force, no wall motion can take place. For fields greater than the anisotropy field, reversal takes place by some form of domain rotation and the crystalline obstructions do not prevent complete magnetization reversal.

Let us consider a statistical distribution of nuclei critical field strengths with respect to the value of local field which must be attained before the wall is free to move. For simplicity, it is assumed that once a wall is free from an obstacle, it will continue to move freely during the remainder of the reversal process. The nuclei or obstructions are assumed to have a distribution of effective critical field intensity between the coercive force and the anisotropy field. The probability that a given nucleating point or obstruction which has not produced a moving domain wall at a given field H will yield a wall as the field increases from H_s to $H_s + \Delta H_s$ will be given by

$$P(H_s)\Delta H_s = \frac{p\Delta H_s}{H_k - H_s} \tag{9.35}$$

where $H_c \leq H_s \leq H_k$. The probability of a wall not being nucleated in the field interval ΔH_s will be equal to one minus the probability that it is nucleated. The

---

[26] D. O. Smith, *J. Appl. Phys.*, **30**: 264S (1959).
[27] R. L. Conger and F. C. Essig, *J. Appl. Phys.*, **28**: 855 (1957).

probability of passing a series of infinitesimal field increases of size ΔH_s without nucleation will be equal to the product of the probability of nonnucleation in each individual ΔH_s. To obtain the probability that nucleation will occur in the next succeeding ΔH_s, this product must be multiplied by the probability of a given wall nucleation at a field H_s. This takes the form

$$G(H_s)\Delta H_s = \left[\prod_{n=H_c/\Delta H_s}^{n=H_k/\Delta H_s} \left(1 - \frac{p\Delta H_s}{H_k - n\Delta H_s}\right)\right] \frac{p\Delta H_s}{H_k - H_s} \tag{9.36}$$

This equation can be evaluated by converting the product to a sum by taking logarithms and converting the sum into an integral as ΔH_s approaches zero giving the result

$$G(H_s)\,dH_s = \frac{p}{(H_k - H_c)^p} \frac{dH_s}{(H_k - H_s)^{1-p}} \tag{9.37}$$

Since it is assumed that a wall, once nucleated, will move freely, the reversal time at a field H_s will be inversely proportional to the number of walls at H_s. The velocity of each wall will be directly proportional to H_s according to Eq. (9.33). In terms of the damping parameter α in the Gilbert equation instead of λ in the Landau–Lifshitz equation, Eq. (9.33) becomes for $\gamma^2 M^2 \gg \gamma^2$ [27]

$$v = 4|\gamma|AH_s/e_{Bo}\alpha \tag{9.38}$$

Thus, the reversal time will be some constant divided by the product of the field strength and the number of walls that have been nucleated. The fraction of the total number of walls that have been nucleated will be given by the integral of the probability function given by Eq. (9.37) between the limits H_c and H_s. The total number of moving walls contributing to the magnetization reversal will be the number of walls possible times this integral. The reciprocal of τ will be the product of v, the number of moving walls, and the width of the film, assumed here to be 1 cm. The number of moving walls will be the product of the fraction of the total and the largest number of walls equal to the film width divided by wall thickness D where $D = \pi(A/2K_1)^{1/2}$ and the wall energy is $2(AK_1)^{1/2}$. Thus,

$$\frac{1}{\tau} = \frac{2\sqrt{2}|\gamma|H_s}{\pi\alpha}\left[1 - \left(\frac{H_k - H_s}{H_k - H_c}\right)^p\right] \tag{9.39}$$

where H_k is the anisotropy field $2K_1/M$. The time required to nucleate a wall can be ignored if it is small compared to the time the wall is in motion, but for fields near H_k, this assumption is invalid. This finite nucleation time will therefore limit reversal by wall motion to a value less than the maximum given by Eq. (9.39).

Before closing this discussion of nucleation process in thin films, it is important to recall that this process is usually effective only if the effect of the edge domains is suppressed by one of the methods discussed above. However, it may be mentioned for completeness that such nucleation near the center of the film has been occasionally observed even in the absence of deliberate suppression of edge effects.

(c) Domain Wall Motion Observation

In the foregoing analysis, we have shown that for wall motion to commence, the applied field must be larger than the wall motion coercive force. However, when a dc field is applied in the easy direction, which is smaller than the critical field for wall motion and an additional ac field is applied in the hard direction, it can be observed that the wall starts to move slowly. This wall motion takes place in a direction such that the domains whose magnetization is parallel to the dc field increase in size. The velocity of the walls is observed to be sensitively dependent upon the magnitude of both the dc and ac fields. This phenomenon known as domain wall creeping is very useful in the study of slow changes in domain configuration. Indeed, as we have already discussed in Sec. 3.1, the method of domain wall creeping can be used to enable a film domain configuration to reach its minimum energy state exhibiting edge domains.

An optical strobing apparatus has been developed which makes it possible to observe magnetization reversal in thin films with reversal taking place during a period of the order of a microsecond.[28] In this apparatus, sunlight strikes a three-sided mirror fastened to a turbine. Light pulses from the spinning mirror pass through a Glan-Thompson prism, which plane polarizes the light reflected from the magnetic film being studied, and pass through a Glan-Thompson analyzer. With the turbine spinning at the maximum speed of 10^6 rpm, the duration of the light pulses at the film is about 10^{-7} sec. Opposing 180° domains of the sample rotate the plane of polarization of the light in different directions. If the film is overcoated with a layer of zinc sulfide a fraction of wavelength of light thick, the domain pattern that is observed is colored, thereby increasing the visual contrast. Observed domain patterns show that the reversal process is dependent upon the speed of reversal. When the magnetization changes at a rate of about once every 10 sec, one observes that reversal starts at the edge of the film and proceeds by small steps across the film. High-speed reversal also starts at the edges but, in addition, there is nucleation at the center of the film which increases the speed of reversal. When a magnetic field is applied suddenly to the film, nucleation sites reverse first. Then, reversal proceeds by the growth of these reversed regions by domain wall motion.

9·4   NONCOHERENT ROTATION THEORY

In Secs. 9.2 and 9.3, we examined in some detail the processes of magnetization reversal via coherent rotation and domain wall motion respectively. In the former case, the switching field H_s and biasing field $H_\perp$ are sufficiently large compared to the coercive force H_c and the anisotropy field H_k that the edge domains, imperfections, etc., play no important role in the reversal process. On the other hand, if $H_c < H_s < H_k$ (for normal films, that is, $H_k > H_c$), the magnetization reversal proceeds by motion of the walls of the demagnetizing domains already existing at the edge of the film. Under certain circumstances, as we have discussed in the last section, nucleation may also occur at the interior of the film. Now, if H_s is larger than H_k but not sufficiently large to cause uniform rotation to occur, experiments have shown that the magnetization reversal process is one of noncoherent rotation. By this, we mean that the magnetization $\mathbf{M}$ rotates by a different amount in different parts of the film so that $\mathbf{M}(\mathbf{r}, t)$ has

---

[28] R. L. Conger and G. H. Moore, *J. Appl. Phys.*, Pt. 2, **34**: 1213 (1963).

neither the dependence of domain wall motion nor that of uniform rotation, that is, $\mathbf{M} \neq f(\mathbf{r})$. Of course, as the magnetization splits up in the film, domain walls would be formed in the film between regions of varying amounts of rotation. It is clearly of importance to examine (1) why partial rotation should occur in thin films and (2) how the resulting domain walls move and complete the reversal.

Before we examine in detail the process of incoherent rotation, it may be surmised that this phenomenon is likely to be related to the imperfection distribution in the film. For, if the film were completely homogeneous in all respects, the reversal process should clearly be one of uniform rotation; for, except for perhaps surface and edge effects, there is no apparent reason for the magnetization to be a function of the coordinate in either the static or dynamic cases. In this connection, see the related discussion in Sec. 11.3(c) on surface waves. For $H_c < H_s < H_k$ in the case of normal films, that is, $H_k > H_c$, the reversal process is one of motion of domain walls which are nucleated due to inhomogeneous demagnetizing fields or physical imperfection centers such as vacancies, dislocations, inclusions, voids, etc. In addition to imperfections of the physical type, there may be imperfections of the magnetic type exemplified by the possible variation of the easy direction and magnitude of the induced uniaxial anisotropy. Of course, this distinction between physical and magnetic imperfections is somewhat uncertain as anisotropy variations, for example, must in turn be due to some physical variation of the film properties such as the spatial compositional dependence of the film. Nevertheless, as we shall demonstrate below, the noncoherent process could best be understood in terms of the anisotropy dispersion in magnetic films.

Many attempts have been made by various workers to explain the mechanism of noncoherent rotation in thin films. Gyorgy[29] attempted to explain the intermediate speed-switching mechanism in ferrite toroids and thin films in terms of a nonuniform rotation model. This model assumes that the magnetization rotates simultaneously but in such a way that demagnetizing effects arising from the boundary can be neglected. The ferrite toroid is first approximated by a cylinder. Then a spiral flux configuration about the cylinder axis is assumed. Now, the discontinuity at the cylinder boundary leads to poles of alternating signs. If the period of the surface poles is much smaller than the diameter of the cylinder, the magnetic field due to these poles will be negligible throughout most of the volume of the cylinder as has been verified by a detailed calculation involving the spiral mode.[30] [Note that in the case of uniform rotation, the surface poles arising from the discontinuity at the boundary would give rise to large demagnetizing fields ($\sim 10^3$ Oe)]. Thus, we may treat the rotation in this region as occurring in applied field only providing the anisotropy field is neglected. If we further assume that the appropriate damping constant has a value which yields the minimum switching time, the results of this model are in good agreement with experiment. However, the threshold fields for nonuniform rotation cannot be predicted correctly. This is not surprising when we recall that anisotropy has been neglected along with the supposition of a model which has not been independently verified. In this connection, it may be noted that anisotropy, being due to spin-orbit interaction and pseudo-dipole coupling, is a microscopic quantity which presumably cannot be locally annihilated by macroscopic averaging over the sample.

In the case of thin films, no specific model has been proposed by Gyorgy although a nonuniform rotational mechanism is also implied for thin films. Indeed, using the

[29] E. M. Gyorgy, *J. Appl. Phys.*, **31**: 110S (1960).
[30] E. M. Gyorgy, *J. Appl. Phys.*, **29**: 1709 (1958).

theoretical results of the nonuniform rotation model, Humphrey and Gyorgy were able to obtain impressive correlation between the observed and theoretical voltage transient wave form during switching of a Permalloy film.[30] It is clear, however, that to proceed further, a specific model for thin film which is based upon some variation of certain pertinent physical variables, such as the anisotropy, is required. In this connection, it should be mentioned that the longitudinal voltage in this intermediate speed region is usually characterized by a fast initial spike followed by a slow tail, suggesting, as pointed out by Humphrey,[31] an initial coherent rotation which breaks up into some noncoherent process before switching is completed.

Hagedorn[32] has further studied the noncoherent switching process in Permalloy films by means of interrupted pulse experiments. The procedure was to interrupt the switching process before completion and then to complete the reversal with a second switching pulse. Two different types of wave form were observed, namely, complete and partial switching ones for cases where $H_c < H_s < H_k$ and $H_s > H_k$ by about 30%. The most striking difference between these two sets of partial switching wave forms, as compared to their respective complete switching wave forms, is that the two parts approximately reproduce the complete wave form in the case where $H_c < H_s < H_k$ but not for the case where $H_s > H_k$. This difference exists if either more or less flux is switched by the first pulse and is direct evidence that the switching process in the latter case (nonuniform rotation) is not the same as that in the former (domain wall motion). Furthermore, domain observations show that the film is divided into many small domains in the static, intermediate state which exists before the commencement of the second switching pulse. Furthermore, it was found that the number of these domains increases with H_s and that the switching process which follows the interruption is slower than would be a continuation of the process prior to interruption.

Harte tried to account for the noncoherent rotation in Permalloy films by a model based upon a small angular dispersion ($\sim 3°$) in the film plane of the easy axis of the induced anisotropy.[33] Whereas the results of this calculation show some resemblance to the experimental data, the small dispersion appears insufficient to correlate the predicted $1/\tau$ vs H_s curves with experiment. Thus, it is reasonable to conclude that small angular dispersion of the easy axis is insufficient to account for the noncoherent switching behavior. If anisotropy variation is indeed to be the source of nonuniform rotation, we are then left with only two possible alternatives. We may either assume that the magnitude of the induced anisotropy has a spatial dependence or that the angular dispersion of the easy axis is much larger. The relative preponderance of these factors may in turn depend upon the film processing variables.

For normal films wherein $H_k > H_c$, Smith and Harte suggested, on the basis of their many domain observations using high resolution Bitter technique, that noncoherent rotation is primarily due to "labyrinth propagation."[34] They found that if parallel wall displacement does not occur after nucleation of an initial reverse domain, reversal takes place by extension from the tip of the initial domain. A striking feature of this form of switching is that regions of unswitched material are left behind, resulting in a labyrinth-like flux pattern; in this context, switched is taken to mean the rotation of **M** beyond the hard axis. This labyrinth configuration is highly unstable with respect to increasing or decreasing applied field.

[31] F. B. Humphrey, *J. Appl. Phys.*, **29**: 284 (1958).
[32] F. B. Hagedorn, *J. Appl. Phys.*, **130**: 254S (1959).
[33] K. J. Harte, *J. Appl. Phys.*, **31**: 283S (1960).
[34] D. O. Smith and K. J. Harte, *J. Appl. Phys.*, **33**: 1399 (1962).

The basic reason for the occurrence of labyrinth switching is postulated to be local variations in the switching threshold. Dispersion in the switching is further assumed to be due to a dispersion in magnitude and direction of the local uniaxial anisotropy. The sequential or propagating nature of labyrinth switching clearly depends upon magnetostatic interaction between the switched region and the region which next switches. A magnetostatic model for the direction of labyrinth propagation as a function of the angle between H_s and the easy axis as given by Smith and Harte is in reasonable agreement with experiment. In this model, the film is considered to be composed of regions k_1 and k_2 with two distinct values of anisotropy K_1 and K_2, with $K_2 > K_1$. The spatial distribution of k_1 and k_2 is assumed to be random with an average spacing between k_1 of r. Since the association of the switched (s) and unswitched (u) labyrinth cells with k_1 and k_2 is desired, it is assumed that magnetostatic coupling plays an important role in defining the effective shape and size of k_1 and k_2. Thus, k_1 can be considered as a long ellipsoid in a matrix of k_2 material. Therefore, there are three regions corresponding to k_1^s, k_2^u and k_1^u. Assuming that k_1^s at the origin is switched, the problem is to determine in which direction the next k_1^u which switches will be found.

In the calculation discussed above, the dispersion of the easy axis of the anisotropy has been neglected; whereas this may be a reasonable approximation in the case of normal films ($H_k > H_c$), it may not be so in the case of inverted films ($H_k < H_c$). According to Smith, there are definite experimental evidences in support of the existence of negative H_k regions in inverted films, i.e., in these films, there are regions whose easy axes are oriented 90° away from the predominant easy direction. The role of these negative H_k regions in the noncoherent switching behavior is obviously dependent upon the size and density of these regions. To date, no detailed calculation in this regard has been carried out. However, Thomas has made theoretical calculations of noncoherent rotation based upon the local variation of the easy-axis direction of the anisotropy.[35] His model is in turn deduced from the experimental observations of Methfessel, Middelhoek, and Thomas[36] who obtained Bitter patterns similar to that found by Smith and Harte[34] and also hysteresis loops. He investigated a simple model which consisted of a set of strips parallel to the easy axis with different anisotropy constant, interacting by the magnetic stray field. It displays an incoherent process similar to the partial rotation process observed in Permalloy films and under certain conditions a unidirectional hysteresis.

Thomas' calculation is mainly intended for inverted films. When $H_c > H_s > H_k$ is applied in the easy direction, the magnetization direction opposite to the field direction becomes unstable and rotation will occur. As a result of the dispersion of the anisotropy direction in some parts of the film, this rotation will occur to the left and other parts to the right as shown in Fig. 5.7. Between different parts of the film will appear walls of the Néel type since the angle through which the magnetization turns in the wall is very small. The appearance of these walls blocks further rotation of the magnetization and the reversal is completed by motion of the walls of the edge domains over the film.

[35] H. Thomas, *J. Appl. Phys.*, **33**: 1117 (1962).
[36] S. Methfessel, S. Middelhoek, and H. Thomas, *J. Appl. Phys.*, **32**: 1959 (1961).

CHAPTER 10

FERROMAGNETIC RESONANCE

Some of the most important parameters in ferromagnetism can be conveniently deduced by the method of ferromagnetic resonance. For example, the Lande g factor, the magnetization, the anisotropy field, the coercive force, the line width, and the magnetic imperfection distribution can all be measured by a magnetic resonance spectrometer. In this chapter we shall begin our discussion of ferromagnetic resonance by first reviewing some of the pertinent features of the simple but related problem of electron paramagnetism. Then we proceed with a detailed discussion of the uniform-mode resonance theory in thin films; in this mode, the spins are all parallel and precess in unison. A brief discussion of the relaxation process and its relation to the observed line width in thin films will also be given. These theoretical discussions will be followed by a detailed description of the experimental method of measurement of the g value, magnetization, anisotropy field, coercive force, line width, magnetic imperfection distribution, etc.

The relatively more complicated problem of spin-wave resonance when the spin direction has a spatial dependence will be treated in Chap. 11.

10·1 GENERAL CONSIDERATIONS

When a ferromagnet is placed in a superimposed static and rf magnetic field, resonance absorption may occur for the proper combination of static field value and frequency. The occurrence of resonance is due to the transition between the different energy levels of ferromagnetic electron spin states. Before we discuss the more complicated many-spin problem in a ferromagnet, it may be instructive to review the elementary facts regarding electron paramagnetism. Consider an electron with spin 1/2 in a magnetic field H_o. The energy level E_o in the presence of H_o is seen from Fig. 10.1 to split into an energy doublet with a separation proportional to H_o:

$$\Delta E = 2|\mathbf{\mu} \cdot \mathbf{H}_o| = 2|\mu_z|H_o \tag{10.1}$$

where μ_z is the component of the magnetic moment in the static field direction z. The ratio of the magnitude of the electron spin magnetic moment to the magnitude of the electron spin angular momentum is just the gyromagnetic ratio $\gamma_e = -|\mathbf{\mu}|/|s\hbar| = -e/mc$ where the electronic charge e is positive. Here m is the electron mass and $\hbar$ is Planck's constant h divided by 2π. Thus, Eq. (10.1) becomes

$$\Delta E = 2|\gamma_e||S_z|\hbar H_o = \hbar|\gamma_e|H_o \tag{10.2}$$

where $|\gamma_e|H_o$ is the familiar Larmor frequency. At thermal equilibrium, the ratio of the population of the upper state to that of the lower state at temperature T is, according to the Boltzmann distribution, $e^{-\Delta E/k_B T}$ where k_B is the Boltzmann's constant. If now an rf field of frequency $\omega = |\gamma_e|H_o$ is applied perpendicular to $\mathbf{H}_o$, transition between the upper and lower states may occur giving rise to resonance absorption. Since S_z changes from $-1/2$ to $1/2$ or vice versa, we conclude that the direction of the spin reverses at resonance.

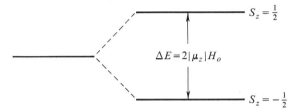

FIG. 10.1. Energy doublet of an electron spin in a z-directed static magnetic field.

If orbital angular momentum as well as spin angular momentum is included, then the energy separation between the doublets becomes

$$\Delta E' = \hbar \frac{g}{2} |\gamma_e| H_o \tag{10.3}$$

where the Lande g factor may be easily derived from geometrical consideration:[1]

$$g = 1 + \frac{J(J+1) + S(S+1) - L(L+1)}{2J(J+1)} \tag{10.4}$$

where $\mathbf{L}\hbar$ and $\mathbf{J}\hbar$ are the orbital and total angular momentum respectively. In this derivation, we implicitly assumed that H_o is not strong enough to break down the coupling between $\mathbf{L}$ and $\mathbf{S}$ and their resultant $\mathbf{J}$ precesses about $\mathbf{H}_o$. We note from Eq. (10.4) that if $S = 0, g = 1$ and if $L = 0, g = 2$ as it should. Since L and J are integers while S must be an integer or a half integer, it follows that g must be a rational number.

In ferromagnetism, g is nearly equal to but not exactly equal to 2 and is usually an irrational number. This implies that ferromagnetism is mainly due to electron spin. The departure from a g value of 2 may be interpreted as due to the incomplete quenching of the orbital angular momentum in the solid state.

The quenching of the orbital but not the spin angular momentum is due to the fact that each atom or ion is subjected to sufficiently asymmetrical electrical forces due to the crystalline field. In the solutions or salts of the iron group, the paramagnetic 3d electrons are the outermost electrons and these are therefore highly exposed to the crystalline field. Consequently, the orientation of the orbit changes as the electrons move about an external magnetic field with the average orbital angular momentum

[1] For derivation see G. Herzberg, *Atomic Spectra and Atomic Structure*, Dover Publications, Inc., New York, 1944, pp. 109–110.

averaging to zero in the field direction. On the other hand, the electron spin has no directional interaction with the electrostatic field and thus orients itself freely in an external magnetic field. We therefore expect the g value of Eq. (10.4) for salts of the iron group to be given essentially by the spin-only value. The quenching is, however, not complete and due to the presence of spin-orbit coupling, the spin carries some orbital angular momentum with it making the g value deviate slightly from its spin-only value of 2.

If the external fields are not strong enough, the Russel–Saunders quantization of the atom will not be appreciably destroyed. In other words, electrostatic forces within the atom are greater than forces from without the atom, so that the squares of the orbital and spin angular momentum are approximately $L(L + 1)$ and $S(S + 1)$, even though the spacial quantization may be greatly disturbed by the asymmetries of the electric fields set up by the neighboring atoms or ions. Thus, whereas the magnitude of **L** may still be approximately a constant of the motion, its components L_x, L_y, and L_z nearly average to zero.

It may be of interest to elaborate somewhat upon the nature of spin-orbit coupling. Often the interaction between spin and orbital angular momenta is small compared to the interaction of orbital angular momenta among themselves, or else of the spins among themselves. Then the spins form a resultant **S**, and similarly the orbital angular momenta form a resultant **L**. If no external field is applied, the vectors **S** and **L** are compounded to form a resultant **J**. This type of coupling is known as the Russel–Saunder's coupling and is the rule in iron and rare-earth groups, so that it is the only type of quantization which we need in our study of magnetism. By vector addition,

$$|\mathbf{J}|^2 = |\mathbf{L} + \mathbf{S}|^2 = L^2 + S^2 + 2\mathbf{L}\cdot\mathbf{S}$$

where **L·S** is the so-called spin-orbit coupling. It is usually small except for heavy elements. This, coupled with the fact that **L** is already well quenched in a salt or a solid of the transition elements means that g should indeed be close to 2 as observed.

10·2 UNIFORM–MODE RESONANCE THEORY

In the uniform precessional mode, the resultant spins of various atoms execute identical motions as a function of time. We may loosely speak of this state as one in which all spins are parallel and precess about the static field in unison. However, we must keep in mind that whereas the projection of each atomic spin upon the static field axis is $\pm S$, their instantaneous relative orientation must be such that the resultant magnitude is $\sqrt{S_T(S_T + 1)}$, where S_T is the total net spin in the direction of the static field as is required by wave mechanics. The number of possible orientations of such a many-spin system is, of course, $(2S_T + 1)$. Since S_T is usually very large in a ferromagnetic solid of macroscopic dimensions ($\sim 6.02 \times 10^{23}$ atoms/gram at. wt), the number of possible orientations of the total spin would be very very large indeed. Thus we may think of the total spin or magnetic moment per unit volume (magnetization) as being capable of orienting in almost any direction with respect to that of the static field. It follows that the magnetization **M** may approximately be considered as a classical vector. A classical equation of motion for the magnetization vector may then be formulated as we shall do in what follows.

It may be instructive to investigate quantitatively a little further the possible orientation of the total spin with respect to the direction of the static field. Let $S_{Tm} = NS$ be the maximum total spin in the static field direction where N is the total number of net spins per unit volume and S is the net spin per atom. Then, if the spins are all oriented along the static field axis, the angle θ_m between the total spin and the static field is, according to wave mechanics,

$$\theta_m = \cos^{-1} \frac{NS}{\sqrt{NS(NS + 1)}} \tag{10.5}$$

Now, if an rf magnetic field of frequency ω is applied perpendicular to the static field H_o with $\omega = |\gamma_e|H_o$, ferromagnetic resonance with accompanying spin reversals will occur. It then follows that if p is the number of reversed spins, the angle θ_p between the new total spin and H_o is

$$\theta_p = \cos^{-1} \frac{(N - 2p)S}{\sqrt{(N - 2p)S[(N - 2p)S + 1]}} \tag{10.6}$$

It is of interest to note that the rf field intensity normally used to excite ferromagnetic resonance in a ferromagnet is usually insufficient to cause a large enough number of spin reversed p compared to N ($p/N \ll 1$) to cause a departure of more than a few degrees of the resultant magnetization direction from H_o.

(a) Resonance in the Plane of the Film

Let the total angular momentum of an atom be $\mathbf{J}\hbar$. Classically, we know that the torque τ acting on a body is equal to the rate of change of angular momentum of the body:

$$\tau = \hbar\dot{\mathbf{J}} \tag{10.7}$$

Since $-|\mu|/|\mathbf{J}\hbar| = -ge/2mc = +g\gamma_e/2 = \gamma$ where μ is the net atomic magnetic moment, Eq. (10.7) becomes

$$\dot{\mu} = \gamma\tau \tag{10.8}$$

Since $\mathbf{M} = N\mu$, we obtain the equation of motion for the magnetization from Eq. (10.8) as

$$\dot{\mathbf{M}} = \gamma\tau \tag{10.9}$$

If $\mathbf{M}$ is placed in a static field H_o, then $\tau = \mathbf{M} \times \mathbf{H}_o$. Thus, if $\mathbf{M}$ is displaced from $\mathbf{H}_o$, it will precess about $\mathbf{H}_o$ at the Larmor frequency $\omega_L = |\gamma|H_o$, as can be seen from Eq. (10.9). This precession would persist for an infinite period of time if it were not for the presence of damping forces. This damping may be introduced in a phenomenological way. However, since the detailed damping mechanism in a ferromagnet has not been completely resolved, different mathematical forms for the damping have been suggested. The three most common damping terms used to augment the right-hand side of Eq. (10.9) are as follows:

1. The Landau–Lifshitz form: $\quad \dfrac{-\lambda}{|\mathbf{M}|^2} \mathbf{M} \times \tau$

2. The Gilbert form: $\quad \dfrac{\alpha}{|\mathbf{M}|} \mathbf{M} \times \dot{\mathbf{M}}$

3. The Bloch–Bloembergen form: $\quad \dfrac{-M_{x,y}}{\tau_2} - \dfrac{M_z - |\mathbf{M}|}{\tau_1}$

The Gilbert form[2] is essentially a modification of the original form proposed first by Landau and Lifshitz in 1935.[3] It is worthwhile to note that the Landau–Lifshitz and Gilbert forms of damping conserve $|\mathbf{M}|$ (τ damp $\perp \mathbf{M}$) while the Bloch–Bloembergen form[4] does not. In their formulation of the damping term, Landau and Lifshitz observed that the ferromagnetic exchange forces between spins are much greater than the Zeeman forces between the spins and the magnetic fields. Exchange will therefore conserve the magnitude of $\mathbf{M}$. Since the approach of $\mathbf{M}$ toward $\mathbf{H}$ is, in this formulation, due entirely to the relatively weak interaction between $\mathbf{M}$ and $\mathbf{H}$, we must require that $\lambda \ll |\gamma||\mathbf{M}|$. In this small damping limit, the Landau–Lifshitz and the Gilbert forms are equivalent so that whether one uses one or the other is simply a matter of convenience or familiarity. On the other hand, the Bloch–Bloembergen form of damping does not conserve $|\mathbf{M}|$ and is therefore equivalent to the forms of Landau–Lifshitz and Gilbert only when α is small *and* for small excursions of $\mathbf{M}$. For large excursions of $\mathbf{M}$, the magnitude of $\mathbf{M}$ is definitely not conserved, as the damping torque is in the direction of the magnetization components in this formulation. Thus, the observation of $|\mathbf{M}|$ in switching experiments in thin films should provide a sensitive test on the appropriate form of the damping term for ferromagnetism since $\mathbf{M}$ rotates over $\pi/2$ or π radius in these experiments. As far as it could be ascertained by results of existing thin-film switching experiments, $|\mathbf{M}|$ is conserved during switching. This would imply that the form of the Bloch–Bloembergen damping term would not be applicable for this type of experiment.

On the other hand, however, Callen has obtained a dynamic equation by quantizing the spin waves into magnons and treating the problem quantum-mechanically.[5] Fletcher, Le Craw, and Spencer subsequently have derived essentially the same equation using energy considerations.[6] In their derivation, they consider the rate of energy transfer between the uniform precession, the spin waves and the lattice. The discussion of these topics shall be deferred until after we have studied the characteristics of spin waves in the next chapter. The important thing to note here, however, is the fact that Callen's and Fletcher *et al.*'s equations are similar to the Bloch–Bloembergen equation and indeed reduce to it if $T_{1o} = T_{1k}$ where T_{1o} and T_{1k} are, respectively, uniform mode to lattice and spin wave to lattice relaxation times. Using a novel Klystron frequency modulation method, Fletcher *et al.* found that the magnitude of the average magnetization $\mathbf{M}$ is not conserved in ferromagnetic resonance experiments with yttrium iron garnet spheres with surface roughness. However, $|\mathbf{M}|$ is found to be nearly conserved as the surface roughness is greatly reduced by polishing. Thus, they interpret this to

   [2] T. A. Gilbert, *Armour Research Foundation Rept. No. 11*, Armour Research Foundation, Chicago, January 25, 1955, unpublished.
   [3] E. Landau and E. Lifshitz, *Physik Z. Sowjetunion*, **8**: 153 (1935).
   [4] N. Bloembergen, *Phys. Rev.*, **78**: 572 (1950).
   [5] H. B. Callen, *J. Phys. Chem. Solids*, **4**: 256 (1958).
   [6] R. C. Fletcher, R. C. Le Craw, and E. G. Spencer, *Phys. Rev.*, **117**: 955 (1960).

mean that whereas microscopically the exchange forces keep adjacent spins very nearly aligned so that locally the magnetization is conserved, spatially averaged magnetization is nevertheless not conserved in the presence of surface imperfections. It is pertinent to note here that the conservation of $|\mathbf{M}|$ in these low-power experiments implies that $T_{1o} \neq T_{1k}$ for otherwise the equations of Fletcher *et al.* reduce to those of Bloch. However, Bloch's equations are in turn equivalent to Landau–Lifshitz for small α and small excursion of $\mathbf{M}$. Thus, we are forced to conclude that volume and surface imperfection effects in rotational thin-film switching experiments must be unimportant as $|\mathbf{M}|$ has been observed to be conserved during switching.

The above questions can not be completely resolved here in this section. A more definitive discussion can be found in Chap. 9 and 11. Consistent with the observation that $|\mathbf{M}|$ is conserved during switching and because of precedence, the Landau–Lifshitz form of damping shall be used here. Thus, Eq. (10.9) when augmented by this damping term becomes

$$\dot{\mathbf{M}} = \gamma\boldsymbol{\tau} - \frac{\lambda}{|\mathbf{M}|^2} \mathbf{M} \times \boldsymbol{\tau} \qquad (10.10)$$

Now consider the experimental configuration of Fig. 10.2. The free energy E of the spin system in the presence of the uniaxial anisotropy and x-y oriented magnetic fields are[7]

$$E = K_1 \sin^2 (\phi - \alpha) - H_s M \sin \theta \cos \phi$$
$$- H_\perp M \sin \theta \sin \phi + \tfrac{1}{2}(4\pi M^2 \cos^2 \theta) \qquad (10.11)$$

where $M = |\mathbf{M}|$ and K_1 is the first order anisotropy constant. Thus, the first term on the right-hand side of Eq. (10.11) represents the uniaxial anisotropy energy with an easy axis oriented at an angle α from the x axis as shown. The second and third terms represent the Zeeman energies due to the interaction between $\mathbf{M}$ and the magnetic fields $\mathbf{H}_s$ and $\mathbf{H}_\perp$. The fourth term represents the demagnetizing energy; the factor of $\tfrac{1}{2}$ comes about because it is a self energy. The torque acting on $\mathbf{M}$ may be derived from the free energy E by the relations

$$\mathbf{F} = -\nabla E \qquad (10.12)$$

and

$$\boldsymbol{\tau} = \mathbf{r} \times \mathbf{F} = -\mathbf{r} \times \nabla E \qquad (10.13)$$

where $\mathbf{F}$ is the generalized force and $\mathbf{r}$ is the radius vector in the direction of $\mathbf{M}$. In spherical coordinates, we have from Fig. 10.2,

$$\mathbf{M} = \hat{r}M \qquad (10.14)$$

and

$$\boldsymbol{\tau} = -\hat{\phi}\frac{\partial E}{\partial \theta} + \hat{\theta}\frac{1}{\sin \theta}\frac{\partial E}{\partial \phi} \qquad (10.15)$$

Because of the extreme geometry of the film, $\mathbf{M}$ would deviate only slightly from the plane of the film in order to minimize the demagnetizing energy. Thus, it would be

---

[7] D. O. Smith, *J. Appl. Phys.*, **29**: 264 (1958).

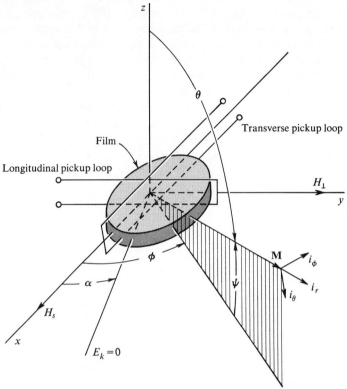

FIG. 10.2.   Anisotropic thin film and associated coordinates (after D. O. Smith, Ref. 7).

expedient to introduce a new variable $\psi = \pi/2 - \theta$. Substituting Eqs. (10.11) and (10.14) into Eq. (10.15) and equating the $\hat{\phi}$ and $\hat{\theta}$ components, we obtain

$$\dot{\phi} M \cos \psi = \gamma \frac{\partial E}{\partial \psi} - \frac{\lambda}{M} \frac{1}{\cos \psi} \frac{\partial E}{\partial \phi} \tag{10.16}$$

and

$$\dot{\psi} M = \gamma \frac{1}{\cos \psi} \frac{\partial E}{\partial \phi} + \frac{\lambda}{M} \frac{\partial E}{\partial \psi} \tag{10.17}$$

Eqs. (10.16) and (10.17) are two coupled linear differential equations in the variables ϕ and ψ and are exact for the problem under discussion. They could, of course, be uncoupled by differentiation and substitution resulting in second-order differential equations in ϕ and ψ:

$$\ddot{\phi} + 4\pi\lambda\dot{\phi} + 4\pi\gamma^2 \frac{\partial E}{\partial \phi} = 0 \tag{10.18}$$

and

$$\psi = - \frac{1}{\gamma 4\pi M} \ddot{\phi} \tag{10.19}[8]$$

where we have made use of the good approximations $4\pi M \gg 2K_1/M$ and $\lambda \ll |\gamma|M$.

---

[8] R. F. Soohoo, *Quart. Prog. Rept.*, Solid State Research, MIT Lincoln Laboratory, January, 1959, p. 15.

For small signals, we may retain only the first-order term in $\partial E/\partial \phi$ in Eq. (10.18) giving

$$\frac{1}{8\pi\gamma^2 K_1} \ddot{\phi} + \frac{\lambda}{2\gamma^2 K_1} \dot{\phi} + (h_s \pm 1)\phi = h_\perp(t) = he^{i\omega t} \tag{10.20}$$

where $\mathbf{h}_s$ is a static field and $\mathbf{h}_\perp(t)$ is a small rf magnetic field of magnitude h both normalized to the anisotropy field $H_k = 2K_1/M$. For $\alpha = 0$, $90°$, the solution of Eq. (10.20) gives

$$\phi = \frac{2h\gamma^2 K_1}{i\omega\lambda} \frac{1}{1 + i(\omega_o/4\pi\lambda)(\omega/\omega_o - \omega_o/\omega)} e^{i\omega t} \tag{10.21}$$

with

$$\omega_{o\pm} = |\gamma|\sqrt{4\pi M(H_s \pm H_k)} \tag{10.22}$$

where $\pm$ signs are associated with $\alpha = 0$ and $90°$, respectively. It is interesting to note that for $\alpha = 0$, that is, for the case with static field applied along the easy axis, the uniaxial anisotropy may be represented by an equivalent field $\mathbf{H}_k$ directed in the same direction as $\mathbf{H}_s$. On the other hand, if $\alpha = 90°$, $\mathbf{H}_k$ is directed in opposition to $\mathbf{H}_s$. Thus, whereas the resonance frequency ω_{o+} increases with increasing H_s with a minimum value of $|\gamma|\sqrt{4\pi M H_k}$ for $\alpha = 0$, ω_{o-} has a finite value only if $H_s > H_k$. As $H_s \to H_k$, the film becomes saturated in the $\mathbf{H}_s$ direction and $\omega_{o-} \to 0$. Thus, in principle, we can study the resonance behavior of thin films at extremely low frequencies perhaps making connection with quasistatic measurements.

If the static field H_s is not applied either parallel or perpendicular to the easy axis ($\alpha \neq 0$, $\pi/2$), then $\mathbf{M}$ and $\mathbf{H}_s$ will not be aligned for finite H_s. Thus, to look at the resonance condition in this general case, we must first determine the equilibrium value of ϕ, ϕ_{eq}, the angle that $\mathbf{M}$ makes with $\mathbf{H}_s$ (x axis) for a given α. This can be easily accomplished by requiring that $\partial E/\partial \phi = 0$ at $\phi = \phi_{eq}$. From Eq. (10.11), we find

$$K_1 \sin 2(\phi_{eq} - \alpha) + H_s M \sin \phi_{eq} = 0 \tag{10.23}$$

ϕ_{eq} is plotted in Fig. 10.3 vs h_s with α as the constant parameter.

To obtain the resonance equation, equivalent to Eq. (10.20), for the general case, we let $\phi = \phi_{eq} + \delta$ and assume δ small. Then, retaining only the first-order terms in δ we have from Eq. (10.11)

$$\frac{\partial E}{\partial \phi} = [2K_1 \cos 2(\alpha - \phi_{eq}) + H_s M \cos \phi_{eq} + H_\perp M \sin \phi_{eq}]\delta$$
$$- K_1 \sin 2(\alpha - \phi_{eq}) + H_s M \sin \phi_{eq} - H_\perp M \cos \phi_{eq} \tag{10.24}$$

Combining Eqs. (10.18) and (10.24), we obtain the desired second-order differential equation in δ as

$$\frac{1}{8\pi\gamma^2 K_1} \ddot{\delta} + \frac{\lambda}{2\gamma^2 K_1} \dot{\delta} + A\delta + B = 0 \tag{10.25}$$

where

$$A = \cos 2(\alpha - \phi_{eq}) + h_s \cos \phi_{eq} + h_\perp \sin \phi_{eq} \tag{10.26}$$

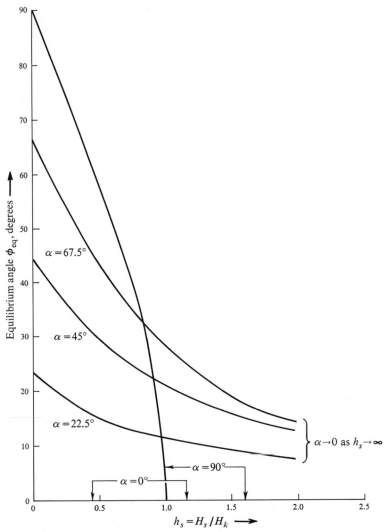

FIG. 10.3.   Equilibrium direction of the magnetization as a function of normalized x-directed static field with the easy-axis orientation relative to the x axis as a constant parameter.

$$B = h_s \sin \phi_{eq} - \tfrac{1}{2} \sin 2(\alpha - \phi_{eq}) - h_\perp \cos \phi_{eq} \qquad (10.27)$$

We see that if $h_\perp = 0$, Eqs. (10.25) and (10.27) yield expression (10.23) for ϕ_{eq} as it should. Furthermore, we note that the last term in Eq. (10.26) multiplied by δ is a second-order term in Eq. (10.25) as $h_\perp$ and δ are both small. Neglecting this term and using Eq. (10.23), Eqs. (10.26) and (10.27) become

$$A' = \cos 2(\alpha - \phi_{eq}) + h_s \cos \phi_{eq}$$
$$B' = -h_\perp \cos \phi_{eq} \qquad (10.28)$$

With this linear approximation, the solution of Eq. (10.25) is easily seen to be of the

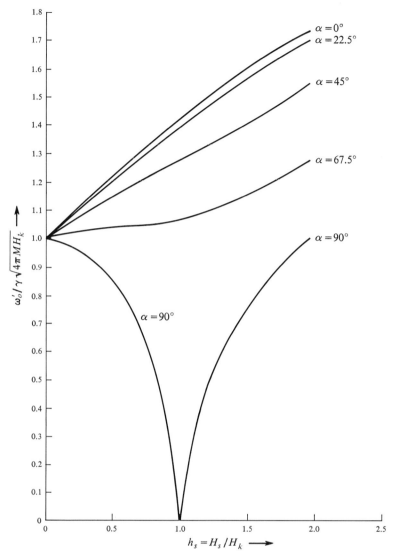

FIG. 10.4.   Normalized resonance frequency as a function of the static field applied in the film plane at various angles with respect to the easy axis.

form $\delta = \delta_m e^{i\omega t}$. Substituting this expression into Eq. (10.25), we easily find that

$$\phi = \phi_{eq} + \delta = \phi_{eq} + \frac{2h\cos\phi_{eq}\gamma^2 K_1}{i\omega\lambda} \frac{1}{1 + i(\omega_o'/4\pi\lambda)(\omega/\omega_o' - \omega_o'/\omega)} e^{i\omega t} \quad (10.29)$$

where the resonance frequency ω_o' is given by

$$\omega_o' = |\gamma|\sqrt{4\pi M[H_s\cos\phi_{eq} + H_k\cos 2(\alpha - \phi_{eq})]} \quad (10.30)$$

Of course Eq. (10.30) reduces to the special form Eq. (10.22), for the special cases $\alpha = 0, \pi/2$. A plot of ω_o vs h_s is given in Fig. 10.4 with H_k and α as constant parameters.

(b) Susceptibility of Film Magnetized in its Plane

For $\alpha = 0, \pi/2$ we have the expression for the susceptibility $x_\| = \phi(\omega, \omega_o)/h$ as

$$\chi_\| = \frac{-2\gamma^2 K_1}{\omega\lambda}\left[\frac{(\omega_o/4\pi\lambda)(\omega/\omega_o - \omega_o/\omega)}{1 + (\omega_o/4\pi\lambda)^2(\omega/\omega_o - \omega_o/\omega)^2} + i\frac{1}{1 + (\omega_o/4\pi\lambda)^2(\omega/\omega_o - \omega_o/\omega)^2}\right] \tag{10.31}$$

Eq. (10.31) exhibits the normal resonance behavior where the real part of $x_\|$ is zero and the imaginary part is maximum at resonance ($\omega = \omega_o$). When the two terms in the denominator are equal, $Im(x_\|) = \frac{1}{2}Im(x_\|)_{\omega=\omega_o}$ and we find the line width ΔH_s defined as the field difference between half imaginary susceptibility points at fixed ω as

$$\Delta H_s = \frac{2\lambda\omega}{\gamma^2 M} \tag{10.32}$$

For the general case where $\alpha = 0, \pi/2$, the rf susceptibility is obtained from Eq. (10.29) as

$$x_\| = \frac{-2\cos\phi_{eq}\gamma^2 K_1}{\omega\lambda}$$

$$\times\left[\frac{(\omega_o'/4\pi\lambda)(\omega/\omega_o' - \omega_o'/\omega)}{1 + (\omega_o'/4\pi\lambda)^2(\omega/\omega_o' - \omega_o'/\omega)^2} + i\frac{1}{1 + (\omega_o'/4\pi\lambda)^2(\omega/\omega_o' - \omega_o'/\omega)^2}\right] \tag{10.33}$$

In a similar fashion, we find the line width $\Delta H_s'$ as

$$\Delta H_s' = \frac{2\lambda\omega}{\gamma^2 M \cos\phi_{eq}} = \frac{\Delta H_s}{\cos\phi_{eq}} \tag{10.34}$$

where ΔH_s, defined by Eq. (10.32), is just the resonance line width for the special cases $\alpha = 0, \pi/2$. Since $\cos\phi_{eq} < 1$ for $\alpha \neq 0, \pi/2$, the line width for the general case is always larger than the saturated case.

(c) Resonance Perpendicular to the Plane of Film

If H_s is applied perpendicular to the plane of the film and $H_\perp$ parallel to the plane of the film, we have the situation depicted in Fig. 10.5. The free energy of the system is

$$E = K_1 \sin^2\theta' - H_s M \sin\theta\sin\phi - H_\perp M \cos\theta + \frac{1}{2}(4\pi M^2)\sin^2\theta\sin^2\phi \tag{10.35}$$

where $\theta' = \cos^{-1}(\cos\theta\cos\alpha - \sin\theta\cos\phi\sin\alpha)$ is the angle between M and the $E_k = 0$ axis. It follows from Eq. (10.15) and (10.35) that

$$\tau = -\hat{\phi}[2\pi M^2 \sin 2\theta \sin^2\phi - H_s M \sin\phi\cos\theta + H_\perp M \sin\theta$$
$$+ K_1 \sin 2\theta(\cos^2\alpha - \sin^2\alpha\cos^2\phi) + K_1 \sin 2\alpha\cos 2\theta\cos\phi]$$
$$- \hat{\theta}(-2\pi M^2 \sin 2\phi\sin\theta + H_s M \cos\phi$$
$$- K_1 \sin^2\alpha\sin\theta\sin 2\phi - K_1 \cos\theta\sin 2\alpha\sin\phi) \tag{10.36}$$

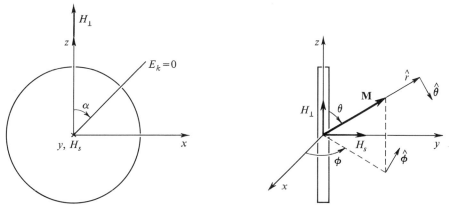

FIG. 10.5.   Magnetic film with static fields applied both parallel and perpendicular to its plane.

In the usual case where $2\pi M^2 \gg K_1$ and H_s does not approach zero, we see from Eq. (10.35) that the terms involving K_1 in Eq. (10.36) can be neglected, considerably simplifying it. Thus, at equilibrium, we easily find that

$$\phi_{eq} = \frac{\pi}{2}$$

$$\theta_{eq} = \sin^{-1}\left(\frac{H_s}{4\pi M}\right)$$

(10.37)

as expected. Letting $\phi = \pi/2 + \delta_\phi$ and $\theta = \theta_{eq} + \delta_\theta$ and neglecting higher-order terms, we easily find from Eq. (10.36) that

$$\boldsymbol{\tau} = -\hat{\phi}M[(4\pi M \cos 2\theta_{eq} + H_s \sin \theta_{eq} + H_\perp \cos \theta_{eq})\delta_\theta$$
$$+ 2\pi M \sin 2\theta_{eq} - H_s \cos \theta_{eq} + H_\perp \sin \theta_{eq}]$$
$$+ \hat{\theta}[H_s M \delta_\phi - 4\pi M^2 \delta_\phi (\sin \theta_{eq} + \delta_\theta \cos \theta_{eq})]$$

(10.38)

First, consider the special case $\theta_{eq} = \pi/2(H_s \geq 4\pi M)$. We find from Eq. (10.38) that

$$\boldsymbol{\tau} = \hat{\phi}M[(4\pi M - H_s)\delta_\theta - H_\perp] + \hat{\theta}M(H_s - 4\pi M)\delta_\phi$$

(10.39)

Eq. (10.39) yields a pair of simultaneous equations in δ_θ and δ_ϕ for small excursions of $\mathbf{M}$ about $\theta_{eq} = \phi_{eq} = \pi/2$:

$$\dot{m}_\phi = M\dot{\delta}_\phi = \gamma[(4\pi M^2 - H_s M)\delta_\theta - H_\perp M] - \lambda(H_s - 4\pi M)\delta_\phi$$
$$\dot{m}_\theta = M\dot{\delta}_\theta = \gamma(H_s M - 4\pi M^2) + \lambda[(4\pi M - H_s)\delta_\theta - H_\perp]$$

(10.40)

For the case in point, it is convenient to introduce the new circularly polarized variables $\delta^+ = \delta_\theta + i\delta_\phi = \delta_o^+ e^{i\omega t}$ and $H_\perp^+ = H_{\perp o}^+ e^{i\omega t}$. We can then easily obtain from Eq. (10.40) the differential equation in δ^+ as

$$\delta^+ = -(H_s - 4\pi M)(i\gamma + \lambda H_s)\delta^+ - \left(\frac{\lambda}{M} + i\gamma\right)H_\perp^+$$

(10.41)

The solution of Eq. (10.41) is

$$\delta_o^+ = \frac{-H_{\perp o}^+\left(\dfrac{\lambda}{M}\right) + i\gamma}{i\omega + (H_s - 4\pi M)(i\gamma + \lambda H_s)} \tag{10.42}$$

with the perpendicular susceptibility $\chi_\perp$ given by

$$\chi_\perp = \frac{M\delta_o^+}{H_{\perp o}^+} = -\frac{\lambda + i\gamma M}{\gamma H_s(H_s - 4\pi M) + i[\omega + \gamma(H_s - 4\pi M)]} \tag{10.43}$$

It follows from Eq. (10.43) that the resonance frequency $\omega_{o\perp}$ is given by

$$\omega_{o\perp} = |\gamma|(H_{s\perp} - 4\pi M) \tag{10.44}$$

For the general case where $\theta_{eq} \neq \phi_{eq} \neq \pi/2$, we must return to Eq. (10.38) and solve it in conjunction with Eq. (10.15).

10·3 MEASUREMENT OF THE MAGNETIZATION, GYROMAGNETIC RATIO, ANISOTROPY FIELD, AND LINE WIDTH

Eqs. (10.22), repeated here, and (10.44) involve three unknowns $|\gamma|$, $4\pi M$, and H_k,

$$(\omega_{o\parallel})_\pm = |\gamma|\sqrt{4\pi M(H_{s\parallel} \pm H_k)} \tag{10.22}$$

in three equations. Consequently, by measuring the resonance static fields $H_{s\perp}$ and $H_{s\parallel}$'s for a fixed value of ω, we may determine all three unknowns. Alternatively, measurements may be made at two different frequencies and use is made of Eq. (10.44) to determine $|\gamma|$ and M. Then Eq. (10.22) may be used to determine H_k. However, due to the limitation of available frequency bandwidth for a given resonance spectrometer, the latter method is not as accurate. The normal procedure is to determine the resonance fields for the perpendicular and parallel cases with a typical spectrum indicated by Fig. 10.6. It follows from Fig. 10.6 that we can determine the anisotropy field H_k by measuring the resonance field separation between the cases where $H_{s\parallel}$ is in the direction of and perpendicular to the easy axis. The dotted extra peaks are resonance peaks

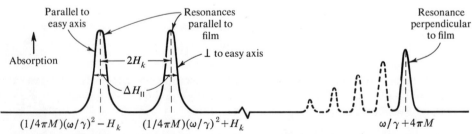

FIG. 10.6.   Absorption as a function of static field applied both parallel and perpendicular to the plane of a film.

excited due to spin pinning at the surfaces of the film as will be discussed in detail in Chap. 11. Likewise, $|\gamma|$ and M can be determined by substituting the measured values of $H_{s\perp}$ and $H_{s\parallel}$ into Eq. (10.44) and either one of equations in Eq. (10.22).

The line widths $\Delta H_{\parallel}$ and $\Delta H_{\perp}$ may be simply determined by measuring the field separation between the $\chi''_{max}/2$ points. However, in a line width measurement using a ferromagnetic resonance spectrometer, the absorption is directly proportional to χ'' only for certain experimental arrangements. To understand this, we must briefly review the elements of perturbation theory for a magnetic sample in a resonance cavity.

The ferromagnetic resonance absorption in a thin film may be detected by two different methods: (1) by putting a tightly coupled loop around the film and monitoring its induced voltage due to magnetization changes directly and (2) by indirectly measuring the perturbation effects upon the cavity due to the presence of the film. In the former case, the film properties are measured by a wide-band bridge in the vhf and uhf ranges.[9] In the latter case, one uses a microwave spectrometer. We shall discuss each of these methods below.

Fig. 10.7 is the schematic diagram of a wide band vhf-uhf bridge. In the original version developed by Smith and Weiss, the film is inserted in a rectangular coaxial line excited through a standard 50Ω coaxial ine. The film may be situated at the bottom of the cavity and surrounded by a pickup loop as shown. In order that the orientation of a film may be changed for the measurement of anisotropy, the film is attached to a demountable holder. To pick up the voltage induced by the changing rf magnetization along the x axis, the loop should have its axis along the x axis. Due to the high demagnetizing factor perpendicular to the plane of the film, the y component of the rf magnetization is negligibly small. The axial static magnetic field is supplied

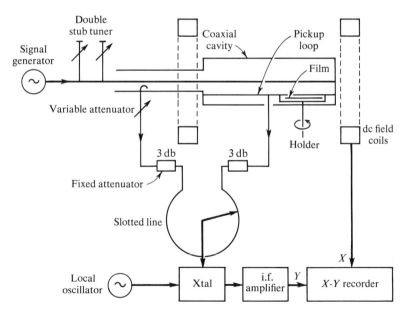

FIG. 10.7.   Schematic diagram of a wide band vhf-uhf bridge for thin-film resonance measurements (after G. P. Weiss and D. O. Smith, Ref. 10).

[9] D. O. Smith and G. P. Weiss, *J. Appl. Phys.*, **29**: 290 (1958).

by a pair of Helmholtz coils made of water-cooled copper tubing and can be varied by changing the coil current. The rectangular coax is a nonresonant cavity thus allowing wide-band operation from 50 Mc/sec to 2100 Mc/sec, while the rf field at the sample can be maximized by using a double-stub tuner. The voltage induced in a pickup loop off resonance (at a clamping field $\gg$ resonance field), can be cancelled by a bucking signal whose amplitude can be adjusted by series attenuators. Phase adjustment is obtained by using a slotted line with a probe in contact with center conductor. Bridge adjustment can be facilitated by adding mechanical reduction gears to the attenuator and phase controls. Detection is accomplished by means of a 32 Mc/sec band-pass crystal mixer, local oscillator and i.f. amplifier combination as shown to obtain minimum noise figure. Annealing of thin films can be accomplished with this vhf-uhf bridge by evacuating the film-containing chamber and heating the film with heating coils in its proximity.[10]

The induced voltage in the pickup loop V is given by

$$V = \dot{\phi} = i\omega A b_x \qquad\qquad (10.45)$$

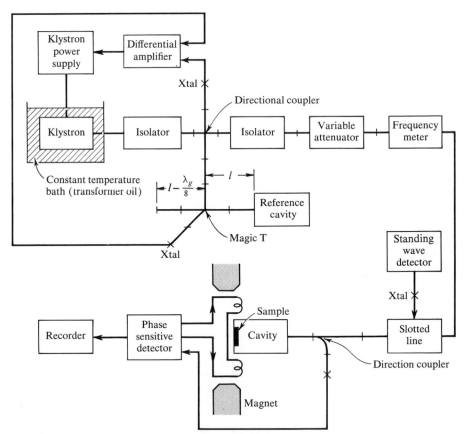

FIG. 10.8.   Schematic diagram of a microwave spectrometer for thin-film resonance measurements.

---

[10] G. P. Weiss and D. O. Smith, *J. Appl. Phys.*, **32**: 85S (1961).

where ω is the frequency, b_x the x component of the flux density, and A is the effective area of the film. Now, since $b_x = h_x + 4\pi m_x$ or $b_x/h_x = 1 + 4\pi\chi_x$ where χ_x is the x component of the susceptibility, the induced voltage V is proportional to $|\chi_x|$ since the air flux is cancelled by a bucking voltage. The frequency and field dependence of the susceptibility is given by Eq. (10.31). To measure ΔH, it would then be necessary only to measure the static field difference between the $(\chi_x)_{max}/\sqrt{2}$ points since what is obtained in this scheme is the amplitude of χ.

For ferromagnetic resonance studies at microwave frequencies (1,000 to 10,000 Mc/sec, say), one uses the microwave resonance spectrometer shown in Fig. 10.8. The film is usually placed at the back or side wall of a rectangular cavity where the electric field is zero while the magnetic field is maximum. The reflected energy from the cavity whose magnitude is dependent upon the static field which is applied to the film is monitored by a directional coupler as shown. As the static field is varied through the resonance value given by Eq. (10.22) or (10.44) for a given frequency and anisotropy field, the absorption of the film and of the cavity passes through a maximum. If the cavity is undercoupled, the reflected energy from the cavity increases with film absorption. Since the reflected energy from the cavity under certain conditions, as discussed below, is proportioned to the imaginary part of the diagonal component of the susceptibility tensor, the reflection vs static field curve has the same shape as the χ'' vs H_o curve that is being sought.

When a ferromagnetic sample, such as a thin film, is placed in a cavity, both the resonance frequency and the Q of the cavity are different from those of the empty cavity. As may be expected, to a first approximation, the change of the cavity resonance frequency is related to the real parts of the susceptibility tensor components (since the insertion of the sample causes a redistribution of the electromagnetic fields in the cavity), and the change in Q is related to the imaginary part of the tensor components (since the film increases the total loss of the cavity).

For the case of the empty cavity resonating at the frequency ω_o, Maxwell's equations are

$$\nabla \times \mathbf{E}_o = -\frac{1}{c} i\omega_o \mathbf{h}_o \qquad (10.46)$$

$$\nabla \times \mathbf{h}_o = \frac{1}{c} i\omega_o \mathbf{E}_o \qquad (10.47)$$

where $\mathbf{E}_o$ and $\mathbf{h}_o$, having the time dependence $e^{i\omega_o t}$, represent empty cavity fields. If the cavity contains a thin film located in a small volume Δv, the cavity will then resonate at a new frequency ω. Then, Maxwell's equations for the sample containing cavity becomes

$$\nabla \times \mathbf{E} = -\frac{1}{c} i\omega \mathbf{h} - \frac{4\pi}{c} \mathbf{J}_m \qquad (10.48)$$

$$\nabla \times \mathbf{h} = \frac{1}{c} i\omega \mathbf{E} + \frac{4\pi}{c} \mathbf{J}_e \qquad (10.49)$$

where the magnetic current $\mathbf{J}_m$ and electric current $\mathbf{J}_e$ are nonzero only at the film.

After some mathematical manipulation involving Eqs. (10.46) to (10.49) and applying the appropriate boundary conditions of the cavity, we find[11]

$$\omega - \omega_o = \frac{4\pi i \int_{\Delta v} (\mathbf{J}_e \cdot \mathbf{E}_o^* + \mathbf{J}_m \cdot \mathbf{h}_o^*)\, d\tau}{\int_v (\mathbf{E}_o^* \mathbf{E} + \mathbf{h}_o^* \cdot \mathbf{h})\, d\tau} \qquad (10.50)$$

Eq. (10.50) is simply a generalization of the well-known Bethe–Schwinger perturbation result for isotropic medium to the case of an anisotropic medium.[12] For a sample sufficiently small compared to the cavity dimensions, the fields in the cavity outside the film (except perhaps in the immediate vicinity of the sample) are not greatly perturbed. Thus, to a first approximation, we can assume that $\mathbf{E} = \mathbf{E}_o$ and $\mathbf{h} = \mathbf{h}_o$ in the denominator of Eq. (10.50), and the volume v can be considered to be the entire volume of the cavity.

A suitable nondegenerate cavity can be constructed from a closed-off section of a rectangular waveguide resonating in the TE_{10n} mode. The sample is usually placed at the center of the end plate where the electric field is zero. The static magnetic field is applied perpendicular to the rf magnetic field which is parallel to the wide dimension of the waveguide at the end wall. Note that $\mathbf{J}_m = 4\pi i \overset{\leftrightarrow}{\mathbf{X}} \cdot \mathbf{h}/c$ where $\overset{\leftrightarrow}{\mathbf{X}}$ is the Polder susceptibility tensor given by [13]

$$\overset{\leftrightarrow}{\mathbf{X}} = \begin{vmatrix} x & -i\kappa & 0 \\ i\kappa & x & 0 \\ 0 & 0 & 0 \end{vmatrix} \qquad (10.51)$$

with

$$x = \frac{(-\gamma H_o + i\omega\alpha)(-\gamma 4\pi M_o)}{(-\gamma H_o + i\omega\alpha)^2 - \omega^2}$$

$$\kappa = \frac{\gamma 4\pi M_o \omega}{(-\gamma H_o + i\omega\alpha)^2 - \omega^2} \qquad (10.52)$$

where $4\pi M_o$ is the saturation magnetization and α is the damping parameter related to λ of Eq. (10.10) by $\lambda = -\alpha\gamma M_o$. $\overset{\leftrightarrow}{\mathbf{X}}$ of Eq. (10.51) was derived in terms of internal fields, i.e., without explicitly taken demagnetization effects into account. However, in a problem of this kind, the field distribution inside the sample is usually not known so that difficulties may be encountered in the application of the perturbation result, Eq. (10.50). However, since $\mathbf{J}_m = 4\pi i \overset{\leftrightarrow}{\mathbf{X}} \cdot \mathbf{h}/c$ and $\mathbf{m} = \overset{\leftrightarrow}{\mathbf{X}} \cdot \mathbf{h} = \overset{\leftrightarrow}{\mathbf{X}}_{ext} \cdot \mathbf{h}_{ext}$ where $\overset{\leftrightarrow}{\mathbf{X}}_{ext}$ is defined in terms of external fields, we can apply the perturbation result, Eq. (10.50), to our problem in terms of external field. By the external fields, we mean the field at the film location in the absence of the sample; thus $\mathbf{h}_{ext}$ is simply equal to $\mathbf{h}_o$ at the end wall of the cavity.

---

[11] J. O. Artman and P. E. Tannenwald, *J. Appl. Phys.*, 26: 1124 (1955); R. F. Soohoo, *Theory and Application of Ferrites*, Prentice-Hall, Inc., Englewood Cliffs, N.J., 1960, p. 260.

[12] H. A. Bethe and J. Schwinger, *Perturbation Theory for Cavities*, Nat. Defense Res. Committee Contractors Rept. D1–117, Cornell Univ., March 4, 1943.

[13] D. Polder, *Phil. Mag.*, 40: 99 (1949).

Carrying out the calculation indicated above for the rectangular cavity with a thin film using Eq. (10.50), we find for the case where the film fills the entire back wall of the cavity

$$4\pi x'_{ext} = -\left(\frac{\Delta\omega}{\omega_o}\right)\left(\frac{d}{\delta}\right)\left[1 + \left(\frac{d}{na}\right)^2\right]$$
(10.53)

$$4\pi x''_{ext} = \Delta\left(\frac{1}{2Q_u}\right)\left(\frac{d}{\delta}\right)\left[1 + \left(\frac{d}{na}\right)^2\right]$$
(10.54)

where $x_{ext} = x'_{ext} - ix''_{ext}$ and $\Delta\omega = \omega - \omega_o$. δ is the thickness of the film while a and d are the width and length of the cavity as shown in Fig. 10.8. Q_u is the unloaded Q of the cavity.

Instead of using the perturbation approach outlined above, we may alternatively solve the exact boundary problem of a thin film at the back wall of the cavity.[14] In this way, it has been found that if the ratio of the film thickness δ to the skin depth of the film is sufficiently small (<0.4), the results obtained in this way are exactly the same as those given by Eqs. (10.53) and (10.54), providing that we recognized the fact that $4\pi x_{ext} = (\mu^2 - \kappa^2)/\mu$ where $\mu = 1 + x$. This equivalence results because μ and κ, unlike x_{ext} associated with perturbation theory, are based upon internal fields; in the solution of the boundary vale problem, no explicit account of the rf demagnetization factors are necessary.

If the film does not completely fill the entire back wall of the cavity, the boundary problem becomes quite complicated and it would only be realistic to use the perturbation formula, Eq. (10.50). In this way, we easily find that for the case where the film is centrally located, the right-hand sides of Eqs. (10.53) and (10.54) should be multiplied by the additional factor

$$\frac{b}{b'}\left(1 + \frac{2a}{a'}\frac{\sin \pi a'/a}{2\pi}\right)^{-1}$$
(10.55)

where b' and a' are, respectively, the height and width of the film.

We now like to look into the actual measuring problem in somewhat more detail. Consider the equivalent circuit of a cavity fed by a transmission line of characteristic impedance Z_o through a $1:n$ transformer as shown in Fig. 10.9; the value of n is

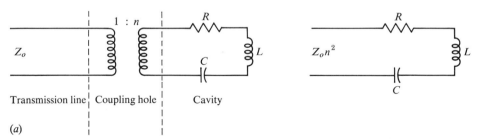

(a)

FIG. 10.9.   Equivalent circuit of a cavity coupled to a transmission line or waveguide. The coupling hole is represented by a $1:n$ ideal transformer in (a) while $Z_o n^2$ in (b) represents the transformed impedance of the waveguide.

[14] R. F. Soohoo, *J. Appl. Phys.*, **31**: 218S (1960).

dependent upon the geometry of the cavity coupling hole. Accordingly, we could define three separate cavity Q's as $Q_u = \omega_o L/R$, $Q_e = \omega_o L/Z_o n^2$, and $Q_L = \omega_o L/(R + n^2 Z_o)$ where Q_u, Q_e, and Q_L are the unloaded, external, and loaded Q of the cavity and where we have neglected the series line loss. Note that $1/Q_L = 1/Q_e + Q_u$. If the cavity is undercoupled, $Q_u < Q_e$ and $R > Z_o n^2$ so that at cavity resonance, the $VSWR$ is simply equal to $R/Z_o n^2$. Thus, it follows that

$$\Delta\left(\frac{1}{Q_u}\right) = \frac{1}{Q_e} \Delta(VSWR) \tag{10.56}$$

Since the value of Q_e depends upon the manner of coupling into the cavity, it is in general a constant during a particular experiment so that $\Delta(1/Q_u) = \Delta(1/Q_L)$. We find from Eqs. (10.53), (10.54), and (10.55) that

$$4\pi\chi''_{\text{ext}} = C_1 \Delta(VSWR) \tag{10.57}$$

where the proportionality constant C_1 is given by:

$$C_1 = 2Q_e\left(\frac{d}{\delta}\right)\left[1 + \left(\frac{d}{an}\right)^2\right] \tag{10.58}$$

For the general case where the film does not completely fill the back wall of the cavity, the right hand side of C_1 should be multiplied by the factor (10.55). According to Eq. (10.57), $\chi''_{\text{ext}} \alpha \Delta(VSWR)$. But $VSWR$ is in turn related to the reflection coefficient ρ by the relation

$$VSWR = \frac{1 + |\rho|}{1 - |\rho|} \tag{10.59}$$

For small $|\rho|$, we see from Eq. (10.59) that $\Delta(VSWR)\alpha\Delta|\rho|$, where $\Delta|\rho| = |\rho| - |\rho_o|$ and ρ and ρ_o are the reflection coefficients with and without the sample. For maximum sensitivity ρ_o should be zero, i.e., the cavity should be perfectly matched to the waveguide when the film is biased off resonance by a large clamping field. However, if $\rho_o = 0$, the reflected power may be very sensitive to mechanical vibrations of the spectrometer; as a compromise between sensitivity and stability, the $VSWR$ of the empty cavity is usually made equal to about 2 by finding an appropriate size of the coupling hole. For thin films, because of their small volume, $|\rho|$ is sufficiently small so that the χ_{ext} vs H_o curve may be simulated by the $\Delta|\rho|$ vs H_o curve. The line width ΔH would then simply be the separation between 1/2 power points of the $\Delta|\rho|$ vs H_o curve. However, if $|\rho|$ is not sufficiently small, $\Delta(VSWR)$ would not be proportional to $\Delta|\rho|$; then the line width would no longer correspond to the separation between 1/2 power points of the $\Delta|\rho|$ vs H_o curve and ΔH must be measured by a more elaborate method.[15]

If dc detection is used, then the reflected power due to a finite $|\rho_o|$ may be balanced out simply by a dc voltage. This method of detection is usually sufficiently sensitive for films whose thickness is more than a few hundred angstroms. However, for thinner films or for the case of selective radiation of a small portion of a film as used in the microwave magnetic microscope to be discussed in the next section, a synchronous

---

[15] R. F. Soohoo, *op. cit.*, p. 95.

or phase-sensitive detection scheme[16] should be used. In this method, the static field H_o is modulated by a small amplitude ac field with a frequency f ranging up to 150 kc/sec. Therefore, the reflected signal will contain an f component which can be detected by amplification. Using this method, the derivative of the absorption or the dispersion curve rather than the absorption curve itself is obtained since the amplitude of the ac reflected signal is proportional to the slope of the $\Delta|\rho|$ vs H_o curve. The advantage of this method lies in the fact that since the output of the synchronous detector is sensitive to the phase of the signal, the effective bandwidth of the device is extremely small with an accompanying reduction in noise. This is accomplished by feeding the detector with both the desired signal and a synchronizing signal from the source; these signals are usually connected to the grids of a twin-triode amplifier. If the time constant of the R–C grid coupling circuit is sufficiently long compared to the periods of the undesired signals, essentially only signals of frequency f would emerge from the detector.

To stabilize the microwave frequency, isolators are used in the measuring system as shown in Fig. 10.8. In addition, a microwave discriminator is also inserted to obtain high-frequency stability (~ 1 part in 10^6 long term and 1 part in 10^8 short term). Such a discriminator is simply a microwave analogue of the ordinary radio frequency discriminator.[17] The output from the two arms of the discriminator are equal when the Klystron output frequency is equal to the resonance frequency of the reference cavity. If these signals were applied to the inputs of a differential amplifier, there would be no output from the amplifier. However, if the frequency deviates from the desired value, the outputs from the discriminator arms will not be equal and the differential amplifier will have an amplified output proportional to their difference. If this signal is in turn applied to the reflector plate of the Klystron, the Klystron frequency will be changed until the signal frequency is equal to the reference value. (However, since the dc component of the amplifier output is positive with respect to ground while the reflector voltage is negative with respect to ground, a large bucking voltage of several hundred volts is also required.) Oscillations of the feedback loop should be avoided and typically a gain of some 30 db is required for the differential amplifier.

10·4 MEASUREMENT OF IMPERFECTION DISTRIBUTION (MICROWAVE MAGNETIC MICROSCOPE)

In order to determine the imperfection distribution in a thin film, some means must be provided to measure the local properties of the film. The microwave magnetic microscope[18] is a probe that is capable of measuring the spatial variations of the magnetic properties directly. The principles of operation of the microscope may be briefly described as follows. If the magnetic sample is placed against the outer face of the back wall of a cavity which has a small centered hole, only that portion of the material directly opposite the opening is exposed to the microwave radiation from the cavity. If the static magnetic field applied to the sample is varied, the resonance spectrum of the radiated portion may be ascertained. The magnetic properties of other portions of

---

[16] B. Chance *et al.*, *Waveforms*, MIT Rad. Lab. Ser. No. 19, McGraw-Hill Book Company, Inc., New York, 1949, p. 515.

[17] F. E. Terman, *Radio and Electronic Engineering*, McGraw-Hill Book Company, Inc., New York, 1955, p. 696.

[18] R. F. Soohoo, "A Microwave Magnetic Microscope," *J. Appl. Phys. Suppl.*, **33**: 1276 (1962).

the material may likewise be obtained by shifting these portions against the cavity hole successively. In this way, the spatial variation of the magnetic properties of the entire sample may be determined.

Since the radiation emanates from a coupling hole that is quite small compared to the wavelength, there will be a diffraction of the microwaves. This implies that the field at the sample, aside from being nonuniform, will also be not completely confined to the vicinity of the hole. However, experiments to date, using a hole as small as 0.001 in., indicate that the uniformity and confinement problem is not severe enough to limit the use of the microscope.

CHAPTER 11

SPIN-WAVE RESONANCE

In the last chapter, we discussed the subject of ferromagnetic resonance involving the uniform precessional mode. In this chapter, we shall generalize the discussion of ferromagnetic resonance to include cases where the magnetization has a spatial dependence. We shall begin our study by examining the theory of spin waves quantum-mechanically, semiclassically and classically. Then, we shall proceed to calculate the spin-wave absorption spectra by assuming various film surface conditions and compare the theoretical results with experiment. In this connection, we shall formulate the general exchange boundary condition, including the effect of a surface anisotropy energy. The physical origin of this anisotropy will be discussed at some length in order to clarify several aspects of thin-film behavior, e.g., the problems of surface spin pinning and thin-film magnetization. The experimental determination of the surface anisotropy energy density and exchange constant will also be considered.

11·1 THEORY OF SPIN WAVES

If a ferromagnetic ellipsoid is placed in a uniform rf and static magnetic field at 0°K and if boundary effects are neglected, uniform precession may be excited whereby the directions of the spins throughout the sample volume do not change from point to point. However, at finite temperatures, or if the physical dimensions of the samples are such that boundary effects can not be neglected, as is the case with thin films, the spin direction may vary from point to point. Macroscopically, we may expand the magnetization in the form of a Fourier series of plane waves with each spatial harmonic identified as a "spin wave." Before we consider in detail the subject of spin waves quantum-mechanically in terms of creation and destruction operators, it seems desirable to discuss their physical significance in classical and semiclassical terms.

(a) Classical Theory

Classically, if the magnetization varies from point to point continuously and with continuous first derivatives, we may expand the magnetization $\mathbf{m}(\mathbf{r}, t)$, for monochromatic radiation at frequency ω, as

$$\mathbf{m}(\mathbf{r}, t) = \sum_{\mathbf{k}} \mathbf{m}_k e^{i(\omega t - \mathbf{k} \cdot \mathbf{r})} \tag{11.1}$$

where **k** is the wave vector of wave number k and the summation is over all possible modes of oscillation. If Eq. (11.1) is solved in conjunction with the equation of motion of the magnetization and Maxwell's equations with appropriate electromagnetic and exchange boundary conditions, we can, in principle at least, evaluate the unknown coefficients $\mathbf{m}_k$ for any experimental situation and sample configuration. In practice, however, it is usually impractical to do so. Fortunately, for the case of thin films, the geometry of the specimen is such that manageable mathematical calculations may be carried out to obtain the desired solution.

Since the exchange energy E_{ex} of an assembly of spins S is given by[1]

$$E_{ex} = -2 \sum_{i,j}' J_{ij} \mathbf{S}_i \cdot \mathbf{S}_j \tag{11.2}$$

where S is in units of $\hbar = h/2\pi$ and h is Planck's constant. [A constant term which is of no consequence in the subsequent discussion is omitted in Eq. (11.2).] The ground state for ferromagnetism (exchange integral J_{ij} positive) is one in which all spins are parallel. If the direction of the spins were to vary from point to point, the value of the exchange energy would be increased to that above its maximum negative value. As may be expected, this excess energy may be represented equivalently by an exchange field given by the expression [see Eqs. (11.21) to (11.25) for derivation]

$$\mathbf{H}_{ex} = \frac{2A}{|\mathbf{M}|^2} \nabla^2 \mathbf{M} \tag{11.3}$$

where $A = 2JS^2/a$ is the exchange constant and a is the lattice constant. Combining Eqs. (11.1) and (11.3), we find

$$\mathbf{H}_{ex} = \frac{2A}{|\mathbf{M}|^2} \sum_{\mathbf{k}} k^2 \mathbf{m}_k e^{i(\omega t - \mathbf{k} \cdot \mathbf{r})} \tag{11.4}$$

Thus, the equation of motion of the magnetization should be augmented by the term given by Eq. (11.3) or (11.4) when the spatial variation of the magnetization is of consequence to become

$$\mathbf{M} = \gamma \mathbf{M} \times \left(\mathbf{H} + \frac{\alpha}{|\mathbf{M}|} \dot{\mathbf{M}} + \frac{2A}{|\mathbf{M}|^2} \nabla^2 \mathbf{M} \right) \tag{11.5}$$

Eq. (11.5) must be solved in conjunction with Maxwell's equations:[2]

$$\nabla \times \mathbf{h} = \frac{\varepsilon}{c} \frac{\partial \mathbf{e}}{\partial t} + \frac{4\pi\sigma}{c} \mathbf{e} \tag{11.6}$$

$$\nabla \times \mathbf{e} = -\frac{1}{c} \frac{\partial \mathbf{h}}{\partial t} - \frac{4\pi}{c} \frac{\partial \mathbf{m}}{\partial t} \tag{11.7}$$

where ε and σ are, respectively, the dielectric constant and the conductivity of the medium. Of course, **e** and **h** are the electric and magnetic fields. Taking the curl

---

[1] See, e.g., J. H. Van Vleck, *Rev. Mod. Phys.*, **17**: 27 (1945).
[2] R. F. Soohoo, *Phys. Rev.*, **120**: 1978 (1960).

of Eq. (11.6) and solving the resulting equation for $\nabla \mathbf{x} \mathbf{e}$ for substitution into Eq. (11.7), we obtain the expression

$$\nabla^2 \mathbf{h} - \frac{1}{c^2}\left(\varepsilon\frac{\partial}{\partial t} + 4\pi\sigma\right)\frac{\partial \mathbf{h}}{\partial t} = \frac{4\pi}{c^2}\left(\varepsilon\frac{\partial}{\partial t} + 4\pi\sigma\right)\frac{\partial \mathbf{m}}{\partial t} - 4\pi\nabla(\nabla\cdot\mathbf{m}) \qquad (11.8)$$

where we have made use of the constitutive Maxwell's equation $\nabla\cdot\mathbf{b} = \nabla\cdot(\mathbf{h} + 4\pi\mathbf{m}) = 0$. Note that if $\mathbf{m} = 0$, Eq. (11.8) reduces to the well-known wave equation for a dielectric medium with dielectric constant ε and conductivity σ. Assuming that

$$\mathbf{h} = \sum_k \mathbf{h}_k e^{i(\omega t - \mathbf{k}\cdot\mathbf{r})} \qquad (11.9)$$

$$\mathbf{m} = \sum_k \mathbf{m}_k e^{i(\omega t - \mathbf{k}\cdot\mathbf{r})} \qquad (11.1)$$

we find upon substituting Eqs. (11.9) and (11.1) into Eq. (11.8) the relationship between $\mathbf{h}_k$ and $\mathbf{m}_k$ as

$$\mathbf{h}_k = \frac{4\pi(\omega^2\varepsilon_e/c^2)\mathbf{m}_k - 4\pi\mathbf{k}(\mathbf{k}\cdot\mathbf{m})}{k^2 - \omega^2\varepsilon_e/c^2} \qquad (11.10)$$

where $\varepsilon_e = \varepsilon(1 + 4\pi\sigma/i\omega\varepsilon)$ is the equivalent dielectric constant of the material with finite conductivity. We note from Eq. (11.10) that if $k^2\cos\phi \gg \omega^2\varepsilon_e/c^2$ where ϕ is the angle between $\mathbf{m}$ and $\mathbf{k}$, then Eq. (11.10) reduces to

$$\mathbf{h}_k \simeq -4\pi\mathbf{k}\frac{\mathbf{k}\cdot\mathbf{m}}{k^2} \qquad (11.11)$$

This is the often used expression for $\mathbf{h}_k$ in the so-called static approximation. It is worth noting, however, that if $\mathbf{k}\cdot\mathbf{m} = 0$, then $\mathbf{h}_k$ is properly given by $(4\pi\omega^2\varepsilon_e/k^2c^2)\mathbf{m}_k$ in the static approximation. Furthermore, for a conductor, it is seldom true that $k^2\cos\phi \gg \omega^2\varepsilon_e/c^2$, so that the exact expression for $\mathbf{h}_k$ given by Eq. (11.10) must be used for the case of conducting materials such as Permalloy films.

Returning now to Eq. (11.10), we find that for the uniform precession ($k = 0$) to exist,

$$\mathbf{h}_o = -4\pi\mathbf{m}_o \qquad (11.12)$$

Under this condition, the flux density $\mathbf{b}_o = \mathbf{h}_o + 4\pi\mathbf{m}_o$ inside the medium is zero because $\mathbf{h}_o$ and $4\pi\mathbf{m}_o$ are equal in magnitude but oppositely directed. Strictly speaking, this experimental situation can never occur and thus the uniform mode of precession so commonly referred to cannot truly exist.[2]

Combining Eqs. (11.5) and (11.10), we obtain two linear algebraic equations in the x and y components of $\mathbf{m}$:

$$(i\omega + C_d\gamma M_o k_x k_y)m_x + (C_d\gamma M_o k_y^2 - C_e\gamma M_o - \gamma H_o + i\alpha\omega)m_y = 0$$
$$- (C_d\gamma M_o k_x^2 - C_e\gamma M_o - \gamma H_o + i\alpha\omega)m_x + (i\omega - C_d\gamma M_o k_x k_y)m_y = 0 \qquad (11.13)$$

where
$$C_d = \frac{i2\pi\delta'^2}{1 - i\frac{1}{2}\delta'^2 k^2} \tag{11.14}$$

$$C_e = \frac{4\pi}{1 - i\frac{1}{2}\delta'^2 k^2} + \frac{2A}{M_o^2} k^2 \tag{11.15}$$

In the derivation of Eq. (11.13), we have used in addition to the terms in expressions (11.9) and (11.1) for h_k and m_k the additional static components $\hat{z}H_o$ and $\hat{z}M_o$ respectively. $\delta'^2 = -i2c^2/\omega^2\varepsilon_e$ is a generalized skin depth of the medium. Setting the determinant of Eq. (11.13) equal to zero, we obtain the secular equation biquadratic in k^2:

$$(K^2)^4 + A(K^2)^3 + B(K^2)^2 + CK^2 + D = 0 \tag{11.16}$$

where
$$\begin{aligned}
A &= 2\eta' + \sin^2\theta_k + i4\xi^2 \\
B &= \eta'(\eta' + \sin^2\theta_k) - \Omega^2 + i4\xi^2(2\eta' + 1 + \tfrac{1}{2}\sin^2\theta_k) - 4\xi^4 \\
C &= i4\xi^2[\eta'(1 + \tfrac{1}{2}\sin^2\theta_k) + \tfrac{1}{2}\sin^2\theta_k - \Omega^2 + \eta'^2] - 8\xi^2(\eta' + 1) \\
D &= 4\xi^4[\Omega^2 - (\eta' + 1)^2]
\end{aligned} \tag{11.17}$$

where θ_k is the angle between the wave vector $\mathbf{k}$ and $\hat{z}$, the direction of the static field $\mathbf{H}_o$, and K, η', ζ^2 and Ω are dimensionless parameters given by

$$\begin{aligned}
K &= k\xi\delta' \\
\eta' &= (H_o/4\pi M_o) - i\alpha\Omega \\
\xi^2 &= A/2\pi M_o^2\delta'^2 \\
\Omega &= \omega/\gamma 4\pi M_o
\end{aligned} \tag{11.18}$$

In the static approximation, as mentioned previously, the expression $-4\pi\mathbf{k}(\mathbf{k}\cdot\mathbf{m})/k^2$ instead of that given by Eq. (11.10) is used for $\mathbf{h}_k$. Correspondingly, $C_d \to -4\pi/k^2$ and $C_e \to 2Ak^2/M_o^2$. Within the framework of these approximations, Eq. (11.16) reduces to the Herring-Kittel formula[3] which is quadratic in k^2. Thus, the other two pairs of possible solutions have been implicitly discarded in such an approximate calculation. Again, for conducting thin films, we must use the more exact Eq. (11.16), as the static approximation would not be applicable.

If $\theta_k \neq 0$, the solution of Eq. (11.16) is quite complicated. We should like to first investigate two special cases, that is $\theta_k = 0$ and $\theta_k = \pi/2$. First consider the solution of Eq. (11.16) when $\theta_k = 0$. In this case, it can be factored into two terms, each quadratic in K^2 having the solutions

$$\begin{aligned}
K_{1,2}^2 &= \tfrac{1}{2}\{\Omega - \eta' - i2\xi^2 \pm [(\Omega - \eta' - i2\xi^2)^2 + i8\xi^2(\Omega - \eta' - 1)]^{1/2}\} \\
K_{3,4}^2 &= \tfrac{1}{2}\{-(\Omega + \eta' + i2\xi^2) \pm [(\Omega + \eta' + i2\xi^2)^2 - i8\xi^2(\Omega + \eta' + 1)]^{1/2}\}
\end{aligned} \tag{11.19}$$

[3] C. Herring and C. Kittel, *Phys. Rev.*, **81**: 869 (1951).

In the special case where $\theta_k = \pi/2$, Eq. (11.16) becomes

$$(K^2 + 2i\xi^2)\{K^6 + (2\eta' + 1 + i2\xi^2)K^4$$
$$+ [\eta'(\eta' + 1) - \Omega^2 + i4\xi^2(\eta' + 1)]K^2$$
$$- i2\xi^2[\Omega^2 - (\eta' + 1)^2]\} = 0 \qquad (11.20)$$

We see from Eq. (11.20) that one of the solutions for K^2 is $-i2\zeta^2$.

In Figs. 11.1 and 11.2, we have plotted the real and imaginary components of the magnitude of $K(= K' - iK'')$, that is, K' and K'' as a function of frequency for an insulator whose $\varepsilon = 12$ and $\alpha = 0.05$ and for a conductor whose resistivity $1/\sigma = 21 \times 10^{-6}$ ohm-cm and $\alpha = 0$ for the case of $\theta_k = 40°$. The exchange constant was assumed to be equal to 10^{-6} erg/cm for both cases. For simplicity, we have assumed

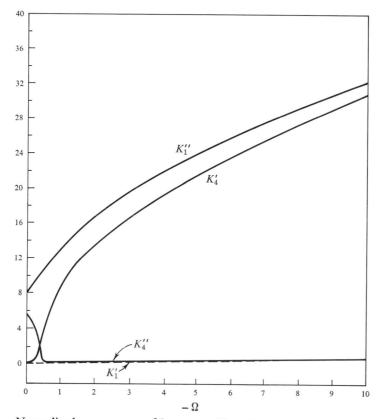

FIG. 11.1. Normalized components of k vs normalized frequency for an insulator ($\sigma = 0$) whose $\varepsilon = 12$, $\alpha = 0.05$, and $A = 10^{-6}$ erg/cm with $\theta_k = 40°$ and $\eta = 0.3$ (after R. F. Soohoo, Ref. 2).

that α for the insulator case to be a constant independent of frequency. We have shown here only plus K's and associated K''s. The positive K's correspond to waves traveling in the positive $\mathbf{r}$ direction. Thus, there are a total of eight waves, four each traveling in opposite directions.

For the problem of spin-wave resonance in thin films, θ_k is usually zero, that is, **k** is the direction of the static field $\mathbf{H}_o$ applied perpendicular to the film. Thus, the explicit solutions for K given by Eq. (11.19) can be used directly in the boundary

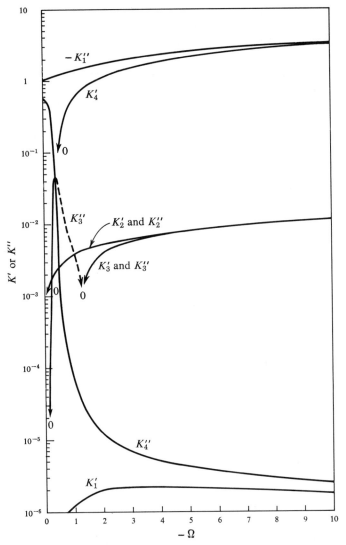

FIG. 11.2. Normalized components of **k** vs normalized frequency for a conductor whose $1/\sigma = 21 \times 10^{-6}$ ohm/cm, $\alpha = 0$, and $A = 10^{-6}$ erg/cm with $\theta_k = 40°$ and $\eta = 0.3$ (after R. F. Soohoo, Ref. 2).

value problem. In order to solve the problem of spin-wave resonance in thin films in the presence of microwave radiation, however, we need to know the exchange boundary condition for the magnetization as well as the ordinary electromagnetic boundary conditions. We shall defer this detailed calculation until we have examined the semiclassical and quantum-mechanical theories of spin waves.

(b) Semiclassical Theory[4]

The Hamiltonian corresponding to the exchange energy given by Eq. (11.2) is

$$H_{ex} = -2J \sum_{i,j}' \mathbf{S}_i \cdot \mathbf{S}_j \qquad (11.21)$$

where $\mathbf{S}_i$ is the spin operator in units of $\hbar$ for the ith atom. Here, we assume that each atom has $2S_o$ resultant electron spins. The quantum-mechanical equation of motion for the spin $\mathbf{S}_m$ is

$$i\hbar\dot{\mathbf{S}}_m = [\mathbf{S}_m, H'] = 2J[(\sum \mathbf{S}_i \cdot \mathbf{S}_j)\mathbf{S}_m - \mathbf{S}_m(\sum \mathbf{S}_i \cdot \mathbf{S}_j)]$$

$$= 2J \sum_j [(\mathbf{S}_m \cdot \mathbf{S}_j)\mathbf{S}_m - \mathbf{S}_m(\mathbf{S}_m \cdot \mathbf{S}_j)]$$

$$= -2J \sum_j \mathbf{S}_j \times [\mathbf{S}_m \times \mathbf{S}_m] \qquad (11.22)$$

Upon using the commutation relation $\mathbf{S} \times \mathbf{S} = i\mathbf{S}$, Eq. (11.22) becomes

$$\hbar\dot{\mathbf{S}}_m = 2J\mathbf{S}_m \times \sum_j \mathbf{S}_j \qquad (11.23)$$

In any macroscopic sample, the number of spins N is very, very large so that the corresponding number of allowable spin orientations $2NS + 1$ is also extremely large. It is then not unreasonable to treat the $\mathbf{S}$'s as classical vectors whose directions are not per se quantized. Thus, for a cubic lattice with lattice constant a, we obtain by series expansion, treating S_m as the center

$$\sum_j \mathbf{S}_j = 6\mathbf{S}_m + a^2\nabla^2\mathbf{S}_m + \cdots \qquad (11.24)$$

For small deviation of the spin system from the completely aligned state, we may neglect higher orders in the series expansion and obtain from Eqs. (11.23) and (11.24) the final expression

$$\hbar\dot{\mathbf{S}} = 2Ja^2(\mathbf{S} \times \nabla^2\mathbf{S}) \qquad (11.25)$$

Strictly speaking, Eq. (11.25) should really be a difference rather than a differential equation because the spin locations are discrete. However, in the continuum limit, this distinction is unimportant.

Now, let

$$\mathbf{S} = \mathbf{S}_o + \boldsymbol{\varepsilon} \qquad (11.26)$$

where $\mathbf{S}_o$ is the unperturbed spin vector, and $\boldsymbol{\varepsilon}$ represents a spin wave of small amplitude. The solution of Eq. (11.25) should be of the form

$$\varepsilon_x = \varepsilon_o \sin \omega t \sin k_x x \sin k_y y \sin k_z z$$
$$\varepsilon_y = \varepsilon_o \cos \omega t \sin k_x x \sin k_y y \sin k_z z \qquad (11.27)$$

---

[4] C. Kittel, *Introduction to Solid-State Physics*, John Wiley & Sons, Inc., New York, 1953, p. 360.

Substituting Eq. (11.27) into Eq. (11.25), we find the expression for the frequency of the spin wave as a function of its wave number to be

$$\hbar\omega = 2S_o Ja^2 k^2 \tag{11.28}$$

In contrast to the cases of some lattice vibrations and electromagnetic waves whose ω is proportional to k, Eq. (11.28) shows that $\omega \propto k^2$ for spin waves.

The energy of a spin wave E_{sw} is given by

$$E_{sw} = -Ja^2 \sum_m \mathbf{S}_m \cdot \nabla^2 \mathbf{S}_m \tag{11.29}$$

Eq. (11.29) was derived from Eqs. (11.21) and (11.24). For periodic boundary conditions applied to standing waves in a rectangular box, we find

$$E_{sw} = \frac{Jk^2\varepsilon_o^2}{a} \int_V \sin^2 k_x x \sin^2 k_y y \sin^2 k_z z \, d\tau \tag{11.30}$$

where we have replaced the summation $a^3\Sigma$ by an integral. Integrating Eq. (11.30), we find

$$E_{sw} = \frac{Jk^2\varepsilon_o^2 V}{8a} \tag{11.31}$$

where V is the volume of the specimen. Since E_{sw} is also equal to $n\hbar\omega$ where n is

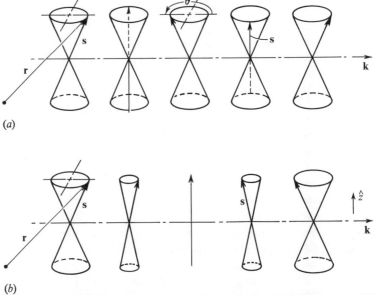

(a)

(b)

FIG. 11.3.   (a) Pictorial representation of a traveling spin wave. Note that the phase angle $\theta = \omega t - \mathbf{k} \cdot \mathbf{r}$ of the spin S changes with distance in the direction **k**. (b) Pictorial representation of a standing spin wave. Note that the z component of the spin S changes with distance in the direction **k**.

an integer quantum number, we finally get

$$\varepsilon_o^2 = \frac{16 S_o a^3 n}{V} \tag{11.32}$$

A pictorial representation of traveling and standing spin waves is given in Fig. 11.3. In the former case, we note that the phase of the spin changes with distance in the direction $\mathbf{k}$ while in the latter case, the amplitude of the spin deviation changes from one lattice point to another.

(c) Quantum-Mechanical Theory

To begin our discussion of the quantum-mechanical theory of spin waves, let us first generalize the exchange Hamiltonian of Eq. (11.21) by including also the dipole-dipole and Zeeman terms:[5]

$$\mathcal{H} = -\frac{1}{2} \sum_{l,m=1}^{N} 2 J_{lm}(R_{lm}) \mathbf{S}_l \cdot \mathbf{S}_m + \frac{1}{2} \sum_{l,m=1}^{N} \frac{4\mu_B^2}{R_{lm}^5}$$

$$\times (R_{lm}^2 \mathbf{S}_l \cdot \mathbf{S}_m - 3\mathbf{S}_l \cdot \mathbf{R}_{lm} \mathbf{S}_m \cdot \mathbf{R}_{lm}) - \sum_{l=1}^{N} 2\mu_B S_{lz} H \tag{11.33}$$

Here N is the total number of atoms, while the sums over l and m each run from 1 to N with $l \neq m$. $R_{lm} = |\mathbf{R}_l - \mathbf{R}_m|$ is the distance between the centers of gravity of the lth and n^{th} atoms with J_{lm} as the exchange integral between them. $\mathbf{S}_l$ is the spin angular momentum operator of the atom at $\mathbf{R}_l$ in units of $\hbar$ while μ_B is the spin magnetic moment which is equal to a Bohr magneton. Finally, the magnetic field $\mathbf{H}$ is directed along the z axis.

The first term in Eq. (11.33) is the Heisenberg exchange energy while the second term represents the magnetic dipole-dipole interaction between electrons on different atoms. The effects of exchange and of higher magnetic poles on the magnetic interaction are both neglected. Thus, the centers of gravity of the atoms constitute the locations of magnetic dipoles, each with magnetic moment $2\mu_B S$. The last term is simply due to the interaction of the magnetic moment of each atom with the external magnetic field. It may be noted that spin-orbit coupling effects have not been included in the Hamiltonian of Eq. (11.33). However, it can be shown that these effects are in general negligible as far as spin-wave behavior is concerned.[5]

At temperatures sufficiently low compared to the Curie temperature, the fractional deviation of the magnetization $M(T,H)$ from its maximum value, M_o, is small. Thus, for this state of "quasisaturation" whereby $[M_o - M(T,H)]/M_o \ll 1$ we shall seek only eigenvalues E whose corresponding eigenfunctions, ψ_E, specify states where the expectation value of the z component of the total spin of the specimen $\sum_{l=1}^{N} S_{lz}$ is close to its maximum possible value NS. To proceed with our calculations, let us introduce the customary circular operators:

$$S_{l+} = S_{lx} + i S_{ly}$$
$$S_{l-} = S_{lx} - i S_{ly} \tag{11.34}$$

---

[5] T. Holstein and H. Primakoff, *Phys. Rev.*, **58**: 1098 (1940).

and also the operator $\eta_l = S - S_{lz}$. Let n_l or the spin deviation of the lth atom be the eigenvalue of η_l and S_{lz} for the state $\psi_{n_1,\ldots,n_l,\ldots,n_N} = \psi_{n_l}$. Thus, it follows that the difference between the z component of the spin of the lth atom and its maximum value $\langle \eta_l \rangle_E$ is the expectation value of the spin-deviation operator η_l, averaged over the eigenstate:

$$\psi_E = \sum_{n_1,\ldots,n_N} b_E(n_1, \ldots, n_l, \ldots, n_N)\psi_{n_1,\ldots,n_l,\ldots,n_N} \tag{11.35}$$

Thus,

$$\langle \eta_l \rangle_E = \sum_{n_1,\ldots,n_N} |b_E(n_1, \ldots, n_l, \ldots, n_N)|^2 n_l \tag{11.36}$$

whereas

$$\langle\!\langle \eta_l \rangle\!\rangle_{AV} \equiv \frac{\displaystyle\sum_E \langle \eta_l \rangle_E e^{-E/kT}}{\displaystyle\sum_E e^{-E/kT}} \tag{11.37}$$

is the expectation value of the spin-deviation operator when the temperature of the specimen is T and involves first an average over ψ_E and then an average over the Boltzmann distribution of the eigenstates of the specimen.

The operators S_{l+}, S_{l-}, and η_l have the following properties:

$$S_{l+}\psi_{n_l} = (2S)^{1/2}\left(1 - \frac{n_l - 1}{2S}\right)^{1/2}(n_l)^{1/2}\psi_{n_l-1}$$

$$\tag{11.38}$$

$$S_{l-}\psi_{n_l} = (2S)^{1/2}(n_l + 1)^{1/2}\left(1 - \frac{n_l}{2S}\right)^{1/2}\psi_{n_l+1}$$

and

$$\eta_l\psi_{n_l} = n_l\psi_{n_l} \tag{11.39}$$

Now, let us introduce the well-known creation and destruction operators defined by

$$a_l^*\psi_{n_l} = (n_l + 1)^{1/2}\psi_{n_l+1}$$

$$a_l\psi_{n_l} = (n_l)^{1/2}\psi_{n_l-1} \tag{11.40}$$

Comparing Eqs. (11.38) and (11.39) with Eq. (11.40), we find

$$S_{l+} = (2S)^{1/2}\left(1 - \frac{a_l^*a_l}{2S}\right)^{1/2}a_l$$

$$\tag{11.41}$$

$$S_{l-} = (2S)^{1/2}a_l^*\left(1 - \frac{a_l^*a_l}{2S}\right)^{1/2}$$

and

$$\eta_l = a_l^*a_l \tag{11.42}$$

Substituting Eqs. (11.41) and (11.42) into the Hamiltonian, Eq. (11.33), and making a number of approximations based upon the quasisaturation condition

$$\frac{1}{2}\frac{M_o - M(T, H)}{M_o} = \frac{\langle\!\langle \eta_l \rangle\!\rangle_{AV}}{2S} = \frac{\langle\!\langle a_l^*a_l \rangle\!\rangle_{AV}}{2S}$$

we find[5]

$$\mathcal{H} = C - \sum_{l,m} 2SJ_{lm}(a_l^* a_m - a_l^* a_l) + \frac{1}{2} \sum_{l,m} \frac{4\mu_B^2}{R_{lm}^3}(2S)(a_l^* a_m - a_l^* a_l)$$

$$- 3S \sum_{l,m} \frac{4\mu_B^2}{R_{lm}^3} [\tfrac{1}{2}(x_{lm}^2 + y_{lm}^2)a_l^* a_m - z_{lm}^2 a_l^* a_l$$

$$+ \tfrac{1}{4}(R_{lm+}^2 a_l^* a_m^* + R_{lm-}^2 a_l a_m)] + \sum_l 2\mu_B H a_l^* a_l \qquad (11.43)$$

with

$$C = -\sum_{l,m} J_{lm} S^2 - 2\mu_B S N H - \frac{1}{2} \sum_l 2\mu_B S$$

$$\times \left[\sum_m \frac{-2\mu_B S}{R_{lm}^2 \left(1 - \dfrac{3z_{lm}^2}{R_{lm}^2}\right)} \right] \qquad (11.44)$$

and

$$R_{lm+} = x_{lm} + i y_{lm}$$
$$R_{lm-} = x_{lm} - i y_{lm} \qquad (11.45)$$

The numerical constant C represents the value of the energy when all the spins are in the direction of $\mathbf{H}$. The first term in C is the exchange energy, the second the interaction energy between the spins and the external field, and the last the mutual dipole-dipole interaction between the spins. Indeed, the expression in the brackets of Eq. (11.44) can be shown to be the sum of the Lorentz local field $4\pi M_o/3$ and the demagnetizing field.

From the form of the Hamiltonian Eq. (11.43), it is apparent that the "*spin deviations*" *specified by the integer* n_l *are not localized on any one atom but are* "*propagated*" *through the crystal.* That this propagation is essentially of a wavelike character can be seen by introducing a set of new variables defined by the following equations:

$$a_\lambda = \frac{1}{\sqrt{N}} \sum_l e^{i\mathbf{K}_\lambda \cdot \mathbf{R}_l} a_l$$

$$a_\lambda^* = \frac{1}{\sqrt{N}} \sum_l e^{-i\mathbf{K}_\lambda \cdot \mathbf{R}_l} a_l^* \qquad (11.46)$$

and

$$a_l = \frac{1}{\sqrt{N}} \sum_\lambda e^{-i\mathbf{K}_\lambda \cdot \mathbf{R}_l} a_\lambda$$

$$a_m^* = \frac{1}{\sqrt{N}} \sum_\lambda e^{i\mathbf{K}_\lambda \cdot \mathbf{R}_l} a_\lambda^* \qquad (11.47)$$

Since, from Eq. (11.40), we have

$$a_l a_m^* - a_m^* a_l = \delta_{ml} \qquad (11.48)$$

we find that a_λ and a_μ^* satisfy the relation

$$a_\lambda a_\mu^* - a_\mu^* a_\lambda = \delta_{\mu\lambda} \tag{11.49}$$

In Eqs. (11.46) and (11.47), $\mathbf{R}_l$ is the vector from an arbitrary origin to the lth atom, whose magnitude measures the corresponding distance in units of the lattice constant, in contrast to the formulas of the above text where $|\mathbf{R}_l|$ is in centimeters while $\mathbf{K}_\lambda$ is a dimensionless reduced wave vector. The usual periodicity conditions require its components to take the values

$$K_{\lambda x} = \frac{2\pi\lambda_x}{G_x}$$

$$K_{\lambda y} = \frac{2\pi\lambda_y}{G_y} \tag{11.50}$$

$$K_{\lambda z} = \frac{2\pi\lambda_z}{G_z}$$

where λ_x, λ_y, and λ_z assume any integral values between $-\frac{1}{2}G_x$ and $\frac{1}{2}G_x - 1$, $-\frac{1}{2}G_y$ and $\frac{1}{2}G_y - 1$, $-\frac{1}{2}G_z$ and $\frac{1}{2}G_z - 1$ respectively. Here, G_x, G_y, and G_z are the lengths of the specimen in the x, y, and z direction, divided by the lattice spacing a.

By applying the transformations (11.46) and (11.47) to the Hamiltonian, Eq. (11.43), and by neglecting contributions from the surface of the specimen so that summations l and h, where $\mathbf{R}_h = \mathbf{R}_l - \mathbf{R}_m = \mathbf{R}_{lm}$, can be carried out independently,

where
$$\mathscr{H} = C + \sum_\lambda A_\lambda a_\lambda^* a_\lambda + \sum_\lambda (\tfrac{1}{2} B_\lambda a_\lambda a_{-\lambda} + \tfrac{1}{2} B_\lambda^* a_\lambda^* a_{-\lambda}^*) \tag{11.51}$$

$$A_\lambda = 3\mu_B \sum_h \left(-\frac{2\mu_B S}{a^3 R_h^3} \right) \left(1 - \frac{3z_h^2}{R_h^2} \right)$$

$$+ \mu_B \sum_h \frac{2\mu_B S}{a^3 R_h^3} \left(1 - \frac{3z_h^2}{R_h^2} \right)(1 - e^{i\mathbf{K}_\lambda \cdot \mathbf{R}_h})$$

$$+ \sum_h 2S J_h(R_h)(1 - e^{i\mathbf{K}_\lambda \cdot \mathbf{R}_h}) + 2\mu_B H \tag{11.52}$$

$$B_\lambda = -3\mu_B \sum_h \left(\frac{2\mu_B S}{a^3 R_h^3} \right) \frac{x_h^2 - y_h^2 - 2ix_h y_h}{R_h^2}$$

$$+ 3\mu_B \sum_h \left(\frac{2\mu_B S}{a^3 R_h^3} \right) \frac{x_h^2 - y_h^2 - 2ix_h y_h}{R_h^2} (1 - e^{i\mathbf{K}_\lambda \cdot \mathbf{R}_h})$$

The surface contributions are obviously negligible for the exchange forces. In this case, the summation over h comprises only nearest neighbors of l, and hence surface terms arise only if the atom l is, itself, on the surface. However, the number of such terms is smaller than the total number of terms by a factor $\cong 1/G$. As far as the magnetic forces are concerned, although their short-range character is not immediately obvious, it can be shown, in the sum over h, again only small values of $|R_h|$ are important; hence the argument just given above again applies. Whereas these arguments are strictly applicable to bulk specimens whose G is very, very large, the

G value corresponding to the thickness of a thin film may be sufficiently small that surface effects cannot be neglected. This question and related matters are discussed in detail in Chap. 6 in relation to the subject of magnetization in thin films.

When the sums over h in A_λ and B_λ are evaluated, the results for $|\mathbf{K}_\lambda| \ll 1$ are

$$A_\lambda = A_{-\lambda} = 2SJK_\lambda^2 + 2\mu_B H + 4\pi\mu_B M_o \sin^2 \theta_\lambda$$
$$B_\lambda = B_{-\lambda} = 4\pi\mu_B M_o \sin^2 \theta_\lambda e^{-2i\phi_\lambda} \tag{11.53}$$

Here, $J \equiv J_h(R_h)$ where R_h is the distance between nearest neighbors while θ_λ, ϕ_λ are polar angles of K_λ with polar axis parallel to the field $\mathbf{H}$. It can be shown that the values of A_λ and B_λ which make important contributions to the magnetization M are those with $|\mathbf{K}_\lambda| \ll 1$.

If the dipole-dipole interactions are neglected, the Hamiltonian, Eq. (11.51), reduces simply to

$$\mathscr{H} = -N \sum_h J_h S^2 - 2\mu_B SNH + \sum_\lambda \left[\sum_h J_h 2S(1 - e^{i\mathbf{K}_\lambda \cdot \mathbf{R}_h}) + 2\mu_B H \right] a_\lambda^* a_\lambda \tag{11.54}$$

Since the eigenvalues n_λ of $\eta_\lambda \equiv a_\lambda^* a_\lambda$ are 0, 1, 2, 3 ... according to Eq. (11.49), we find that the eigenvalues of the Hamiltonian, Eq. (11.54), are just the energy values first found by Bloch[6] and Möller.[7] Also, n_λ can be interpreted as the number of spin-wave quanta associated with the wave vector $\mathbf{K}_\lambda$. Furthermore, $\sum_\lambda \ll \eta_\lambda \gg_{AV}$ which is equal to $\sum_l \ll \eta_l \gg_{AV}$ gives directly the expectation value of the deviation from its maximum value of the z component of the total spin of the specimen. The eigenvalues E of the Hamiltonian, Eq. (11.54), can be found by introducing an additional transformation to yield

$$E = C + \sum_\lambda \left[\tfrac{1}{2}(A_\lambda^2 - |B_\lambda|^2)^{1/2} - \tfrac{1}{2}A_\lambda \right] + \sum_\lambda (A_\lambda^2 - |B_\lambda|^2)^{1/2} N_\lambda \tag{11.55}$$

where N_λ takes on the values 0, 1, 2, 3, ... and it follows from Eqs. (11.53) that

$$A_\lambda = A_{-\lambda} = 2SJK_\lambda^2 + 2\mu_B H$$
$$B_\lambda = B_{-\lambda} = 0 \tag{11.56}$$

since the dipole-dipole terms are neglected.

The magnetization of the specimen at temperature T can be obtained from the partition function $Z = \sum_E e^{-E/k_B T}$ by the relation

$$M = \frac{k_B T}{V} \frac{\partial}{\partial H} \log Z \tag{11.57}$$

where k_B is Boltzmann's constant and V is the volume of the sample. This result is utilized in Chap. 6 in connection with the calculation of the magnetization in thin films.

[6] F. Bloch, *Z. Physik*, **61**: 206 (1930); **74**: 295 (1932).
[7] C. Möller, *Z. Physik*, **82**: 559 (1933).

In the foregoing derivation we made use of the exchange interaction model of a ferromagnet wherein the electrons responsible for ferromagnetism are assumed to be localized at the lattice sites. Since the 3d electrons are mainly responsible for ferromagnetism in the transition ferromagnetic elements like iron, nickel and cobalt, this assumption is, to a first approximation, reasonably valid. (For ferrimagnetic insulators such as ferrites and garnets, the ferromagnetic electrons are indeed localized so that the exchange model is strictly applicable.) However, energy can evidently be transferred from the ferromagnetic system to the lattice by way of the conduction s electrons. This relaxation process has been studied by Abrahams and Mitchell.[8] Since the conduction electron-lattice interaction is so strong (with a characteristic time of the order of 10^{-13} sec), we may consider the s electrons to be part of the lattice, and we can treat the energy transfer as a "spin-electron" relaxation. The conduction electrons will then be treated as a degenerate electron gas by means of a single particle model in the plane wave approximation. The results of Abrahams' calculation show that the effect due to the interaction of ferromagnetic spins with conduction electron current is much more important than that due to the dipolar interaction of ferromagnetic spin with the conduction electron spins. On the other hand, Mitchell has found that the 4s–3d exchange interaction gives rise to a relaxation time which is 1/10 that due to dipolar effects.

In the classical treatment of spin waves discussed in part (a) of this section, the current effects are included by solving the equation of motion of the magnetization in conjunction with Maxwell's equation. The eddy-current damping so introduced is partly responsible for the line width observed in uniform-mode and spin-wave resonance experiments.

11·2 FERROMAGNETIC RELAXATION AND SPIN WAVES

A phenomenological description of electron-spin relaxation in ferromagnetic insulators has been developed using the rate of energy transfer between the uniform precession, the spin waves, and the lattice.[9] This leads to an equation of motion containing T_{1o}, the relaxation time of the uniform precession to the lattice; T_{2k}, the relaxation time of the uniform precession to the kth spin wave; and T_{1k}, the relaxation time of the kth spin wave to the lattice. This is accomplished by using the rate of transfer of energy between the main precession, the spin waves, and the lattice. Each spin wave state is treated separately; it is not necessarily at equilibrium with other spin wave states, nor with the uniform precession, nor with the lattice.

The relaxation process involved is depicted in Fig. 11.4. In the figure, W_o represents the energy of the principle mode directly excited by the rf field while W_k represents the energy of the kth spin mode. P is defined as the net power per unit volume absorbed by the sample. Carrying out the indicated calculations, we find the following equations:

$$\frac{d}{dt}(M_x^2 + M_y^2) = \frac{2M_o P}{H + (N_T - N_z)M_o} - (M_x^2 + M_y^2)\left(\frac{1}{T_{1o}} + \sum_k \frac{1}{T_{2k}}\right) \quad (11.58)$$

[8] E. Abrahams, *Phys. Rev.*, **98**: 387 (1955); A. H. Mitchell, *Phys. Rev.*, **105**: 1439 (1957).
[9] R. C. Fletcher, R. C. LeCraw, and E. G. Spencer, *Phys. Rev.*, **117**: 955 (1960).

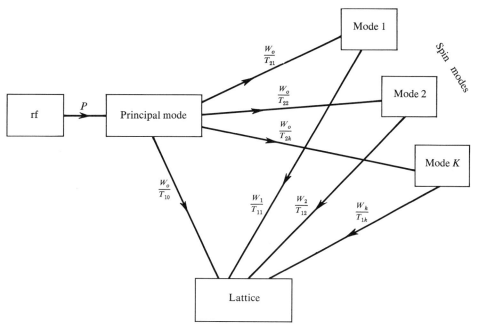

FIG. 11.4. Schematic representation of the energy-transfer process between the uniform precessional mode, the spin modes, and the lattice (after R. C. Fletcher, R. C. LeCraw, and E. G. Spencer, Ref. 9).

and

$$\frac{d}{dt}(M_o - M_z) = \frac{P}{H + (N_T - N_z)M_o} - \frac{M_x^2 + M_y^2}{2M_o}\left(\frac{1}{T_{1o}} - \frac{1}{T_{1k}}\right) - \frac{M_o - M_z}{T_{1k}} \quad (11.59)$$

where M_x, M_y, M_z are respectively the x, y, and z components of the magnetization. M is the saturation magnetization while H is the magnetic field. N_T and N_z are, respectively, the demagnetizing factors transverse to and along the direction of the applied field.

In the absence of relaxation, the torque equation is

$$\frac{d\mathbf{M}}{dt} = \gamma(\mathbf{M} \times \mathbf{H}_e) \quad (11.60)$$

where $\mathbf{H}_e$ is the effective magnetic field. Making the above equation consistent with Eqs. (11.58) and (11.59), we find the basic equations of motion:

$$\frac{dM_{x,y}}{dt} = \gamma(\mathbf{M} \times \mathbf{H}_e)_{x,y} - \frac{M_{x,y}}{2}\left(\frac{1}{T_{1o}} + \sum_k \frac{1}{T_{2k}}\right) \quad (11.61)$$

and

$$\frac{d(M_o - M_z)}{dt} = -\gamma(\mathbf{M} \times \mathbf{H}_e)_z - \frac{M_x^2 + M_y^2}{2M_o}\left(\frac{1}{T_{1o}} - \frac{1}{T_{1k}}\right) - \frac{M_o - M_z}{T_{1k}} \quad (11.62)$$

Eq. (11.61) is exactly equivalent to the Bloch–Bloembergen equation[10] for transverse relaxation provided that

$$\frac{1}{T_2} = \frac{1}{2}\left(\frac{1}{T_{1o}} + \sum_k \frac{1}{T_{2k}}\right) \tag{11.63}$$

where T_2 corresponds to Bloch's transverse relaxation time. Furthermore, if $T_{1o} = T_{1k}$, the second term on the right-hand side of Eq. (11.62) vanishes, and this equation for longitudinal relaxation is also identical with that of Bloch. If $T_{1o} \neq T_{1k}$, the Bloch equations can be shown to still give a description of the motion of the system which has most of the essential features provided we find the appropriate expression for T_1.[9] Thus, it is very comforting to note that the time-honored Bloch equations can be deduced from basic energy considerations involving a transfer of energy between the uniform precession and spin modes, between uniform precession and lattice, and between spin modes and lattice. Of course these equations are linearized; no reaction of the spin modes back upon the uniform mode has been assumed. Furthermore, the actual relaxation process is probably much more complicated than that depicted in Fig. 11.4. In particular, the rf field could excite any one or a combination of the spin modes instead of just the uniform mode. Also, one spin mode could excite other spin modes which may excite still others instead of relaxing directly toward the lattice.

As we noted in Sec. 10.2(a), the Bloch equations are exactly equivalent to the also commonly used Landau–Lifshitz equation of motion for the magnetization[11] provided that the excitation and the magnetization excursion are both small. Furthermore, the Landau–Lifshitz and Gilbert equation[12] (a modified form of the Landau–Lifshitz equation) are in turn equivalent for small damping (long relaxation time).

The equation of motion for the magnetization obtained above using energy considerations is furthermore equivalent to Callen's equation:[13]

$$\frac{d\mathbf{M}}{dt} = \alpha\mathbf{M} - \gamma(\mathbf{M} \times \mathbf{H}) - \lambda\mathbf{M} \times (\mathbf{M} \times \mathbf{H}) \tag{11.64}$$

where the expressions for α, γ and λ are derived in terms of magnon (spin-wave) transition probabilities. Only first-order processes were considered in the derivation of Eq. (11.64) since low-level excitation was assumed.

The foregoing analysis is strictly applicable only to insulators. For conductors like Permalloy films, additional relaxation due to eddy currents may be expected. Thus, we should be mindful of this additional loss when we try to interpret relaxation processes in terms of measured line widths in conducting films.

In a ferromagnetic resonance experiment, the line width is usually measured at a fixed frequency but variable field. From Eq. (10.32), we have found that the damping parameter λ for the uniform mode may be calculated from the measured line width

[10] N. Bloembergen, *Phys. Rev.*, **78**: 572 (1950).

[11] L. Landau and E. Lifshitz, *Physik Z. Sowjetunion*, **8**: 153 (1935).

[12] T. A. Gilbert, *Armour Res. Foundation Rept. No. 11*, Armour Research Foundation, Chicago, January 25, 1955, unpublished.

[13] H. B. Callen, *J. Phys. Chem. Solids*, **4**: 256 (1958).

ΔH_s and frequency as

$$\lambda = \frac{\gamma^2 M}{2\omega} \Delta H_s \tag{10.32}$$

for the cases where the static H_s is applied either along or perpendicular to the easy axis. Using Eq. (10.32) and ΔH_s measured from 100 Mc/sec to 12 kMc/sec, Smith[14] found that in the range above about 1 kMc/sec, λ is nearly independent of frequency indicating that ΔH_s increases directly as frequency. However, in the vhf–uhf range he found that λ decreases with increasing frequency. Similar behavior has also been found by Kingston and Tannenwald who observed that ΔH_s decreases with increasing frequency in the uhf range.[15] The question naturally arises as to whether this frequency dispersion in λ actually indicates a basic dependence of the damping on frequency. It is difficult to imagine that the relaxation times T_{1o}, T_{1k} and T_{2k} (or equivalently the magnon-magnon transition probabilities) should be a function of frequency. Furthermore, in the vhf–uhf range, simple calculations show that, because of the small thickness of the film, eddy-current effects are negligible. Therefore, eddy-current damping cannot be the source of this dispersion in λ. In a later paper, Smith and Harte[16] pointed out that this increase in apparent damping could be attributed to a dispersion throughout the film. The experiments of Rossing substantiate this explanation and indeed he showed that dispersion in the amplitude of the anisotropy can be determined from measurements of ferromagnetic resonance in the uhf range.[17] In the 100–1600 Mc/sec range, using a coaxial bridge similar to that shown in Fig. 10.7, Rossing found that, for the cases where the magnetic field is applied along and perpendicular to the easy direction, the line width of the uniform mode can be described by an equation:

$$\Delta H_s = (\Delta H)_{so} + \frac{2\omega\lambda}{\gamma^2 M} \tag{11.65}$$

It is interesting to note that the second term on the right-hand side of Eq. (11.65) is identical to that given by Eq. (10.32). The frequency independent term $(\Delta H)_{so}$ can be related to the variation in the magnitude of the anisotropy throughout the film. Observed values of $(\Delta H)_{so}$ range from 2 to 5 Oe consistent with the value of dispersion inferred by Smith and Harte[16] from the reversal measurements of several investigators.

Ferromagnetic resonance at radio frequencies has also been studied by Hasty and Boudreaux[18] (1–20 Mc/sec with field in the plane of the film) and by Hasty[19] (1–50 Mc/sec with field perpendicular to the plane of the film). In the former case, only the anisotropy field and the width of the absorption line can be measured. The latter method, on the other hand, provides a direct means of measuring the saturation magnetization, as well as ΔH_s and H_k, since the rf uniform-mode resonance absorption

---

[14] D. O. Smith, *J. Appl. Phys.*, **29**: 264 (1958).
[15] R. H. Kingston and P. E. Tannenwald, *J. Appl. Phys.*, **29**: 232 (1958).
[16] D. O. Smith and K. J. Harte, *J. Appl. Phys.*, **33**: 1399 (1962).
[17] T. O. Rossing, *J. Appl. Phys.*, **34**: 995 (1963).
[18] T. E. Hasty and L. J. Boudreaux, *J. Appl. Phys.*, **32**: 1807 (1961).
[19] T. E. Hasty, *J. Appl. Phys.*, **34**: 1079 (1963).

occurs when the applied field is equal to $4\pi M + H_k$. The main problem with this method is that of keeping the film oriented so that at least parts of it are exactly perpendicular to the applied field. A misorientation of 20 sec causes the resonance frequency at $H = 4\pi M + H_k$ to shift from 0 to 90 Mc. This problem was overcome by a cross-modulation field.

The standard method of determining the rf susceptibility of a material is to place the specimen inside a coil which is part of a resonant circuit.[20] The real part of the susceptibility is then determined by a shift in the resonance frequency and the imaginary part by the change in the Q of the circuit. When the sample is a conductor, the situation is usually complicated by the fact that the eddy-current losses cannot be separated from the magnetic losses. However, since the skin depth at rf frequencies is much larger than the film thickness, the eddy-current losses are found to be negligible.

Observation of ferromagnetic resonance at rf, vhf and uhf frequencies is usually difficult because the effective field at which resonance occurs is quite low. In most specimens it is either impossible to magnetize the material with such low fields or the crystalline anisotropy fields obscure the resonance. However, due to the presence of the uniaxial anisotropy, neither of these difficulties appears for Permalloy films provided that anisotropy dispersion and internal stress are not unusually large. Thus, thin Permalloy films afford a unique opportunity for the study of ferromagnetic resonance at very low frequencies. Indeed, according to Eq. (10.22), the resonance frequency approaches zero as $H_s \rightarrow H_k$ for the case where the field is applied perpendicular to the easy axis and in the plane of the film.

Of particular interest to our present discussion of relaxation phenomena is the experimental result on the line width of the uniform-mode resonance. In the Hasty and Boudreaux experiment,[18] the measured line width at 2.8 Mc/sec ranged from 0.5 to 3 Oe, depending upon composition and deposition conditions. This corresponds to a λ of 10^9, an abnormally high value. Like Harte and Smith,[16] they also attribute this dispersion in λ as due to the dispersion of the anisotropy. In the Hasty[19] experiment, the width of the absorption line at 2 Mc/sec for a typical film was 22 Oe. The line width increased with frequency until a maximum width of 65 Oe was observed at 15 Mc/sec. For frequencies exceeding 15 Mc/sec, the line width began to decrease again and a number of subsidiary absorption peaks began to appear below the main line. This rather strange behavior is attributed to film surface roughness.

In the above discussion, we confined ourselves to the damping of the uniform mode. Since a spin wave could relax between other spin waves or the lattice, it too must possess a finite line width. Unfortunately, no systematic data on the wave number k dependence of λ has been reported in the literature, although it has been observed in spin-wave resonance experiments that the line width first decreases and then increases as k increases to sufficiently large values. For lower k values, the eddy-current relaxation broadens the line at microwave frequencies. Since spin-wave resonance experiments are usually performed at microwave frequencies (10 kMc/sec, say), the skin depth may be comparable to film thickness so that eddy-current effects cannot be neglected. Thus, in deducing λ from the measured line width at microwave frequencies, we must be mindful that the λ so obtained has an eddy-current contribution which is inherently a function of frequency.

---

[20] For the description of such an rf bridge, see H. A. Thomas and R. D. Huntoon, *Rev. Sci. Instr.*, **20**: 516 (1949).

11·3 SPIN-WAVE RESONANCE SPECTRUM

Some very fundamental information on ferromagnetism could be obtained by observing the spin-wave resonance spectrum in thin films. Since Seavey and Tannenwald's[21] first very convincing observation of spin-wave resonance in thin films, there has been considerable theoretical and experimental activity in the study of the absorption spectrum of various kinds of magnetic thin films. Although Jarrett and Waring[22] have observed multiple spin-wave resonances in $NiMnO_3$ which could possibly be identified as spin-wave resonances, the results are not nearly as convincing as the clear pictorial spin-wave resonance peaks due to standing spin-wave resonances observed in thin films. Furthermore, a wealth of information on the fundamental quantities in ferromagnetism could be obtained by the spin-wave resonance method. In particular, the magnetization, gyromagnetic ratio, exchange constant, surface and volume anisotropy energy, as well as relaxation times of spin waves in thin films could be easily determined. In this section we shall study the theoretical and experimental methods of spin-wave resonance in thin films in some detail.

Assuming only nearest neighbor exchange interactions with exchange constant J, we may write down the Hamiltonian of a spin system in a magnetic field as

$$\mathscr{H} = -2J \sum_{i, j}' \mathbf{S}_i \cdot \mathbf{S}_j - g\mu_B \sum_i \mathbf{S}_i \cdot \mathbf{H}_i \tag{11.66}$$

where $\mathbf{H}_i$ is the effective magnetic field at the ith spin resulting from applied, demagnetizing, and anisotropy fields. Since S^2 commutes with the Hamiltonian if $\mathbf{H}_i$ is the same for all spins, no spin waves can be coupled to the uniform mode for the spin system represented by the Hamiltonian, Eq. (11.66). However, if dipole-dipole interactions are included, the uniform mode could be coupled to the degenerate spin-wave modes if these dipolar forces are spatial dependent.[23] At high signal levels, this coupling leads to a saturation of the amplitude of the uniform precession and to the excitation of a subsidiary spin-wave resonance peak well substantiated in the study of ferrites.[24, 25] If the exciting rf field is inhomogeneous, we can also observe magnetostatic modes,[26] which are modes whose wavelengths are in the order of sample dimensions but sufficiently large that exchange forces can be neglected.[27, 28] It is also possible to excite spin-wave modes by a uniform rf field in a thin film if surface spins are partially or completely pinned by local anisotropy interactions. Such interactions may arise, for example, from the lower symmetry for atoms at the surface due to pseudodipole forces or with differences in chemical composition, such as the formation of antiferromagnetic oxide layer at the surface.[29, 30] We shall begin our discussion by first formulating the general exchange boundary condition applicable

[21] M. H. Seavey, Jr., and P. E. Tannenwald, *Phys. Rev. Letters*, **1**: 168 (1958).
[22] H. S. Jarrett and R. S. Waring, *Phys. Rev.*, **111**: 1223 (1958).
[23] A. M. Clogston *et al.*, *J. Phys. Chem. Solids*, **1**: 129 (1956).
[24] N. Bloembergen and S. Wang, *Phys. Rev.*, **93**: 72 (1954).
[25] H. Suhl, *J. Phys. Chem. Solids*, **1**: 209 (1957).
[26] R. L. White and J. H. Solt, *Phys. Rev.*, **104**: 56 (1956).
[27] T. E. Mercereau and R. P. Feynman, *Phys. Rev.*, **104**: 63 (1956).
[28] L. R. Walker, *Phys. Rev.*, **105**: 390 (1957).
[29] C. Kittel, *Phys. Rev.*, **110**: 1295 (1958).
[30] P. Pincus, *Phys. Rev.*, **118**: 658 (1960).

to a line of spins placed in a static field of arbitrary orientation and whose end spins are subjected to different environments.[31]

(a) Formulation of Problem

Consider a system of spins in a magnetic field. The Hamiltonian of the spin system is given by Eq. (11.66). However, in accordance with the discussion above, we shall generalize H_i to include dipolar fields due to dynamic interaction between spins themselves as well as applied, static demagnetizing, and anisotropy fields. The quantum-mechanical equation of motion of S_{im} can be easily shown to be (see Eq. 11.23)

$$i\hbar\dot{S}_m = [S_m, \mathscr{H}] = i2JS_m \times \sum_j S_j + i\hbar\gamma S_m \times H_m \tag{11.67}$$

If we consider a finite chain of N spins and nearest neighbor exchange interaction only, we find the equations of motion for the end spins S_1 and S_N as

$$\frac{\partial S_1}{\partial t} = \frac{2J}{\hbar} S_1 \times S_2 + \gamma S_1 \times H_1 \tag{11.68}$$

$$\frac{\partial S_N}{\partial t} = \frac{2J}{\hbar} S_N \times S_{N-1} + \gamma S_N \times H_N \tag{11.69}$$

where H_1 and H_N are not necessarily equal. Considering the spins semiclassically as vectors, we can expand $S_{2,N}$ in terms of $S_{1,N-1}$ and their derivatives,

$$S_{2,N-1} = S_{1,N} + a \frac{\partial S_{1,N}}{\partial y} + \frac{1}{2} a^2 \frac{\partial^2 S_{1,N}}{\partial y^2} + \cdots \tag{11.70}$$

where a is the lattice constant and the direction of the spins varies only in the y direction. Strictly speaking, Eq. (11.70) should be a difference rather than differential equation since the spin locations are discrete. However, this distinction is unimportant for the continuum approximation considered below. Combining Eq. (11.70) with Eqs. (11.68) and (11.69) we obtain

$$\frac{\partial S_{1,N}}{\partial t} = \frac{2J}{\hbar} S_{1,N} \times \left(a \frac{\partial S_{1,N}}{\partial y} + \frac{1}{2} a^2 \frac{\partial^2 S_{1,N}}{\partial y^2} \right) + \gamma S_{1,N} \times H_{1,N} \tag{11.71}$$

where we have neglected terms involving derivatives higher than the second.

Macroscopically, $S_{1,N}$ may be replaced by the magnetization $M_{1,N}$. By $M_{1,N}$ we then mean the magnetization of the surface layers whose dimensions are large compared to the lattice constant but small compared to the pertinent dimensions of the sample. Thus Eq. (11.71) becomes

$$\frac{\partial M_{1,N}}{\partial t} = \frac{2J}{\gamma\hbar N_o} M_{1,N} \times \left(a \frac{\partial M_{1,N}}{\partial y} + \frac{1}{2} a^2 \frac{\partial^2 M_{1,N}}{\partial y^2} \right) + \gamma M_{1,N} \times H_{1,N} \tag{11.72}$$

---

[31] R. F. Soohoo, *Phys. Rev.*, **131**: 594 (1963).

where N_o is equal to the number of spins per unit volume. The reason for the transformation to this approximation is its obvious connection with macroscopic ferromagnetic resonance experiments. Furthermore, the components of $\mathbf{H}_{1,N}$ can now be easily identified and derived from the classical energy density function:

$$E = \tfrac{1}{2}(4\pi M^2) \sin^2\theta \sin^2\phi - MH_o \sin\theta \cos(\phi_H - \phi) + E_K(\theta, \phi) \qquad (11.73)$$

where θ and ϕ are the angles that the magnetization $\mathbf{M}$ makes with the z and x axis respectively with the film lying parallel to the x–z plane. ϕ_H is the angle $\mathbf{H}_o$ makes with the x axis with $\mathbf{H}_o$ lying in the x–z plane. This situation is depicted in Fig. 11.5.

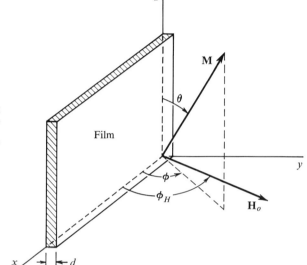

FIG. 11.5. Thin magnetic film in a static field of arbitrary orientation (after R. F. Soohoo, Ref. 31).

The torque may be found from a generalized force $\mathbf{F} = -\nabla E$ using the expression

$$\boldsymbol{\tau} = \mathbf{r} \times \mathbf{F} = -\mathbf{r} \times \nabla E \qquad (11.74)$$

Assuming that the character of the surface energy is uniaxial with the easy axis parallel to the surfaces of the film, we have $E_k(\theta, \phi) = K_s \sin^2\theta \sin^2\phi$. Thus, from Eq. (11.73) we find

$$\nabla E = \hat{\phi}\,\frac{1}{r}\,[(2\pi M^2 + K_s')\sin\theta \sin 2\phi - MH_o \sin(\phi_H - \phi)]$$

$$+ \hat{\theta}\,\frac{1}{r}\,[(2\pi M^2 + K_s')\sin^2\phi \sin 2\theta - MH_o \cos\theta \cos(\phi_H - \phi)] \qquad (11.75)$$

where $\hat{\theta}$ and $\hat{\phi}$ are unit vectors in the θ and ϕ direction respectively and $K_s' a = K_s$ is the surface energy per unit area. It follows from Eqs. (11.74) and (11.75) that

$$\boldsymbol{\tau} = \hat{\theta}[(2\pi M^2 + K_s')\sin\theta \sin 2\phi - MH_o \sin(\phi_H - \phi)]$$

$$- \hat{\phi}[(2\pi M^2 + K_s')\sin 2\theta \sin^2\phi - MH_o \cos\theta \cos(\phi_H - \phi)] \qquad (11.76)$$

For small excursions about the equilibrium position $\theta_{eq} = \pi/2$ and ϕ_{eq}, we may let $\theta = \pi/2 + \delta_\theta$ and $\phi = \phi_{eq} + \delta_\phi$ where $\delta_\theta \ll \pi/2$ and $\delta_\phi \ll \phi_{eq}$. Then Eq. (11.76) approximates to

$$\tau = \hat{\theta}\{(2\pi M^2 + K_s')(\sin 2\phi_{eq} + 2\cos 2\phi_{eq}\delta_\phi)$$
$$- MH_o[\sin(\phi_H - \phi_{eq}) - \cos(\phi_H - \phi_{eq})\delta_\phi]\}$$
$$- \hat{\phi}\{-(2\pi M^2 + K_s')2\delta_\theta(\sin^2\phi_{eq} + \sin^2\phi_{eq}\delta_\phi)$$
$$+ MH_o\delta_\theta[\cos(\phi_H - \phi_{eq}) + \sin(\phi_H - \phi_{eq})\delta_\phi]\} \tag{11.77}$$

Now, let $M_{1,N} = {}_r M + \hat{\theta}m_{1\theta,N\theta} + \hat{\phi}m_{1\phi,N\phi}$, where $m_{1\theta,N\theta} = M\delta_{1\theta,N\theta}$ and $m_{1\phi,N\phi} = M\delta_{1\phi,N\phi}$. Combining Eq. (11.72) and (11.77), we obtain the final component equations as

$$\frac{\partial m_{\theta 1,N}}{\partial t} = -\gamma \frac{2A}{M}\left(\frac{1}{a}\frac{\partial m_{\phi 1,N}}{\partial y} + \frac{1}{2}\frac{\partial^2 m_{\phi 1,N}}{\partial y^2}\right)$$
$$+ \gamma\left(4\pi M + \frac{2K_{s1,N}'}{M}\right)\cos 2\phi_{eq1,N}m_{\phi 1,N} + \gamma H_o\cos(\phi_H - \phi_{eq1,N})m_{\phi 1,N}$$
$$+ \gamma M\left[\left(2\pi M + \frac{2K_{s1,N}'}{M}\right)\sin 2\phi_{eq1,N} - H_o\sin(\phi_H - \phi_{eq1,N})\right] \tag{11.78}$$

and

$$\frac{\partial m_{\phi 1,N}}{\partial t} = \gamma \frac{2A}{M}\left(\frac{1}{a}\frac{\partial m_{\theta 1,N}}{\partial y} + \frac{1}{2}\frac{\partial^2 m_{\theta 1,N}}{\partial y^2}\right)$$
$$+ \gamma\left(4\pi M + \frac{2K_{s1,N}'}{M}\right)\sin^2\phi_{eq1,N}m_{\theta 1,N} - \gamma H_o\cos(\phi_H - \phi_{eq1,N})m_{\theta 1,N} \tag{11.79}$$

where we have replaced $JSM\,a^2/\gamma\hbar$ by its equivalent A, the exchange constant.

For the interior spins the terms linear in a and in K_s' vanish by symmetry while the term quadratic in a is doubled. Thus, Eqs. (11.78) and (11.79) become

$$\frac{\partial m_\theta}{\partial t} = -\gamma \frac{2A}{M}\frac{\partial^2 m_\phi}{\partial y^2} + \gamma 4\pi M\cos 2\phi_{eq}m_\phi$$
$$\gamma H_o\cos(\phi_H - \phi_{eq})m_\phi + \gamma M[2\pi M\sin 2\phi_{eq} - H_o\sin(\phi_H - \phi_{eq})] \tag{11.80}$$

$$\frac{\partial m_\phi}{\partial t} = \gamma \frac{2A}{M}\frac{\partial^2 m_\theta}{\partial y^2} + \gamma 4\pi M\sin^2\phi_{eq}m_\theta - H_o\cos(\phi_H - \phi_{eq})m_\theta \tag{11.81}$$

The equilibrium condition for the magnetization according to Eq. (11.80) is given by

$$H_o\cos\phi_H\sin\phi_{eq} = (H_o\sin\phi_H - 4\pi M\sin\phi_{eq})\cos\phi_{eq} \tag{11.82}$$

[Note the following: For the atomic layers near the surfaces of the film, the equilibrium value of ϕ, that is $\phi_{eq1,N}$, is determined by the expression

$$H_o \cos \phi_H \sin \phi_{eq1,N} = \left[H_o \sin \phi_H - \left(4\pi M + \frac{2K'_{s1,N}}{M} \right) \sin \phi_{eq1,N} \right] \cos \phi_{eq1,N}$$

obtained from Eq. (11.78). If the surface anisotropy field $2K'_s/M$ is small compared to the static magnetization $4\pi M$, as is usually the case, $\phi_{eq1,N}$ would be nearly the same as ϕ_{eq} as can be seen by comparing the above expression with Eq. (11.82). Under these conditions, the entire film is uniformly magnetized and our calculation is strictly correct. If $2K'_{s1,N}/M$ is not small compared to $4\pi M$, $\phi_{eq1,N}$ would differ from ϕ_{eq}. In this case, due to the presence of exchange forces between spins of the surface layers and those of the film proper, a domain wall within which the angle that the spins make with the film surface varies gradually from ϕ_{eq} to $\phi_{eq1,N}$ will presumably be formed. In this case the magnetization distribution corresponding to the surface modes, discussed in Sec. 11.3(c), would be rather complicated. However, so long as $2K'_{s1,N}/M$ is not too large compared to $4\pi M$, the difference between ϕ_{eq} and $\phi_{eq1,N}$ is not too great and the domain wall width is correspondingly small. Under these circumstances the magnetization distribution calculated for the surface modes would still closely resemble that of the actual case providing that the characteristic decay distance of the rf magnetization $1/k$ is large compared to the domain wall width. In any case, the magnetization of the bulk of the film should be at an equilibrium angle ϕ_{eq} and our calculation of the resonance spectrum of the spin-wave modes should be rather insensitive to the slight variation of the equilibrium value of ϕ across the film in realistic cases.]

For a general orientation of H_o, the rf magnetization will not be circularly polarized. Thus, we look for solutions of Eqs. (11.80) and (11.81) of the form

$$m_\phi = R(k) \cos \omega t (\alpha' \sin ky + \beta' \cos ky)$$
$$m_\theta = \sin \omega t (\alpha \sin ky + \beta \cos ky) \tag{11.83}$$

Substituting Eq. (11.83) into Eqs. (11.80) and (11.81), we obtain the dispersion relation for spin waves in a thin film as

$$\left(\frac{\omega}{\gamma} \right)^2 = \left[H_o \cos(\phi_H - \phi_{eq}) - 4\pi M \sin^2 \phi_{eq} + \frac{2A}{M} k^2 \right]$$
$$\times \left[H_o \cos(\phi_H - \phi_{eq}) + 4\pi M \cos 2\phi_{eq} + \frac{2A}{M} k^2 \right] \tag{11.84}$$

and the expression for $R(k)$ as

$$R(k) = \left[\frac{H_o \cos(\phi_H - \phi_{eq}) + \dfrac{2A}{M} k^2 - 4\pi M \sin^2 \phi_{eq}}{H_o \cos(\phi_H - \phi_{eq}) + \dfrac{2A}{M} k^2 + 4\pi M \cos 2\phi_{eq}} \right]^{1/2} \tag{11.85}$$

Substituting Eq. (11.83) into Eqs. (11.78) and (11.79) using Eq. (11.85), and letting $y = 0$ for the first spin, we find

$$\frac{\alpha'}{\beta'} = -\frac{1}{2}ka + \frac{\dfrac{2K'_{s1}}{M}}{\dfrac{2A}{M}k^2}ka\cos 2\phi_{eq} \qquad (11.86)$$

and

$$\frac{\alpha}{\beta} = -\frac{1}{2}ka + \frac{\dfrac{2K'_{s1}}{M}}{\dfrac{2A}{M}k^2}ka\sin^2\phi_{eq} \qquad (11.87)$$

From Eq. (11.86), we see that there is a particular value of ϕ_{eq} whereby $\alpha'/\beta' = 0$ and the ϕ component of the spin system becomes unpinned. Denoting this value of ϕ_{eq} by $(\phi_{eq})_u$, we find from Eq. (11.86) that

$$(\phi_{eq})_u = \tfrac{1}{2}\cos^{-1}\left(\frac{ka}{2}\frac{2Ak}{2K_s}\right) \qquad (11.88)$$

where $K_s = K'_s a$ is the uniaxial surface energy constant in ergs/cm². For this value of $(\phi_{eq})_u$ there is a corresponding value of ϕ_H denoted by ϕ_{Hu} as determined by Eq. (11.82) for a given value of H_o. However, for a given value of ω, H_{ou} and ϕ_{Hu} must be of such values as to satisfy both Eqs. (11.82) and (11.84). Thus ϕ_{Hu} may be determined as a function of $2Ak^2/2K'_s$, the ratio of exchange to surface energy.

It is of interest to investigate the case where $K_s \rightarrow \infty$ corresponding to complete pinning of the surface spins. We see from Eq. (11.88) that under this condition $(\phi_{eq})_u \rightarrow \pi/4$. Then we find from Eq. (11.82) that $H_{ou} = 4\pi M/\sqrt{2}(\sin\phi_H - \cos\phi_H)$. Substituting this expression into Eq. (11.84) for H_o we readily find the quadratic expression for ϕ_{Hu} as

$$\phi_{Hu} = \tan^{-1}\left[1 + \left(\frac{\gamma 2\pi M}{\omega}\right)^2 \pm \sqrt{\left[1 + \left(\frac{\gamma 2\pi M}{\omega}\right)^2\right]^2 + 2\left(\frac{\gamma 2\pi M}{\omega}\right)^2 - 1}\right] \qquad (11.89)$$

In the derivation of Eq. (11.89), we have made the observation that the exchange terms are usually negligible in comparison with others. ϕ_{Hu} is plotted in Fig. 11.6 as a function of $\omega/\gamma 4\pi M$.

If K_s is finite, we find the more general expression from Eqs. (11.82), (11.84), and (11.88) as

$$\left(\frac{\omega}{\gamma 4\pi M}\right)^2 = [\sin\phi_{equ}\cos\phi_{equ}\cot(\phi_{Hu} - \phi_{equ}) - \sin^2\phi_{equ}]$$
$$\times [\sin\phi_{equ}\cos\phi_{equ}\cot(\phi_{Hu} - \phi_{equ}) - \sin^2\phi_{equ} + \cos 2\phi_{equ}] \qquad (11.90)$$

where ϕ_{equ} is given by Eq. (11.88). ϕ_{Hu} for several values of $2Ak^2/2K'_s$ with k corresponding to the disappearance of the peaks with the sine distribution except the

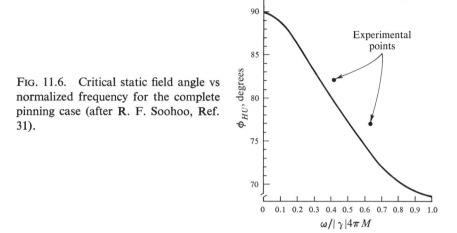

FIG. 11.6. Critical static field angle vs normalized frequency for the complete pinning case (after R. F. Soohoo, Ref. 31).

first, could also be plotted vs $\omega/\gamma 4\pi M$ similar to the $K_s \to \infty$ case of Fig. 11.6. For comparison with experiment, however, it may be more convenient to plot $2Ak^2/2K_s'$ vs ϕ_{Hu} with $\omega/\gamma 4\pi M$ as the constant parameter. This has been done in Fig. 11.7 for $\omega/\gamma 4\pi M = 0.4$ and 0.6. These curves afford an accurate measurement of $2Ak^2/2K_s'$ by a single measurement of the angle ϕ_{Hu}.

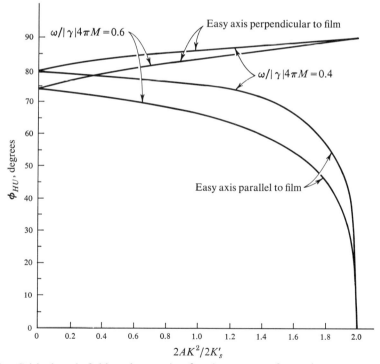

FIG. 11.7. Critical static field angle vs ratio of exchange to surface anisotropy energy for the uniaxial case (after R. F. Soohoo, Ref. 31).

If the surface anisotropy is uniaxial with the easy axis parallel to the film normal and a hard plane perpendicular to it, $E_k(\theta, \phi)$ would be given by $E_k(1 - \sin^2 \theta \sin^2 \phi)$. An entirely analogous calculation would show that as far as the motion of the spin system is concerned, we need only change the sign of K_s in the above equations to render it valid for this case. In a similar fashion we may plot the corresponding curves or ϕ_{Hu} vs $\omega/\gamma 4\pi M$ and $2Ak^2/2K_s'$ as is done in Fig. 11.6 and 11.7.

On the other hand, if the surface anisotropy is unidirectional with its easy axis in the direction of the inward normal to the film surfaces, $E_k(\theta, \phi) = K_s'(1 - \sin \theta \sin \phi)/2$. Analogous calculation would show that the terms involving K_s' in Eqs. (11.78) and (11.79) should be replaced by $-K_{s1,N}'(M \cos \phi_{eq1,N} - \sin \phi_{eq1,N} m_{\phi1,N})/2M$ and $-K_{s1,N}' \sin \phi_{eq} m_{\theta1,N}/2M$ respectively. This change would lead to the corresponding expression for α'/β' as

$$\frac{\alpha'}{\beta'} = -\frac{1}{2} ka + \frac{\dfrac{K_{s1}'}{2M}}{\dfrac{2A}{M} k^2} ka \sin \phi_{eq} \tag{11.91}$$

and α/β is obtained from Eq. (11.91) by changing the sign of $\sin \phi_{eq}$.

If the easy axis is in the direction of the surface outward normal instead, $E_k(\theta, \phi) = K_s'(1 + \sin \theta \sin \phi)/2$ and the only effect as compared to the inward normal case is again the change of sign of K_s'. Of course, curves similar to those given in Figs. 11.6 and 11.7 could be plotted also for the unidirectional cases. However, as we shall see later, since the oxidation experiments indicate that the surface anisotropy energy is uniaxial rather than unidirectional, we shall not pursue this further.

(b) General Exchange Boundary Condition

In the continuum approximation, we must let $a \to 0$ in such a way that $K_{s1,N} = K_{s1,N}' a$, the surface energy coefficient, remains finite. In this case Eqs. (11.86) and (11.87) become, for $K_{s1} = K_{sN} = K_s$,

$$\frac{\alpha'}{\beta'} = \frac{2K_s}{2Ak} \cos 2\phi_{eq}$$

$$\frac{\alpha}{\beta} = -\frac{2K_s}{2Ak} \sin^2 \phi_{eq} \tag{11.92}$$

Combining Eqs. (11.92) and (11.83), we find the macroscopic exchange boundary conditions at $y = 0$ for the uniaxial case with the hard axis in the direction of the film normal as

$$2A \frac{\partial m_{\phi1}}{\partial y} - 2K_s \cos 2\phi_{eq} m_{\phi1} = 0$$

$$2A \frac{\partial m_{\theta1}}{\partial y} + 2K_s \sin^2 \phi_{eq} m_{\theta1} = 0 \tag{11.93}$$

At $y = d$, where d is the thickness of the film, the exchange boundary condition is

$$2A \frac{\partial m_{\phi N}}{\partial y} + 2K_s \cos 2\phi_{eq} m_{\phi N} = 0$$

(11.94)

$$2A \frac{\partial m_{\theta N}}{\partial y} - 2K_s \sin^2 \phi_{eq} m_{\theta N} = 0$$

The difference in sign for the second term of Eqs. (11.93) and (11.94) is due to the fact that the direction of the outward (or inward) normal changes sign for $y = 0$ and $y = d$. Eqs. (11.93) and (11.94) are formally equivalent to the macroscopic expressions derived by Rado and Weertman for the special case where $\phi_{eq} = \pi/2$.[32] If the easy axis of the surface anisotropy is perpendicular rather than parallel to the surface of the film, similar calculation shows that the sign of K'_s or K_s is changed from plus to minus.

If the surface anisotropy is unidirectional with the easy axis in the direction of the surface inward normal, a similar calculation will show that the corresponding macroscopic boundary conditions are given by

$$2A \frac{\partial m_{\phi 1,N}}{\partial y} - \frac{K_s}{2} \sin \phi_{eq} m_{\theta 1,N} = 0$$

(11.95)

at both $y = 0$ and $y = d$. If the easy axis is in the direction of the surface outward normal, calculation shows that K_s in Eq. (11.95) changes sign. For $m_{\theta 1,N}$ the sign of the second term in Eq. (11.95) should be changed.

(c) Line Spectrum

Let us consider the location of the various spin-wave resonance peaks on the static field axis for different shapes of the surface anisotropy energy surface. For the special case where $\phi_H = \phi_{eq} = \pi/2$, the boundary conditions for the θ and ϕ components are the same, as is evident by an examination of Eqs. (11.93) and (11.95). For the uniaxial case with the hard axis in the direction of the film normal, we find by combining Eqs. (11.83), (11.93), and (11.94) the expression determining the location of the spin-wave peak as

$$\tan kd = \frac{-8AkK_s}{(2Ak)^2 - (2K_s)^2}$$

(11.96)

Again, for the case where the easy axis is in the direction of the film surface normal, K_s in Eq. (11.96) should be replaced by $-K_s$.

For the unidirectional cases, we find by combining Eqs. (11.83) and (11.95) the expression determining the location of the spin-wave peaks:

$$\tan kd = 0$$

(11.97)

Eqs. (11.96) and (11.97) have been plotted in Fig. 11.8 for different values of K_s. We note from the figure that whereas the location of the spin-wave peaks moves toward the right or left as K_s is changed for the uniaxial case, it is stationary for the

[32] C. T. Rado and T. R. Weertman, *J. Phys. Chem. Solids*, **2**: 315 (1959).

unidirectional cases. These results may have been surmised by observing that the direction of the equivalent surface fields are antisymmetric and symmetric with respect to the median plane $y = d/2$ for the uniaxial and unidirectional cases respectively. For the uniaxial case, an examination of Eqs. (11.93) and (11.94) will show that the direction of the equivalent field acting on the surface spins are in the $-y$ direction at $y = 0$ and d for the case where the hard axis is in the direction of the film normal. For the case where the easy axis is in the direction of the film normal, the equivalent surface fields are in the $+y$ direction at $y = 0$, d. On the other hand, for the unidirectional cases, the equivalent surface fields for the ϕ component are in the direction of the inward normal at $y = 0$, d for the case where the easy direction is parallel to the inward normal at the surfaces of the film. Correspondingly, if the easy direction is along the outward normal of the surfaces, the equivalent surface fields are also in the direction of the outward normals at $y = 0$, d.

The foregoing results may be easily generalized to include the case of unequal spin pinning at the two surfaces of the film. Denoting the surface energy density constants by K_{s1} and K_{sN} for $y = 0$ and d, respectively, we find, for example, for the uniaxial case with the easy axis in the direction of the film normal the pertinent equation

$$\left[\left(-\frac{1}{2}ka + \frac{2K_{s1}}{2Ak}\right)\left(-\frac{1}{2}ka + \frac{2K_{sN}}{2Ak}\right) + 1\right]\tan kd = 2\frac{K_{s1} - K_{sN}}{2Ak} \qquad (11.98)$$

for the location of the spin-wave peaks. Both equations (11.96) and (11.98) may be satisfied by real or imaginary values of k. The imaginary k solutions correspond not to the ordinary volume resonance modes (real k) but to surface modes. The rf magnetization of these modes should decrease rapidly from the surface and therefore may have an important influence upon the nature of the magnetization reversal process in thin films. Thus, the possible existence of these surface modes may contribute to prevent the magnetization from rotating in unison in the exterior and interior parts of the film. With reference to Fig. 11.8, we note that for the uniaxial cases, H_o changes with K_s. According to the spin-wave dispersion relation (11.84) for the special case $\phi_H = \pi/2$, the relationship between k and H_o is given by

$$k^2 = \frac{\omega/\gamma - H_o + 4\pi M}{2A/M} \qquad (11.99)$$

Thus, at a given ω, k changes with changes in K_s as H_o required for resonance for a given spin-wave mode is dependent upon K_s for these cases. Thus, if the modes are numbered according to the asymptotic approach of H_o as $K_s \to \infty$ so that $n = dk/\pi$ with n odd, the k^2 law for spin waves will be apparently violated as H_o departs from its asymptotic values with finite K_s. This "numbering ambiguity"[33] is particularly significant as K_s is typically of the order unity[34, 35] so that there is significant departure of H_o from its $K_s \to \infty$ values. Furthermore, inasmuch as the substrate side of the film appears to be strongly pinned, presumably due to the presence of oxidized layer on the film substrate interface, the curves of Fig. 11.8 according to Eq. (11.98) would

[33] R. F. Soohoo, *J. Appl. Phys.*, **34**: 1149 (1963).
[34] R. F. Soohoo, *J. Appl. Phys.*, **32**: 148S (1961).
[35] C. F. Kooi et al., *J. Phys. Soc. Japan*, Suppl. B1, **17**: 599 (1962).

vary somewhat as K_s on the nonsubstrate side is changed. This would introduce further complications into the determination of the exchange constant A by means of spin-wave resonance.

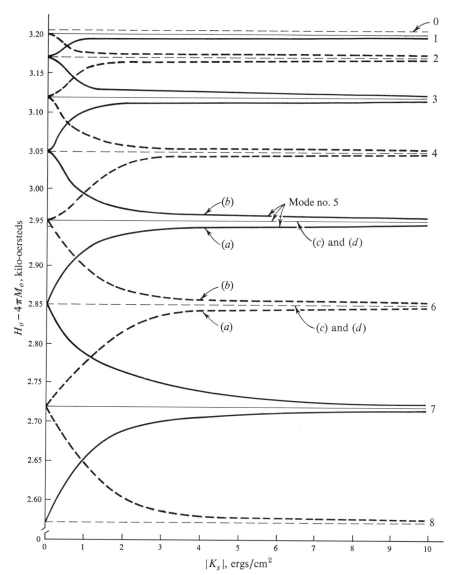

Fig. 11.8. Resonance field of spin-wave modes vs surface anisotropy energy of a thin insulating film ($d = 5 \times 10^{-5}$ cm, $4\pi M = 10^4$ gauss, $|\gamma| = 2.8$ Mc/sec, $A = 10^{-6}$ erg/cm, and $f = 9$ kMc/sec). (a) Uniaxial, easy axis $\perp$ to film; (b) uniaxial, easy axis $\parallel$ to film; (c) and (d) unidirectional (after R. F. Soohoo, Ref. 31).

(d) Absorption Spectrum

Since most spin-wave resonance experiments are done with conducting films, it would be pertinent to calculate the absorption spectrum including conductivity. However, relaxation damping will be neglected for simplicity.

For the special case where $\phi_H = \pi/2$ so that H_o is perpendicular to the film (see Fig. 11.4), we can use the explicit expressions for the wave numbers given by Eq. (11.19). From this equation, it can be easily shown that $K_{1,2}^2(-|\Omega|) = [K_{3,4}^2]^*(|\Omega|)$. For Ω negative, $K_{3,4}$ and $K_{1,2}$ represent respectively the wave numbers for the positive and negative circularly polarized waves. Because of this degeneracy, we may deal with each sense of polarization independently. Thus, for this special case the magnetization can be expressed in terms of a linear combination of four plane spin waves.[34] For the positive circularly polarized waves,

$$m_p = (m_3^+ e^{-ik_3 y} + m_4^+ e^{-ik_4 y} + m_3^- e^{ik_3 y} + m_4^- e^{ik_4 y})e^{i\omega t} \tag{11.100}$$

where the first two terms represent waves traveling in the positive y direction while the last two terms represent waves traveling in the negative y direction. The expression for h_p can be derived from Maxwell's equations. Imposing the exchange boundary condition, Eqs. (11.93) and (11.94), and the usual requirement of the continuity of the tangential component of $\mathbf{h}$ or $\mathbf{e}$ at the surfaces of the film, we find

$$Z_{po} = i \frac{e_{po}}{h_{po}} = \frac{i\omega\delta'^2}{2c} \frac{k_3 C_{e3}(m_3^+ - m_3^-) + k_4 C_{e4}(m_4^+ - m_4^-)}{C_{e3}(m_3^+ + m_3^-) + C_{e4}(m_4^+ + m_4^-)} \tag{11.101}$$

where Z_{po} is the impedance of the film at the surface $z = 0$ and $C_{e3,4} = 4\pi/[1 - i(\frac{1}{2})\delta'^2 k_{3,4}^2]$ and $\delta'^2 = i2c^2/\omega\varepsilon_e$ is the generalized skin depth where $\varepsilon_e = \varepsilon[1 + (4\pi\sigma/i\omega\varepsilon)]$ and ε and σ are the dielectric constant and conductivity of the ferromagnet, respectively. For the uniaxial case, we have

$$
\begin{aligned}
D \frac{m_3^+ + m_3^-}{h_o} = {}& -4C_{e3}[(K_s^2 - 4A^2 k_4^2)\sin k_4 d \\
& - 4Ak_4 K_s \cos k_4 d]\sin k_3 d \\
& + 4C_{e4}\{(K_s \sin k_3 d - 2Ak_3 \cos k_3 d) \\
& \times [K_s \sin k_4 d - 2Ak_4(\cos k_4 d - 1)] \\
& - 4A^2 k_3 k_4 + 2Ak_3(K_s \sin k_4 d + 2Ak_4 \cos k_4 d)\}
\end{aligned}
\tag{11.102}
$$

$$
\begin{aligned}
D \frac{m_3^+ - m_3^-}{h_o} = {}& 4iC_{e3}[(K_s^2 - 4A^2 k_4^2)(\cos k_3 d - 1)\sin k_4 d \\
& - 4Ak_4 K_s(\cos k_3 d - 1)\cos k_4 d] \\
& - 4iC_{e4}\{(K_s \cos k_3 d + 2Ak_3 \sin k_3 d) \\
& \times [K_s \sin k_4 d - 2Ak_4(\cos k_4 d - 1)] \\
& - K_s[2Ak_4 + K_s \sin k_4 d - 2Ak_4 \cos k_4 d]\}
\end{aligned}
$$

K_s is positive and negative respectively for the cases where the hard and easy axis are in the direction of the film normal. For the unidirectional case with easy direction in the direction of the inward normal, which is of no practical interest here, the expressions for $m_3^+ \pm m_3^-$ have been given previously[34] and are similar to the ones given above. To obtain the expressions for $m_4^+ \pm m_4^-$, we need only change k_3 to k_4, c_{e3} to C_{e4} and vice versa on the right-hand side of the equations for

$D(m_3^+ \pm m_3^-)/h_o$, respectively. For the other sense of polarization we need only change k_3 to k_2 and k_4 to k_1.

A plot of Eq. (11.102) vs $H_o - 4\pi M$ is given in Fig. 11.9 for two different values of K_s. The movement of the peaks as K_s is changed shown in Fig. 11.8 for the uniaxial case is clearly indicated. Furthermore, detailed numerical calculations show that the location of the absorption peaks are practically the same as those given in Fig. 11.8 for an insulator even in the presence of conductivity.[36]

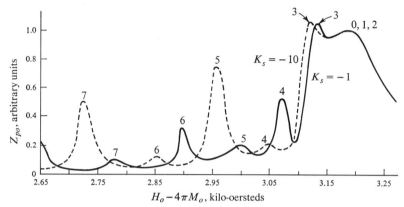

FIG. 11.9. Spin-wave absorption spectrum of a thin conducting film ($1/\sigma = 21 \times 10^{-6}$ ohm/cm and other film data same as that given in Fig. 11.8). Surface anisotropy is uniaxial with easy axis $\perp$ to film (after R. F. Soohoo, Ref. 31).

11·4 DETERMINATION OF EXCHANGE CONSTANT

One of the most important aspects of spin-wave resonance is that the observed absorption spectrum enables us to determine the value of the exchange constant of the film. If the surface spins were assumed completely pinned, then for the uniaxial as well as unidirectional case $\tan kd = 0$ for $\phi = \pi/2$ according to Eqs. (11.96) and (11.97). Correspondingly $k = n\pi/d$ where n is an odd integer. Thus, for this case where the static field is applied perpendicular to the plane of the film, the dispersion relation Eq. (11.84) simply becomes

$$\frac{\omega}{\gamma} = H_o - 4\pi M + \frac{2A}{M}\left(\frac{n\pi}{d}\right)^2 \tag{11.103}$$

Thus, at a fixed frequency ω, the separation between spin-wave peaks i and j (identified by integers n_i and n_j) is given by

$$H_{oi} - H_{oj} = \frac{2A}{M}\left(\frac{\pi}{d}\right)^2(n_j^2 - n_i^2) \tag{11.104}$$

where $H_{oi}(>H_{oj})$ is the resonance field for the ith spin-wave peak. Clearly, the

---

[36] R. F. Soohoo, *MIT Lincoln Lab. Rept. 53-G-0062*, August, 1961.

exchange constant A could be obtained from Eq. (11.104) if H_{oi} and H_{oj} are measured for a given film, providing that we know how to correctly number the various peaks. Difficulties in numbering arise because frequently the first few low k modes ($n = 1$, 3, 5, say) overlap each other so that they cannot be easily distinguished from each other. In practice, the peaks are numbered in such a way that the exchange constant A is as nearly a constant as possible. Furthermore, as we have shown in Sec. 10.3(d), if the surface spins are only partially pinned, the exchange constant A and the surface anisotropy energy K_s must be determined simultaneously. In that case, the exchange constant will not be given by the simple expression, Eq. (11.104), but is determined by the general expressions, Eqs. (11.96) and (11.84), for the uniaxial case.

If the surface spins are assumed completely pinned and use is made of Eq. (11.104), we find experimentally that the mean value of A for various experiments is about 0.9×10^{-6} erg/cm. This value is lower than that determined by other methods. For example, by measuring the complex permeability of bulk Permalloy, the value of which is influenced by the exchange interaction existing in the skin depth, Rado and Weertman[32] deduced a value of $(3.3 \pm 0.5) \times 10^{-6}$ erg/cm. This discrepancy may be partly attributed to the fact that the surface spins are not usually completely pinned. Although the rf field inside the film is not completely uniform due to the presence of eddy currents, it is nearly so because of the small film thickness[37] so that eddy-current effects cannot adequately account for this discrepancy.

Most spin-wave resonance experiments in thin films are made with the static field H_o applied perpendicular to the plane of the film ($\phi_H = \pi/2$). However, some spin-wave resonance experiments have been carried out with H_o applied in the plane of the film[38,39] or with the field at an arbitrary orientation with respect to the film plane.[40] In these cases, the number of spin-wave peaks are usually fewer and not as well resolved as those of the perpendicular case. The reason for this is thought to be due to the nature of the surface anisotropy. If the surface anisotropy is assumed uniaxial with the easy axis along the film normal (see Sec. 10.5 for verification of the validity of this assumption with respect to Permalloy films), it can be shown from our general analysis in Sec. 10.3 ($\phi_H = 0$) that the absorption spectrum with two or three peaks is theoretically predicted, similar to those experimentally observed.[38,39] The absorption spectrum for this special case has been studied in some detail by Wolf.[41] However, he pointed out that without further experimental investigation, it is not possible to decide whether the experimental findings of Chan and Morrish[39] can be explained by surface effects as described or by magnetostatically coupled layers within a stratified film as they assumed.

In all the above experiments, spin-wave resonances were observed using Permalloy film. Nosé has observed spin-wave resonances in polycrystalline Ni,[42] Pd-Ni,[43] and Ni-Cu[44] films. In the case of polycrystalline nickel films, stress and associated magnetostriction was invoked to explain the observed results. Ferromagnetic resonance in

[37] R. F. Soohoo, *J. Appl. Phys.*, **31**: 218S (1960).

[38] C. F. Kooi and R. W. Moss, *Bull. Am. Phys. Soc.*, Ser. II, **4**: 353 (1959).

[39] D. Chan and A. H. Morrish, *J. Appl. Phys.*, **33**: 1146 (1962).

[40] P. E. Wigen *et al.*, *Phys. Rev. Letters*, **9**: 206 (1962).

[41] P. Wolf, *IBM Zurich Res. Lab. Res. Note NZ-23*. Paper presented at 8th Annual Conference on Magnetism and Magnetic Materials, Pittsburgh, November 12–15: 1962.

[42] H. Nosé, *J. Phys. Soc. Japan*, **15**: 1714 (1960).

[43] H. Nosé, *J. Phys. Soc. Japan*, **16**: 838 (1961).

[44] H. Nosé, *J. Phys. Soc. Japan*, **16**: 342 (1961).

single crystal nickel which is relatively free of strain has also been observed.[45] Spin-wave resonance in cobalt films has also been observed.[46, 47]

11·5 ORIGIN OF SURFACE ANISOTROPY

By observing the spin-wave spectrum of a thin film with various values of K_s, it should be possible to determine the nature, and in the uniaxial cases the value as well, of the surface anisotropy energy. Kooi, Holmquist, Wigen, and Doherty have performed such experiments by repeatedly oxidizing and reducing the film surface not adjacent to the substrate.[35] By using their data, we found that the spin-wave resonance peaks move to lower values of the static field H_o as K_s is increased by oxidation. It therefore appears, by comparison with the theoretical curves in Fig. 11.8, that the surface anisotropy is uniaxial in character with the easy axis of magnetization parallel to the film normal. This behavior could be qualitatively accounted for by either a low magnetization layer, as recently proposed by Wigen et al.,[40] or an antiferromagnetic layer at the surfaces of the film with an easy axis along the film normal and a hard plane perpendicular to it. This is so because according to Eq. (11.75) the existence of an uniaxial surface energy is mathematically equivalent to a difference in demagnetizing field for the surface and interior parts of the film. To the first order, this is equivalent to the case of a lower magnetization layer at the surface of the film and our theoretical results with regard to the disappearance of the spin pinning at some critical angle ϕ_{Hu} for a given $\omega/\gamma 4\pi M$ is consistent with that observed by Wigen et al. as indicated in Fig. 11.6. The discrepancy between theoretical and observed values of ϕ_{Hu} may be due to incomplete pinning. However, according to Eqs. (11.86) and (11.87), only the ϕ component of the magnetization becomes unpinned at ϕ_{Hu} and $\phi_{eq} = 45°$, while m_θ remains pinned. Consistent with experiments, one can show that m_θ as well as m_ϕ becomes unpinned when the magnetization makes an angle of 45° with the film normal.

It is very likely that a combination of antiferromagnetic surface layer and a lower magnetization layer exists as the interface between ferromagnetic and antiferromagnetic layers could be rather complicated and there is no assurance of complete ferromagnetic to antiferromagnetic order. Although this phenomenon could be equally accounted for by inhomogeneous demagnetizing field due to the films' nonellipsoidal shape, our detailed calculations (see Appendix A) show that the inhomogeneity is only of order $(d/D)4\pi M$, where d/D is the thickness to diameter ratio of the film, entirely too small compared to the line width to account for pinning.

Of course, for effective pinning to occur, the surface energy K_s, or equivalently $4\pi\Delta M$, where ΔM is the difference between the magnetization of the surface layer and that of the film interior, must be sufficiently large. In this connection, it is of interest to examine this question further by noting that the value of the surface anisotropy in ergs/cm^2 is of the order unity.[35] These values of K_s were estimated by observing the relative magnitudes of the odd and even modes similar to those shown in Fig. 11.9. Now, the equivalent surface field $H_s = 2K_s'/M$ where $K_s' = K_s/a$ would then be of the order $2/aM$. Assuming that the lattice constant a is equal to

[45] M. Kuriyama, H. Yamanouchi, and S. Hosoya, *J. Phys. Soc. Japan*, **16**: 701 (1961).
[46] Z. Frait and M. Ondris, *Czech. J. Phys.*, **B11**: 360 (1961).
[47] P. E. Tannenwald and R. Weber, *Phys. Rev.*, **121**: 715 (1961).

3 Å and $4\pi M$ equal to 10^4 gauss, we find a value of H_s equal to about 8×10^4. It is inconceivable that a $4\pi \Delta M$ of this magnitude could even occur in a Permalloy film whose normal $4\pi M$ is equal to 10^4 gauss. Thus, it appears that whereas a lower magnetization surface layer is capable of explaining the disappearance of the spin-wave modes at a given field orientation, it can not in general account for the high intensity of the peaks. (However, for films whose spin-wave resonance peak intensity falls off very rapidly with increasing k, we obviously cannot rule out the possibility of a lower surface magnetization layer.) In this connection, we should mention that Portis has extended the hypothesis of Wigen *et al.* of a lower magnetization surface layer to include the possibility of a nonuniform magnetization distribution throughout the film.[48] By assuming *ad hoc* that the magnetization drops parabolically from the center of the film, he was able to account for the linear ($\omega \alpha k$) rather than quadratic ($\omega \alpha k^2$) spacing of the low-lying spin-wave modes for rapidly deposited films which were permitted to oxidize. He therefore suggested that the variation in magnetization of these films arises from oxide inclusions whose fractional density increases as the surface is approached. He also assumed that the magnetization is free rather than pinned at the actual surface; this assumption appears reasonable providing that the magnetization variation near the surface is not too drastic. It may be recalled from the discussion above that the presence of lower surface magnetization layer is mathematically and physically equivalent to a surface anisotropy of uniaxial anisotropy. Although Portis was also able to account approximately for the intensity of the modes in these films by a 10% magnetization variation, there is at present no convincing collaborating experiment to substantiate his model or that of Wigen *et al.*

Another source of uniaxial anisotropy is that of the lower-order symmetry of the surface spin environment calculated by Néel.[49] This source of surface anisotropy can best be understood by considering the short-range nature of the pseudodipole interaction. As discussed in Chap. 7, the pseudodipole potential, unlike the ordinary magnetic dipole potential, decays more rapidly than the inverse cube of the space coordinate. Thus, it is customary to assume that the pseudodipole potential can be restricted to nearest neighbor interaction only. In the presence of such short-range potential, it is evident that the surface spins are subject to different forces in different directions since there are neighboring spins on the inner but not on the outer side of the surface. Therefore, we may expect the presence of an anisotropy energy localized at the surface of the specimen. It is of interest to note that if the interaction were long range, e.g., similar to that due to the magnetic dipole, the surface spins would be subjected to essentially the same environment as those in the interior as the long-range interaction concerned is a volume rather than a surface effect. As shown in Appendix B, the resulting surface anisotropy density E_s is given by the equation

$$E_s = K_s \cos^2 \theta \qquad (11.105)$$

where θ is the angle between the spontaneous magnetization and the normal to the surface. The value of K_s depends on the nature of the lattice structure and the surface orientation. Néel has estimated that K_s has values of the order of 0.1 to 1 erg/cm^2. Our calculation and experiment,[36] however, have shown that this Néel surface energy

---

[48] A. M. Portis, *Appl. Phys. Letters*, **2**: 69 (1963).
[49] L. Néel, *J. Phys. Radium*, **15**: 225 (1954).

(~ 0.05 erg/cm^2 for 80–20 Permalloy) is at least an order of magnitude too small to account for the relative intensity of the observed spin-wave resonance peaks.

We now come to a discussion of that source of surface anisotropy due to the presence of an antiferromagnetic layer at the film surface. The most likely antiferromagnetic layer that may exist at the surface is NiO ($T_N = 518°C$) although the existence of ferrite layers for some films have also been confirmed by electron diffraction. FeO could also exist but since its Néel temperature T_N (198°K) is below room temperature, it can not account for the spin-wave resonances observed at room temperature. Furthermore, it has been found that separation between spin-wave peaks in thin films does not vary much for a given film at liquid helium, liquid nitrogen, and room temperatures. Potentially, this source of anisotropy could give rise to a very high value of K_s as required by experiment. Indeed Pincus has shown that only ten antiferromagnetic layers are sufficient to pin the surface spins,[30] although it is not clear why such surface anisotropy should be uniaxial in symmetry. It is evident, however, that the nature of the anisotropy is related closely to complicated film formation and oxidation process. Since most films, being deposited in ordinary vacuum of 10^{-6} to 10^{-5} mm Hg and subsequently exposed to the atmosphere, inevitably are partially oxidized, we consider the oxidized layer as the most important source of surface anisotropy. In this connection, it is interesting to note that Neugebauer has found in his nickel film oxidation experiments, that the uniaxial anisotropy with its axis in the direction of the film normal increases quite significantly after oxidation.[50]

11·6   DETERMINATION OF SURFACE ANISOTROPY

As can be seen from Fig. 11.9, the relative amplitude and location of spin-wave peaks on the static field axis are dependent upon the magnitude of the anisotropy constant K_s for the important uniaxial case. However, the magnitude and location of these peaks are dependent also upon the exchange constant A as the curves in Fig. 11.9 were calculated with A as a constant parameter. This fact thus complicates the process of determination of K_s and A as they must be determined simultaneously.

Since the magnitude of the resonance peaks is dependent upon the conductivity and damping constant of film, comparison of their relative intensities would not afford a simple determination of A and K_s. The situation is further complicated by the fact that we do not know a priori the possible wave-vector dependence of the damping constant. Therefore, it would be more expedient to utilize the experimentally determined static field values H_o for the various peaks for this purpose; H_o could be easily and accurately measured by a nuclear magnetic resonance probe. As the location of these peaks is independent of the values of conductivity and damping constant of the film, a measurement of the peak locations is sufficient to accurately determine K_s and A. However, since there may be several combinations of A and K_s which yield the same peak locations, an independent measurement of another parameter which is dependent upon both A and K_s is necessary. The appropriate quantity in question turns out to be the critical field angle with respect to the film plane ϕ_{Hu} at which the spin system becomes unpinned. Using the measured critical angle ϕ_{Hu}, $2Ak^2/2K_s'$, the ratio of the exchange to surface energy, could be determined from Fig. 11.7. Then, using this ratio and curves similar to those of Fig. 11.8 plotted with

---

[50] C. A. Neugebauer, *Gen. Elec. Res. Lab. Sci. Rept. No. 2*, 1961.

A as a constant parameter, we may determine K_s and A simultaneously. This procedure can be facilitated by plotting curves representing loci of constant $2Ak^2/2K'$ obtained from Fig. 11.7 in Fig. 11.8. Since ϕ_{Hu} is a single-value function of $2Ak^2/2K'_s$, this is tantamount to plotting curves of constant ϕ_{Hu} in the H_o–K_s plane of Fig. 11.8.

The only remaining complication to this problem is the difficulty in identifying the various spin-wave peaks according to wave numbers k. As we discussed in Sec. 11.3(c), the modes could only be numbered meaningfully by the asymptotic approach of their resonance field values as $K_s \to \infty$. For thinner films (1000 Å, say), the various peaks are usually well resolved[51] so that the identification is trivial. If the film is thick (5000 Å, say), the low-k peaks are not well resolved so that their experimental identification is somewhat more tentative; this situation is illustrated by the absorption spectrum shown in Fig. 11.9.

As we have already mentioned above, the relative amplitudes of the spin-wave peaks are dependent upon the exchange constant, surface energy, conductivity, and damping constant of the film. Therefore, experimentally, it is not very useful to compute the relative amplitudes based upon the line spectrum, i.e., a spectrum which neglects both eddy-current and relaxation damping. Nevertheless, it is interesting to note that for the case where static field is along the film normal, the peak amplitudes of the line spectrum decrease as n^2 where n is the integer mode number.[30]

---

[51] T. D. Rossing, *J. Appl. Phys.*, **34**: 1133 (1963).

CHAPTER 12

APPLICATIONS

In the previous chapters we discussed in detail the physical behavior of magnetic thin films. In this concluding chapter we shall indicate how these physical properties are utilized for technological applications. For the physicists whose interests are mainly in the basic physics of thin films, the treatise in this chapter represents a bird's-eye view of the present applications and future potentialities of magnetic thin films. For those who are inclined more toward engineering, aside from the general treatment given this chapter, pertinent references and a rather extensive bibliography are given at the end of this book.

Magnetic thin-film applications may be broadly divided into four main categories: (1) application as computer memories, (2) application as computer logic elements, (3) radio-frequency and microwave applications, and (4) miscellaneous applications. The associated devices include such diverse items as planar and cylindrical binary storage elements, the twister memory, domain wall logic components, rf parametron, millimeter wave resonance isolators using thin films, Hall effect probe, delay line, thin-film magnetometer, etc. We shall touch upon the behavior of these devices to illustrate the capabilities and limitation of magnetic thin films.

In order for the treatment in this chapter to be essentially self-contained and to avoid undue cross references to materials in the rest of the book, a brief resumé of the properties of thin films that are pertinent from the technological viewpoint will first be given.

12·1 RÉSUMÉ OF FILM PROPERTIES

Since the chief application of magnetic thin films to date is as computer memories, it is pertinent to review the subject of hysteresis loops and changes of magnetic state in thin films. These would lay the groundwork for the analysis of different memory selection schemes and of the requirements on the associated driving and sensing circuitry.

To begin with, let us consider the thin-film switching configuration of Fig. 8.4. The free energy of the system is given by

$$E = K_1 \sin^2(\phi - \alpha) - H_s M \sin\theta\cos\phi - H_\perp M \sin\theta\sin\phi + 2\pi M \cos^2\theta \quad (8.9)$$

where M is the magnetization, and K_1 the uniaxial anisotropy constant, H_s and $H_\perp$ are orthogonal fields, and the angles θ, ϕ, and α are as indicated.

The first term represents the anisotropy energy attributed to the existence of a preferred orientation of the magnetization while the second and third terms represent energies of interaction between the magnetization and the applied fields. The last term is the demagnetizing energy and is equal to the work required to rotate the magnetization from the film plane up to the film normal; an infinitely thin film has been implicitly assumed.

An uniaxial anisotropy occurs when a nickel-iron alloy (Permalloy) film is deposited in the presence of a magnetic field. The origin of this induced anisotropy was discussed in great detail in Chap. 7. It was shown then that there are a number of contributing sources to the anisotropy. Preferential iron-pair orientation in the nickel lattice and imperfection alignment are probably the important ones for a typical normal-incidence Permalloy film. For films that are deposited with the vapor beam inclined to the film normal and for so-called anomalous films produced by certain deliberate preparation techniques, the origin of the anisotropy is somewhat more complex and controversial. Since these films are not usually used in any applications, we shall not further review their properties here.

Since $4\pi M$ of a typical Permalloy film is about 10^4 gauss, in the absence of a large field comparable in magnitude to $4\pi M$ applied perpendicular to the plane of the film, the magnetization would lie in the film plane. It then follows from Eq. (8.9) that the strength of the magnetic fields H_s and $H_\perp$ required to change the magnetic state corresponding to a change in E increases with increasing anisotropy constant K_1. From an application point of view, this implies that K_1 should be small in order to minimize the requirements on the driving circuitry. In general, K_1 varies with composition, and experimentally it has been shown that it attains a minimum in the neighborhood of the 80% Ni–20% Fe composition. As is shown in Fig. 7.10, the magnetostriction also goes through zero near the same composition. When the magnetoelastic constant B is zero, there is no interaction between the magnetic system and the stress in the film. If $B \neq 0$, a nonuniform deformation of the crystal would occur which may give rise to additional contribution to the anisotropy.

(a) Hysteresis Loop

Let us now return to the discussion of the hysteresis loop. Now, the torque τ acting on the magnetization is given by $\mathbf{r} \times \mathbf{F}$ where $\mathbf{r}$ is the coordinate vector and $\mathbf{F}$ is the generalized force. Since $\mathbf{F}$ is conservative, we have $\mathbf{F} = -\nabla E$ where the energy E is given by Eq. (8.9). Thus, $\tau = \hat{\phi}(1/\sin\theta)(\partial E/\partial\phi)$ where $\hat{\phi}$ is a unit vector in the ϕ direction. It follows that the equilibrium position of $\mathbf{M}$ can be obtained by setting $\partial E/\partial\phi = 0$. When there exists an extremum as in the case of the longitudinal loop, i.e., the loop obtained in the direction of the easy axis, we may also set $\partial^2 E/\partial\phi^2$ equal to zero (point of inflection).

Let us first consider two special cases of interest, namely $\alpha = 0$ and H_s or $H_\perp$ equals zero. For the case where $\alpha = 0$ and $H_s = 0$, the switching magnetic field $H_\perp$ is applied perpendicular to the easy axis and the resultant $M\sin\phi$ vs $H_\perp$ hysteresis loop is termed the transverse loop. For simplicity, let $\theta = \pi/2$ so that the $\mathbf{M}$ lies in the plane of the film. Setting $\partial E/\partial\phi = 0$ as described above, we readily find

$$M\sin\phi = M\frac{H_\perp}{2K_1/M} \tag{8.10}$$

where $2K_1/M$, having the dimension of $H_\perp$, is known as the anisotropy field. The transverse loop as determined by Eq. (8.10) was plotted in Fig. 8.5. It is seen from that figure that the loop has no hysteresis and that it saturates at $H_\perp = 2K_1/M$. In practice, the close loop exists only for $H_\perp \ll 2K_1/M$. At higher drives, the loop opens up and encloses a finite area as shown by the dotted curve of Fig. 8.5. This phenomenon, as we have discussed in Sec. 9.2, is attributed to the formation of reverse domains of magnetization at higher fields.

From the above discussion, we see that a transverse field of the value $2K_1/M$ is required to rotate the magnetization $\mathbf{M}$ completely to the applied field or hard axis and that magnetization component along the field axis increases linearly with $H_\perp$ up to the saturation value M.

For the longitudinal loop, we set $\theta = \pi/2$, $\alpha = \pi$, $H_\perp = 0$ in Eq. (8.9). Thus, setting $\partial E/\partial \phi = \partial^2 E/\partial \phi^2 = 0$, we find the equations for the longitudinal loop as

$$M \cos \phi = -M \frac{H_s}{2K_1/M} \tag{8.11}$$

$$\cos 2\phi = \left(\frac{H_s}{2K_1/M} \right)^2 \tag{8.12}$$

From Eq. (8.12), we see that when $H_s = 2K_1/M$, $\phi = 0$, π. Thus, when $\partial^2 E/\partial \phi^2 = 0$ giving rise to Eq. (8.12), we pass from the case where the extremum is a minimum to where it is a maximum. In this case, an irreversible magnetization change of $2M$ occurs when $H_s = 2K_1/M$ as shown in Fig. 8.6.

It is seen from Fig. 8.6 that there are two stable states of the system with the magnetization making an angle ϕ of 0 or π with the x axis. These two states may then represent the binary states "0" and "1" of a computer memory. For example, if the magnetization is initially along the $\phi = \pi$ direction and a field H_s equal to $2K_1/M$ is applied in the $\phi = 0$ direction, according to Fig. 8.6, the magnetization will reverse irreversibly to the $\phi = 0$ direction of the applied field. If H_s is now reduced to zero, the magnetization along the $\phi = 0$ direction remains unchanged due to the perfect rectangularity of the loop; in practice, the squareness ratio of the loop, defined as remanent magnetization divided by saturation magnetization, is 0.99 or better. If a pickup loop is placed with its plane perpendicular to the x axis as shown in Fig. 8.4, a voltage proportion to $\dot{M}$ will appear across its terminal indicating a change of state. On the other hand, if $\mathbf{M}$ were initially along the direction $\phi = 0$, a field H_s applied in this direction would not cause a realignment of the magnetization so that $\dot{M} = 0$ and there will be no voltage appearing across the terminals of the pickup loop. Thus, according to whether or not a voltage is generated in the pickup loop when H_s is applied, we can infer about the initial state of the system.

The reason that two identifiable states in a thin film with a rectangular hysteresis loop can perform computer logic has to do with the binary system of numbers.[1] For example, consider the number 433. The decimal number system represents numbers as sums of powers of ten, where each power of ten is weighted by a digit between zero and nine, inclusive. When we write a decimal number, we note down

---

[1] M. Phister, Jr., *Logical Design of Digital Computers*, John Wiley & Sons Inc., New York, 1958, p. 16.

only the weights to be attached to various powers, and a decimal point which tells which powers of ten are to be weighted. Thus, in this system,

$$433 = 4 \times 10^2 + 3 \times 10^1 + 3 \times 10^0 \tag{12.1}$$

In a similar manner, using 2 instead of 10 as the base of the number system, we have

$$433 = 1 \times 2^8 + 1 \times 2^7 + 0 \times 2^6 + 1 \times 2^5$$
$$+ 1 \times 2^4 + 0 \times 2^3 + 0 \times 2^2 + 0 \times 2^1 + 1 \times 2^0$$
$$= (11\ 0\ 11\ 00\ 0\ 1.)_2 \tag{12.2}$$

This number system, having the base two, is known as the binary number system. (In a binary-coded decimal system, used because of the easiness of decimal-binary and binary-decimal conversions at the memory input and output, respectively, each decimal digit is replaced by a set of binary digits or bits. For example, for the decimal digits 0, 1, 2, 3, 4, the binary codes are 0000, 0001, 0010, 0011, 0100, correspondingly. Thus, the number 433 would be written in the binary code as 010000110011.) We note immediately that the weights consist entirely of ones and zeros. It is apparent that using the base two, we may express any number by the states of a group of memory devices, such as ferrite cores or magnetic films with rectangular hysteresis loops, each of which is capable of storing of either a one or a zero. Thus, $+M_r$ and $-M_r$ in Fig. 8.6 correspond to the 1 and 0 states, respectively.

Let us now proceed just a little further to see how a typical problem can be solved by converting its mathematical equivalent into a system of numbers. For example, for the case of easy-axis magnetization reversal in thin films, it is necessary to solve Eqs. (10.18) and (10.19). Once the film parameters M, γ, λ and the switching fields H_s and $H_\perp$ are specified, the orientation angles of $\mathbf{M}$, namely $\phi(t)$ and $\psi(t)$, can be found by specifying the independent variable t as well as the coefficients of the equation by some number, like 10^{-9} sec, say, in a binary code. For this purpose, it would be convenient to expand $\phi(t)$ in terms of a power series in t. Of course, the input and output operations are accomplished via decimal-binary and binary-decimal conversions, respectively.

According to the above discussion, the energy required to switch a film from one stable state to another is dependent upon H_k. However, in practice, the film begins to reverse its state of magnetization at a value of field usually below that of H_k. This is because films usually reverse by domain wall motion, rather than by coherent magnetization rotation, in the easy direction in the absence of a transverse field $H_\perp$. The field at which the magnetization component $M\cos\phi$ is actually zero is the coercive force H_c, as shown in Fig. 8.6. If $H_c/H_k < 1$, the film is termed normal and if $H_c/H_k > 1$, it is termed inverted. Most films are of the normal type and it is not quite certain how inverted films can be consistently produced.[2]

(b) Modes of Switching

To analyze the effect of the application of $H_\perp$ upon the shape of the longitudinal loop, we return to Eq. (8.9) and set $\partial E/\partial\phi = \partial^2 E/\partial\phi^2 = 0$ for finite values of H_s

---

[2] D. O. Smith, *J. Appl. Phys.*, **32**: 74S (1961).

and $H_\perp$. The result of the calculation gives

$$\frac{H_\perp}{H_k} = \sin^3 \phi$$

$$\frac{H_s}{H_k} = \cos^3 \phi$$

(8.13)

which is equivalent to $H_s/H_k = \pm[1 - (H_\perp/H_k)^{2/3}]^{3/2}$. The parametric equations, Eq. (8.13), are plotted in Fig. 9.2 exhibiting the behavior of the threshold fields, i.e., the figure gives the proper combination of the values of H_s and $H_\perp$ at which rotational switching begins to occur. (If similar curves are plotted by reflection of the threshold curve shown in Fig. 9.2 about the H_s and $H_\perp$ axes, a figure of astroidal shape is obtained. Such a figure is known as the Stoner–Wohlfarth switching astroid.) We see from this figure that the field at which the magnetization reverses by rotation is continuously decreased from H_k at $H_\perp = 0$ to 0 at $H_\perp = H_k$. The corresponding hysteresis loop gradually changes from the highly rectangular shape to a collapsed S-shaped loop accompanied by an effective decrease in coercive force as illustrated in Fig. 8.6.

Since the switching speed should decrease with increasing values of H_s above the effective coercive force, application of a transverse field would decrease the switching time τ for a given drive. Conversely, for a given τ, the drive field required is correspondingly decreased. This is an important conclusion for fast switching conditions. It must be noted, however, that according to Fig. 8.6, the loop becomes less rectangular as $H_\perp$ increases; this feature is undesirable for computer memory applications. As discussed in the next section, the reason for this is that in a memory array the unswitched bits may constantly be subjected to half-select fields equal to about $H_k/2$ and that the paths of the minor hysteresis loops are such that the bit may be reversed after the repeated application of these half-select pulses if the hysteresis loop is not highly rectangular.

The actual magnetization reversal process is complicated by the fact that for a range of values of H_s and $H_\perp$ above the threshold curve shown in Fig. 9.2, magnetization reversal has been observed to proceed not by pure coherent rotation of the magnetization but by some sort of an admixture of coherent rotation and a slower reversal process. Measurements of flux changes in the longitudinal and transverse directions show that most of the reversal is occurring by a rotational process, but not completely so.

The various modes of magnetization reversal are shown in Fig. 12.1. It is seen from this figure that if the nonuniform rotation threshold is taken as a reference, the wall motion threshold, the creep threshold and the coherent rotation threshold may vary considerably with respect to it, depending upon the material and peculiarities of the sample and also on the test conditions. The coherent rotation threshold, for example, is sensitive to the rise time of the switching pulses and may vary considerably from sample to sample. The creep threshold (switching field values which will cause irreversible changes in the magnetization after repeated application) also varies from sample to sample and may depend on the rise and decay time of the fields.[3]

---

[3] R. M. Sanders and T. D. Rossing, *J. Appl. Phys.*, **29**: 288 (1958).

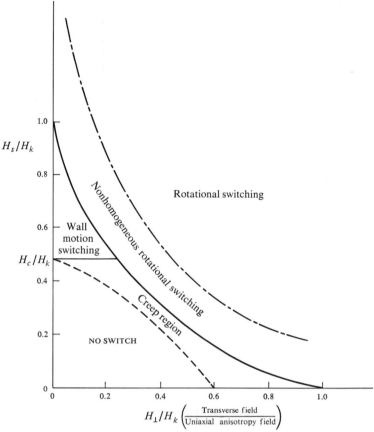

FIG. 12.1.   Various modes of magnetization reversal in thin films (after Pohm and Mitchell, Ref. 24).

A few words regarding the three dominant magnetization reversal mechanisms are in order. Referring to Fig. 9.1, it is seen that the $1/\tau$ vs H_s curves for constant values of $H_\perp$ in general are composed of three segments, each with a different average slope. It is seen from Fig. 9.1 that when the values of H_s and $H_\perp$ are such that τ is large (1 μsec or more), the magnetization reverses by domain wall motion. When τ is quite small ($< 0.1\ \mu$sec), the magnetization reverses by coherent rotation. For intermediate values of τ (0.1 μsec $< \tau < 1\ \mu$sec), the magnetization reverses by incoherent rotation.

For the mode of reversal via the motion of domain walls, the demagnetizing fields and imperfections in the film play a very important role. Usually, reversed domains are already nucleated in the remanent state due to the increased demagnetizing field at the edge of film. This increase is due to the departure of the film from an ellipsoidal shape. When a switching field is applied to the film, these reverse domains propagate first in the direction of the easy axis eventually forming long filaments of reverse domains parallel to the easy direction. The reversal process is then completed by the expansion of these domains in the hard direction. Now, the nature of the imperfections determine the coercive force. Here the coercive force H_c, as measured by a hysteresis looper, is defined as the field required to reverse half the magnetization so as to render the net magnetization of the film in this state zero. It is important to note, however, unless the sides of the hysteresis loop are straight up and down, this coercive force H_c is not equal to the wall motion coercive force H_w. H_w in this context is equal to the field required just to move the walls associated with the edge domain. In computer application terminology, H_w is sometimes called the knee field, synonymous with the value of H_s required to begin to cause an appreciable change in the magnetization. For some situations, nucleation may begin in the film proper after H_s exceeds a certain value called the nucleation field H_n and that the walls associated with these nucleating centers then propagate throughout the film to complete the reversal.

In the intermediate speed region, magnetization reversal proceeds by incoherent rotation. Without going into details, it is clear that this incoherent nature of the magnetization reversal must be related to the imperfections in thin films. For if the film were completely homogeneous in all respects, the reversal process should clearly be one of uniform rotation when the values of H_s and $H_\perp$ are such that the film state corresponds to one above the rotational threshold. In this case, with the exception of perhaps surface and edge effects, there is no apparent reason for the magnetization to be a function of the coordinate in either the static or dynamic states. We know from the discussion above that domain wall motion is influenced by physical imperfections such as vacancies, dislocations, inclusions, voids, etc. In the noncoherent rotation region, H_s is sufficiently larger than the effective coercive force and anisotropy fields for incoherent rotation to occur so rapidly that domain walls have no time to propagate. It is therefore not unreasonable to suspect that the pertinent imperfection of interest here is of magnetic rather than physical type.

Various workers have tried to determine the physical origin for the breaking up of the initial coherent rotation into a noncoherent rotation mode. (Since the rotation starts coherently, the threshold should be correctly predicted by the coherent-rotation model as has been experimentally found.) The results of these investigations indicate that the noncoherent behavior of the magnetization in the dynamic state is due to the presence of a spatial dependence of the magnitude of the induced anisotropy. For normal films, wherein $H_k > H_c$, Smith and Harte suggested, on the basis of their many domain observations using high resolution Bitter technique, that noncoherent rotation is due primarily to "labyrinth propagation."[4] They found that if parallel wall displacement does not occur after nucleation of an initial reverse domain, reversal takes place by extension from the tip of the initial domain. A striking feature of this form of switching is that regions of unswitched material are left behind, resulting in a labyrinth-like flux pattern.

The basic reason for labyrinth switching is postulated to be local variations in the switching threshold. Dispersion in the switching threshold is further assumed to be due to a dispersion in magnitude and direction of the local uniaxial anisotropy. The sequential or propagating nature of labyrinth switching clearly depends upon magnetostatic interaction between the switched region and the region which next switches. A magnetostatic model for the direction of labyrinth propagation as a function of the angle between H_s and the easy axis has been given by Smith and Harte.[4] The results of calculation using this model which takes into account only the magnitude dispersion of anisotropy, i.e., regions of K_2 material imbedded in a K_1 background, are in reasonable agreement with experiment.

---

[4] D. O. Smith and K. J. Harte, *J. Appl. Phys.*, **33**: 1399 (1962).

These low-speed labyrinth propagation experiments were carried out with an optical microscope. It is not immediately obvious that the noncoherent magnetization reversal indeed corresponds to a process of this type. A final resolution of this problem clearly must await the actual determination of the spatial dependence of the anisotropy using an instrument like, for example, the microwave magnetic microscope[5] or by

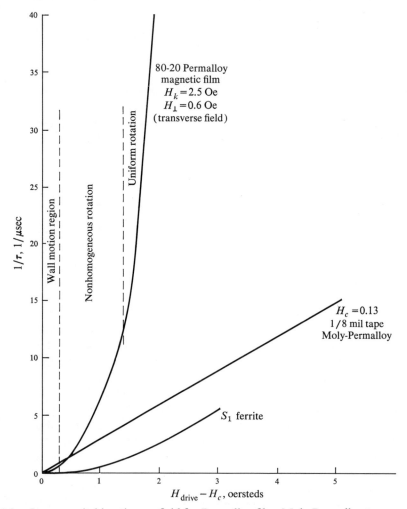

FIG. 12.2.   Inverse switching time vs field for Permalloy film, Moly-Permalloy tape, and bulk ferrite core (after Pohm and Mitchell, Ref. 24, and from the data of Olson and Pohm, Ref. 1, Chap. 9).

a high-speed motion-picture study of the magnetic state similar to that reported by Conger and Moore[6] for the domain wall motion region.

In the high-speed region, the switching and biasing fields are sufficiently large that magnetization reversal proceeds by a coherent rotation of the magnetization

[5] R. F. Soohoo, *J. Appl. Phys.*, **33**: 1276 (1962).

[6] R. L. Conger and G. H. Moore, *J. Appl. Phys.*, **34**: 1213 (1963).

throughout the film. As was shown in Sec. 9.2, a comparatively simple mathematical treatment of this switching mode can be carried out by combining the expression of the free energy, Eq. (8.9), with the Landau–Lifshitz equation of motion of the magnetization, Eq. (10.10).

It is of interest to compare the switching times of thin films with those of ferrite cores and Moly-Permalloy tape. This is done in Fig. 12.2. Depending upon the operating conditions, it is seen from the figure that the rotation mode is 10 to 100 times faster than the mode normally characterizing ferrite or tape core switching, i.e., domain wall motion.

12·2   MEMORY APPLICATIONS

As we discussed in the last section, magnetic thin films could function as memory elements by utilizing the bistable states of their rectangular hysteresis loops. We have also briefly reviewed the various mechanisms of magnetization reversal. Our study so far, however, has been on the behavior of a single film. In memory applications, we must consider the behavior of an assembly of films interconnected by coupling lines to form a computer memory system. Thus, we have to consider such topics as the simultaneous excitation of a number of elements and the magnetostatic coupling between adjacent films.

(a) Selection System

Fields can be applied in the plane of the film by driving current through strips passing over the film and substrate. These strips can be made by printed circuit techniques and therefore complete sets of conductors can be laid over the film quite simply. The width of strips used may, typically, be 50 or 100 mils with an interstrip spacing of the same order. The areas of the film used for storage may be deposited as discrete spots or may be selected from a continuous sheet of film by the field pattern developed by the current in the conductors. However, for simplicity and clarity, the memory shall be considered as consisting of discrete elements in what follows. It is of interest to note that ferrite cores, unlike thin films, must be threaded individually by a difficult and expensive process. Thus, this fact represents an important economic advantage of thin films when compared with ferrite cores. Of course, films, in contrast to cores, have the disadvantage of an open flux path which may increase the coupling between neighboring spots. A number of selection schemes have been proposed which vary widely in effectiveness.[7-11] We shall examine here the two most important ones; these selection schemes are known as the coincident-current system and the cross-field system.

The coincident-current system is widely used in ferrite core storage systems[12] and has also been proposed for use with thin films.[7] In this scheme, both reading and

---

[7] A. V. Pohm and S. M. Rubens, *Proc. Eastern Joint Computer Conference*, December, 1959, p. 120.

[8] J. I. Raffel, *J. Appl. Phys.*, **30**: 60S (1959).

[9] E. E. Bittman, *Electronics*, **32**: 55 (1959); *IRE Trans. Elec. Compt.*, **EC8**: 92 (1959).

[10] Remington Rand UNIVAC, *Proj. Lighting, 2nd Phase, 1st Quart. Rept.*, NObsr, February 28, 1957, pp. 45–47.

[11] E. M. Bradley, *Electronics*, **33**: 78 (1960); *J. Brit. Inst. Rad. Engrs.*, **20**: 765 (1960).

[12] J. W. Forrester, *J. Appl. Phys.*, **22**: 44 (1951).

writing operations are performed by coincident currents. Consider Fig. 12.3(a) show-ing the rectangular easy-axis hysteresis loop with coercive force H_c of a few oersteds and the two remanent states $+M_r$ and $-M_r$, designated by 1 and 0 as indicated in the figure. In addition, a sense loop oriented perpendicular to the easy axis is placed around the film to detect a change of flux in the easy direction.

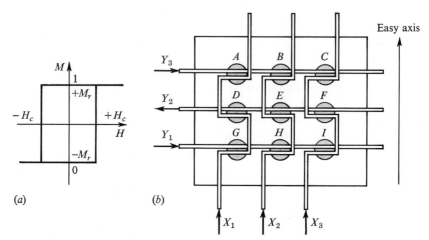

FIG. 12.3.　(a) Easy-axis M-H loop and (b) a 9-bit coincident-current matrix (adopted from C. I. Cowan, Ref. 13).

The operation of this type of memory scheme is as follows.[13] Assume that the film is initially in state 1. Now, if a field of $-H_c/2$ is applied by passing a suitable current through one strip there will be no change of flux and there will be no output from the sense loop for a perfectly rectangular loop. Also repeated application of $-H_c/2$ should not affect the film very much if the loop is highly rectangular although in practice there will be a small change of flux initially.

Now, if a second parallel strip is driven to give a total field of $-H_c$ the core will switch, giving an output voltage at the sense loop and on removal of the field the film will remain at the zero state. On the other hand, if the film were initially in the zero state, applications of $-H_c$ would have produced no flux change and no output voltage. This process then is of "reading" as it allows us to detect whether there was a 0 or 1 stored. The process of "writing" is the converse of the above. As writing will always be carried out after reading, the film is initially in the zero state, so that to write a "1" means applying a total field of $+H_c$.

This method of reading and writing can best be illustrated by a memory plane shown in Fig. 12.3(b). In order to determine the state of film E, a current should be allowed to flow in lines X_2 and Y_2. In this case, film E would be subjected to a full field H_s half of which is supplied by X_2 and by Y_2. On the other hand, films B, D, F, and H are subject to only a half field H_s while films A, C, G and I are not subjected to any fields at all as can be readily seen from an inspection of Fig. 12.3(b). Now, if $H_c < H_s < 2H_c$, film E only will switch to the opposite state. By these means, it is then possible to select one element from a group of n elements with a total of $2\sqrt{n}$ rows and columns, that is, $2\sqrt{n}$ current drivers. This arrangement can be repeated

[13] C. I. Cowan, *Electronic Eng.*, **33**: 642 (1961).

on m planes, where m is the number of bits in the computer word with the corresponding rows and columns on all planes being connected together so that, for example, energizing lines X_2 and Y_2 will drive the elements corresponding to films shown in Fig. 12.3 (b) in each plane. Naturally, the sense lines are separated for each plane. Thus, if the stored word is 10 – – – – then a voltage will be obtained from the sense line on the first plane, no voltage on the second plane, etc.

To write, reverse currents are applied to the appropriate lines and to prevent switching (where a "0" is required) another separate conductor passing over all the elements on each plate parallel to the other strips can also be driven so as to inhibit half the field supplied by these strips. In this case no element on that particular plane will be driven by a field larger than $H_s/2$. Therefore, to write the word 10 – – – –, inhibit current is fed to the first plane, none to the second plane, etc.

To produce a practical memory with the coincident-current selection system, it is clear from the above discussion that the coercive force H_c and the loop squareness ratio of all elements must be practically alike. Otherwise, half-selection currents may have an appreciable switching effect upon the unselected film elements which would have a serious effect upon the storage and noise level properties of the system. In the case of ferrite cores, the required uniformity in their magnetic characteristic can sometimes be obtained by a judicious selection of the cores themselves. In the case of thin films, it is clear that planes rather than individual films must be selected. Although it is difficult to produce large planes with the same coercive force for all films, it has been possible to obtain yields as high as 50% on small planes (32 ten-bit words, say) and these planes are now available from several commercial concerns. It may be noted that the 50% plane yield is comparable to the 50% individual core yield for ferrite memories.

In the coincident current scheme, it is necessary to apply driving fields along the easy axis so that the magnetization reversal proceeds by the rather slow mechanism of domain wall motion as discussed in Sec. 12.1(b). In the case of ferrite cores, domain wall motion appears to be the dominant mechanism for realistic drives so that the aforementioned limitation is not a severe one. On the other hand, for thin films, if the domain wall reversal mode is invoked, the high-speed potentialities of the coherent rotation or incoherent rotational modes are not realized. This situation can be alleviated somewhat by using a system where the film is driven at an angle to the easy axis. Although this scheme would allow the reversal to proceed by some rotational process, it would severely aggravate the problem of half-select currents partially switching the film since the loop will now be less rectangular. (This scheme is of course equivalent to applying switching fields along both the easy and hard axes. We know from the discussion in Sec. 12.1(b) that although the effective coercive force is lowered by the application of the transverse field, the loop becomes S-shaped and less rectangular.) For the level of technological control in the production of thin films to date, it is at present impractical to use the coincident-current selection system herein described.

A word is in order regarding the switching time via domain wall motion in the coincident-current scheme of selection. Since the film will not switch until the applied pulse drive NI exceeds the coercive force, we may write

$$NI_o = CH_S$$

where NI_o is the minimum pulse drive in ampere turns required to switch the film, and C is a constant which depends upon the inertia of the magnetic domains to change direction and, hence, upon the characteristic of the film material. The switching time τ is related to the drive by the following expressions:

$$\tau = \frac{K}{NI - NI_o} \tag{12.3}$$

where K is a constant applicable over a certain range of $(NI - NI_o)$ and is related to the damping or loss mechanisms in the film material. Since the switching field $H_s/2$ supplied by a single drive line must not exceed the coercive force H_c, for otherwise the half-select films would unintentionally switch, it is clear that the minimum switching time in this coincident-current scheme would occur when $NI - NI_o$ corresponds to a field of H_c.

A method of selection which considerably eases the requirement on the magnetic characteristics of the film has been described by Raffel[8] and Raffel et al.[14] Referring to Fig. 12.4(a), consider first the read operation with the magnetization initially in the "1" state. If the drive field with a value larger than H_k is applied along the hard direction, the magnetization will rotate from the direction of the easy axis to that of the hard axis giving rise to an output voltage at the terminals of a sense loop oriented with its axis along the easy direction as illustrated in Fig. 12.4(b). If the film were initially in the "0" state, the direction of the flux change and the phase of the output voltage would be reversed. Upon removal of the drive field, the magnetization would be in a state of instability. If, however, a digit field is applied along the easy direction before the drive field has been removed, **M** will switch either to the "0" or "1" state depending upon the direction of the digit field as illustrated in Fig. 12.4(c). Furthermore, if the digit field is less than the coercive force of the film, it should have no effect upon a film which has not been switched to the hard direction by the drive field. Fig. 12.4(d) shows the relative timing of the pulses, used in such a cross-field selection system. Note the output voltage occurs only due to the rise and fall of the drive currents and that the second pulse is superfluous and is therefore usually gated out.

A slightly different mode of operation may be used in order to eliminate the need for both a "1" and "0" digit driver.[14] A dc current in the "0" direction flows continuously, and a "1" pulse twice as large overrides the dc for writing "1's". The only difference between the two modes is that the "1" and "0" signals are equal but opposite in polarity for the first, while in the second, the dc bias during read time increases the "1" and decreases the "0" signal.

An alternate system which requires also only one set of digit current drivers has also been described.[11] Here the elements are driven at an angle of about $5°$ to the hard direction and since **M** is not brought to the unstable position, the anisotropy torque at an angle of $85°$ from the easy axis acts to return the film to the "1" state, so that only one direction of digit current pulse is required to return **M** to the "0" state. The disadvantage of this method is that tighter control must be exercised over the dispersion of the easy axis. This problem has been successfully solved by depositing a continuous film of an alloy known as Gyrolloy I onto an aluminum plate and using current-carrying wires to define the active film area. (It is claimed that a small addition of Co to the Ni-Fe alloy on aluminum substrate reduces

---

[14] J. I. Raffel et al., *Proc. IRE*, **49**: 155 (1961). (Details of the circuits of representative film memory drivers and sense amplifiers can also be found in this reference.)

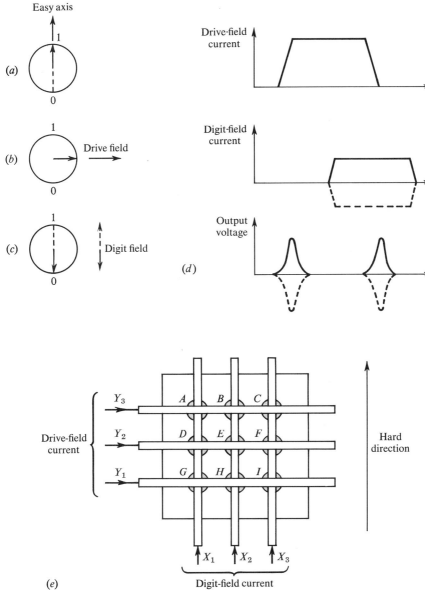

FIG. 12.4. Cross-field switching scheme (after C. I. Cowan, Ref. 13).

easy-axis dispersion by about a factor of 3, although H_k is increased somewhat thereby.[15] The effect of the easy-axis skew upon the performance of memory elements of a continuous film of 80% Ni–17% Fe–3% Co composition deposited on aluminum substrates has also been investigated.[16])

Since the reading process does not inherently provide a means of selection as it does in the case of the coincident-current system, it is necessary to employ a "word-organized" arrangement to build up a memory, rather than the "bit-organized"

[15] E. M. Bradley, *J. Appl. Phys.*, **33**: 1051 (1963).
[16] P. Mussman and M. Williams, *J. Appl. Phys.*, **34**: 1175 (1963).

matrix discussed in the previous section. The difference, from the point of view of the assembly, is that in the word-organized system all bits of a word are on one plane.[17] Fig. 12.4(e) shows a basic system of elements on one plane, with strips for drive and digit current. The sense loop, which is not shown in the figure, is parallel to the digit strip. If a drive current pulse is fed to strip Y_3 bit films, A, B, and C will be switched to the hard direction, producing a voltage at the sense lines of phase dependent upon whether a "1" or "0" was stored. Before removal of this drive current, digit current pulses can be applied to each strip. The direction of the digit currents will determine whether a "1" or "0" is to be stored in each bit position of the word. The other bits on the plane should be unaffected by the currents. The size of the memory can be expanded quite simply by increasing the number of words on a plane and by increasing the number of planes.

The major advantages of the cross-field selection system as compared with the coincident-current scheme are[13]

1. A relaxation in the material requirements since the coercive force and squareness of the easy-axis loop need not be so closely controlled.

2. The wide tolerances allowable in operating currents, since in practice, the drive-field current is limited only by a lower threshold, and the digit-field current can be between limits set, on the one hand, by anisotropy torque due to the maximum angular misalignment of the film with respect to the field and, on the other hand, by the coercive force. Typical values of current amplitudes would be drive-field current $\simeq 0.75$ A, digit-field current $\simeq 0.25$ A with a strip of about 1 mm (~ 40 mils) wide.

3. The output signals corresponding to "0" and "1" read-out are of equal amplitude but of opposite phase. This eases the problem of amplifying the output signal in the presence of noise. A typical signal level may be 3 or 4 mV with an approximate pulse duration of 0.1 μsec.

(b) Film Geometry

Heretofore, we have been concerned only with films of planar geometry. Actually, films could also be deposited on long glass tubes in the presence of a circumferential magnetic field.[18] Thus, the easy axis of the film is also circumferential while the hard axis is along the axis of the cylinder. In contrast to the case of planar films, the flux path is closed in cylindrical films and this fact should, other things being equal, enhance the rectangularity of the easy-axis loop. It further follows that it should be possible to use much thicker films in the cylindrical geometry (10,000 Å, say) and still retain a single-domain state.

If the magnetic film is first subjected to a saturating axial magnetic field, reduction of this field to zero would leave the film in a multidomain state. Subsequent application of a pulse with small amplitude and duration along a wire threading the glass tube substrate then switches the film into a "1" or "0" circumferentially magnetized state. If another axial wire is inserted into the tube, destructive read-out may be accomplished. The destructive axial read-out field is supplied by currents in a multiturn coil coaxial with the tube and external to each film. Although the output signal of a given film is proportional to the cross-sectional area and the length of the film, it is independent of its diameter. Thus, in principle, the inner diameter of the glass

---

[17] W. A. Renwick, *Proc. Inst. Elec. Engrs.*, **104B**: 436 (1957).
[18] G. R. Hollman, J. A. Turner, and T. Kilburn, *J. Brit. Inst. Radio Engrs.*, **20**: 31 (1960).

substrate could be made very small thereby minimizing the currents required to change the state of the film, This, coupled with the much larger permissible thickness of the cylindrical film, as mentioned above, and the decoupling due to orthogonality of the read and read-out fields, presents definite advantages over the planar films. However, it should be noted that the saturating axial read field has to be comparatively larger which increases the demand on the associated circuitry.

The foregoing scheme enables us to observe film hysteresis under pulse field conditions.[18] As the amplitude of a write pulse is increased from zero, the integrated output emf first remains at a fixed negative amplitude due to the set pulse; then when the write pulse reaches the knee of the hysteresis loop, the signal reduces in amplitude until it is zero at the pulse coercive force. Further increase in amplitude changes the sign of the output signal and the amplitude increases to the reversed saturation level. In contrast to the low-frequency hysteresis looper, this scheme enables us to measure the pulse coercive force thus allowing a better assessment of the dynamic performance of a film memory. In this way, it has been found that the pulse coercive force increases as the pulse duration is reduced, and in addition, the rectangularity of the loop deteriorates.

The disturb threshold in cylindrical memory wire has been investigated by Gianola.[19] The measured thresholds for the circumferential and axial fields were found to be smaller than that predicted by the rotational model. Furthermore, the threshold levels were found to be sensitively dependent upon the nature and the sequence of the applied fields. For example, a pulse field applied many times in a direction normal to the magnetization is considerably more effective in reducing the threshold levels than a dc field of the same amplitude. The effect of reduced threshold upon the performance of the memory is also discussed.

A magnetic element consisting of a silver-coated glass rod upon which is electro-plated a Permalloy film may be used to perform both storage and logical functions.[20] A single element for a coincident-current memory requiring two inputs, an inhibit winding, and a sense winding would consist of four separate single-layer concentric solenoids wound over the magnetic rod. The rod is also suitable as a multi-input logical switch. Separate inhibiting windings wound over the rod perform the NOR function of its input literals.

Magnetic devices which utilize a helical flux path along a cylindrical wire were first studied by Bobeck.[21] The helical flux path is accomplished by an applied torsion on a magnetic wire, the effect of which is to shift the direction of magnetization into a helical path inclined at an angle of 45° with respect to the axis. This device, called the twistor, could also be fabricated by electroplating a ferromagnetic material (Ni-Fe or Ni-Fe-Mo) on a wire upon the surface of which a helical microstratch is applied.[22] In this way, a helical easy axis is developed without the application of a torsion to the wire which is a rather expensive step in the twistor fabrication process.

The write process is composed of passing currents through the twistor and a coaxial solenoid such that the resultant magnetic field will switch the film from one helical direction of easy magnetization to the other. Read-out of stored information is accomplished by sensing across the twistor while pulsing the solenoid with a

[19] V. F. Gianola, *J. Appl. Phys.*, **34**: 1131 (1963).
[20] D. A. Meier, *J. Appl. Phys.*, **30**: 45S (1959).
[21] A. H. Bobeck, *Bell System Tech. J.*, **36**: 1319 (1957).
[22] S. J. Schwartz and J. S. Sallo, *IRE Trans. Electronic Computers*, **EC-8**: 465 (1959).

current sufficient to saturate the film in the helical sense opposite to the existing state of magnetization.

Yet another geometry has been used in the woven-screen technique which represents an attempt to produce a large number of elements in a single structure. The technique consists of weaving an array of insulated and conducting wires, then plating the conducting wires with magnetic material, thereby forming square "toroids" with prefabricated sense and drive wires.[23] The platings in general have been of nickel-iron alloys and most of these have been in the neighborhood of 80 Ni–20 Fe, or close to the zero magnetostriction point of the system. The substrate can be divided into two areas: (1) base material and (2) interface layer. The base material, which may be copper or aluminum, is the bare metal wire which is woven into the plane. The most usable interface layers have been found to be gold, tin, nickel, copper, and rhodium.

The woven-screen memory has been envisioned as a word-organized memory with a 3:1 selection ratio. Interestingly, Wells, Davis, Howard, and Cann[23] estimated that by extending conventional techniques, the cost of the memory elements alone of a random access linear-select memory of 1 million fifty-bit words is some 85% of the total cost of the memory. On the other hand, the woven-screen memory technique offers a means of fabricating large memories economically. It is estimated that for large memory planes the cost of the memory elements could be reduced to less than 1 cent per bit. Using a 1-cent per bit figure, the cost of the 1 million word memory considered above would be reduced to 32% of that constructed using conventional techniques. Correspondingly, the cost of the memory elements now is only 53% rather than 85% of the total cost.

(c) Coupled Films

One of the major limitations of the single spot memory element is the existence of a permissible upper bound to its thickness to diameter ratio. If the thickness to diameter ratio of the spot is larger than this maximum value, the film breaks up into multidomains in its plane in order to minimize the magnetostatic energy. This is so because the tendency for the magnetization to have a component along the film normal increases as the film thickness increases. However, since the demagnetizing energy in the direction perpendicular to the plane of the film is very large, it would be energetically more favorable for the film to break up into planar domains so that the magnetization could remain in the plane of the film. Of course, when this state occurs, due to too large a film thickness per diameter ratio, the bistable single-domain storage feature of the film is destroyed. Some means of overcoming this limitation so as to maximize the output signal (due to increase in thickness and/or to increase in the spot density (due to decrease in diameter)) is clearly of interest.

The conflicting requirements of single-domain bits in close packing and of large signal can be reconciled by using two superposed identical films with antiparallel magnetization. The resulting closed magnetic structure, as shown in Fig. 12.5(a), reduces magnetostatic fields so that films of increased thickness to diameter ratio

---

[23] P. E. Wells *et al.*, "Investigation of Woven Screen Memory Techniques." Paper presented at the Symposium on Large Capacity Memory Techniques for Computing Systems, Washington, D.C., May 23–25, 1961.

remain single domains. This structure has been proposed and studied by various investigators.[24-29]

The use of pairs of thin films as memory cells with nondestructive read-out has also been investigated.[30, 31] These are NDRO schemes which utilize a film with high threshold for storing information and another with low threshold for read-out. They all operate on the general principle of storing a binary digit in one film and sensing its remanent state by switching the second film in such a way that the magnetic state of the first is altered.

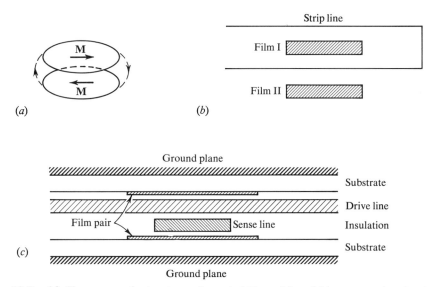

FIG. 12.5. (a) Close magnetic structure of coupled films; (b) and (c) two associated strip-line configurations for coupled films (after H. Chang, Ref. 26, and T. Smay, Ref. 29, respectively).

Several strip-line coupled-film configurations may be devised, one of which is illustrated in Fig. 12.5(b). In this arrangement, a strip line wraps both films, or just one film to provide the same or different fields to the two films. More than one strip line is used to provide fields in different directions or to sense various components of flux changes.[26] Films prepared by multilayer evaporation without breaking vacuum (Ni-Fe, Cu, SiO) were found to possess more homogeneous properties than those prepared by other methods. An airgap between films of 2.4×10^4 Å was found adequate in sustaining single domains in film pairs with dimensions and H_c which result in partial demagnetization in the uncoupled configuration.

[24] A. V. Pohm and E. N. Mitchell, *IRE Trans. Electronic Computers*, **EC-9**: 308 (1960).

[25] J. C. Suits and E. W. Pugh, *J. Appl. Phys.*, **33**: 1057 (1962).

[26] H. Chang, *IBM J. Res. Develop.*, **6**: 419 (1962).

[27] H. Chang, A. Yelon, and O. Vogeli, *J. Appl. Phys.*, **34**: 1209 (1963).

[28] H. Chang, *IBM Res. Note NC-191*, January 4, 1963; also presented at the International Conference on Nonlinear Magnetics in Washington, D.C., April, 1963.

[29] T. Smay, "Energy Transfer Properties of Thin Magnetic Film Coupled Pair Logic Elements." Paper presented at the International Conference on Nonlinear Magnetics in Washington, D.C., April, 1963.

[30] L. J. Oakland and T. D. Rossing, *J. Appl. Phys.*, **30**: 54S (1959).

[31] R. J. Petschaver and R. D. Turnguist, *Proc. Western Joint Computer Conf.*, **19**: 411 (1961).

Another film-coupling line configuration is shown in Fig. 12.5(c).[29] In this arrangement sense-line coupling is not limited by substrate thickness, and image currents flowing in the enclosing ground planes tend to restrict drive-line fields to drive-line vicinity, minimizing the problem of interaction between adjacent bit locations, thus allowing larger packing densities. A theoretical and experimental investigation of the effect of the coupling strip lines upon the dynamic behavior of the film magnetization in high-speed switching applications has been made by Smay. Flux penetration time constants for the strip lines were also estimated.

A rather extensive analysis of the static and quasidynamic behavior of coupled films has been given by Chang.[26] Using the constant field contour plots in the θ_1-θ_2 plane (θ's being the stable orientations of the M's), we can predict multiple stable states, switching threshold, hysteresis, and the detailed paths of magnetization changes as a function of the applied field. Whereas the method of analysis is quite similar to that of uncoupled films, the mathematical formation of the problem and the presentation of results are quite different due to the fact that the orientations of the M's have to be represented by two dependent variables.

Chang also studied the threshold and switching properties of coupled films for the case where the flux reversal is one of rotation.[28] The calculation shows that nearly identical rotational switching speeds occur for single and coupled films, and this prediction has been verified by experiment. (However, J. C. Suits and E. W. Pugh[32] found by magneto-optical means that whereas the switching times for 50% of the film are the same for coupled and uncoupled films, the switching time for 90% of the material is considerably shorter for sandwich elements than for corresponding bits. This may be due to the fact that the films used by Suits and Pugh are not as homogeneous as those used by Chang *et al.*[27] Thus, uncoupled and coupled inhomogeneous films may switch predominantly by incoherent and coherent rotation respectively.) Experimental study of internal field, dispersion, creeping as well as switching speed has also been examined.[27] It was found that coupled films were not susceptible to the word field disturb from neighboring lines. Coupling should make the dispersion of the easy axis less effective in inducing the films to break into multidomains after being subjected to a hard-direction field. Creeping should also be reduced as the number of domains is reduced due to dipolar coupling between films. However further experiments are required to quantitatively substantiate these predictions.

In the foregoing discussion, the films used were composed of a SiO layer sandwiched between two Permalloy films. Multilayer films could also be formed by depositing different films in direct contact with each other. The investigation of a configuration consisting of an electrodeposited uniaxial Permalloy in contact with an electrodeposited isotropic 97Fe-3Ni film on a Be-Cu wire substrate has been reported.[33] It was found that the easy-axis hysteresis loops of these multilayer films are likewise rectangular but with no evidence of the step observed in gross, heterogeneous, magnetic structures. It was also found that the coercive force H_c of these films is a complicated function of the ratio of the thickness of the layers. It is interesting to note that at values of drive fields near H_c of the multilayer, the shape of switching curves was similar to that of the uniaxial Permalloy; but as the drive field

---

[32] J. C. Suits and E. W. Pugh, *J. Appl. Phys.*, **33**: 1057 (1962).
[33] A. Kolk, L. Douglas, and G. Schrader, *J. Appl. Phys.*, **33**: 1061 (1962).

was increased, the shape began to resemble that of the isotropic layer. The switching behavior of these multilayer films has been found to be compatible with the nucleation and growth of domain walls.

The magnetostatic interaction between films in a sandwich configuration has been studied theoretically and experimentally.[34] In particular, localized magnetostatic interactions between the films, such as the effect of the localized fringing field of a domain wall in one film on the neighboring magnetization distribution of the adjacent film, were investigated.

(d) Read-Out and Testing Methods

The information stored in a thin-film memory can be read out by electrical, magneto-optical, or resonance techniques. In what follows, we shall briefly describe these various methods.

A common method for achieving nondestructive read-out is to apply a pulse transverse field $H_\perp$ to a film and sense the voltage induced in the easy-axis loop by the magnetization rotation as has already been discussed in Sec. 12.1(a). Now, the critical angle of rotation, beyond which the film would break up into multidomains thus destroying the stored information, may be as small as $15°$.[35] Therefore, the flux change and the corresponding output is usually small while the magnitude of the $H_\perp$ pulse must be carefully controlled. This severe restriction on the amount of permissible rotation may be eliminated if a passive R–L loading loop is wound on the film with its axis along the easy direction of magnetization.[36] When $H_\perp$ is applied, a current I_s is induced in this loop. This current tends to oppose the magnetization rotation, and if the $H_\perp$ pulse terminates while I_s has an appreciable value, the opposing field causes $\mathbf{M}$ to be restored to its original orientation.

Nondestructive read-out may also be accomplished by optical interrogation techniques.[37] This type of read-out would make use of the longitudinal magneto-optical effect, by which an incident beam of plane-polarized light reflected from a magnetized surface is rotated by an amount determined by the direction of magnetization. As we discussed in Chap. 2, the degree of rotation is detected by an optical polarization analyzer and a photomultiplier. Thus, read-out from small regions of a film can be accomplished by scanning it with a high intensity light spot. Spurious variations in surface reflectivity of the films are sufficiently small so that parts of the film magnetized in opposite directions can be clearly determined. There are several advantages that an optical interrogation method has over the conventional electrical read-out system. For example, the read-out is completely nondestructive and is not affected by drive and other currents. From experimental evidence, it appears that information rates of greater than 1 Mc/sec could be obtained, and reading and writing density of 10^6 bits per cm^2 appears feasible.

The Kerr rotation of light reflected from thin ferromagnetic films has been found to depend on the optical properties of the substrate as well as that of the material itself.[38] Rotations greater than the thick-film longitudinal Kerr rotation were observed at certain thickness of ferromagnetic films deposited on silver substrates.

[34] H. W. Fuller and D. L. Sullivan, *J. Appl. Phys.*, **33**: 1063 (1962).

[35] R. M. Sanders and T. D. Rossing, *J. Appl. Phys.*, **29**: 288 (1958).

[36] J. M. Daughton *et al.*, *J. Appl. Phys.*, **32**: 36S (1961).

[37] R. L. Conger and J. F. Tomlinson, *J. Appl. Phys.*, **33**: 1059 (1962).

[38] A. J. Kolk and M. Orlovic, *J. Appl. Phys.*, **34**: 1060 (1963).

A read-only memory device has been developed using thick films.[39] It consists of a relatively thick film sandwiched between the conductors of a strip transmission line. A current applied to the strip line magnetizes the film in the hard direction. Upon removal of the drive current, the film relaxes toward a multidomain state providing the film thickness is sufficiently large that the demagnetizing field in its plane exceeds its coercive force. Experimental and theoretical results indicate that both the switching and relaxation of these films take place in time intervals as short as 3 nsec with an applied field of 2 nsec rise and decay times. Individual elements have been operated with a pulse repetition rate of 20 Mc/sec.

Nondestructive read-out of magnetic film memories could also be accomplished by a uhf ferromagnetic resonance technique.[40] If a field $H < H_c$ is applied along the easy axis, the resonance frequency of the film is either increased or decreased from its value at $H = 0$ depending upon whether $\mathbf{H}$ is parallel or antiparallel to $\mathbf{M}$. According to Eq. (10.22), the resonance frequency as a function of the applied field is given by

$$f_o = f_k\sqrt{1 \pm \frac{H}{H_k}} \qquad (12.4)$$

where $f_k = \gamma\sqrt{4\pi M H_k}$ is the resonance frequency of the film in the anisotropy field H_k and demagnetizing field $4\pi M$. The plus sign in Eq. (12.4) corresponds to the parallel case, the minus sign to the antiparallel case. This asymmetry provides the possibility of a method for sensing the direction of the magnetizing vector and therefore the state of the film. Note that Eq. (12.4) is applicable only if $H < H_c$; when $H > H_c$, the film switches by domain wall motion giving rise to an abrupt change in the resonance signal. When $H > H_c$ the relative direction of $\mathbf{H}$ and $\mathbf{M}$ changes from antiparallel to parallel so that the $+$ and $-$ signs in Eq. (12.4) should be interchanged accordingly. This phenomenon has been studied in Sec. 8.3(c) in connection with the resonance method of measuring the coercive force.

In the resonance read-out experiment, the film is placed under a strip transmission line which is driven by a uhf generator and is terminated by a video diode detector. The easy axis of the film, being axial in orientation, is perpendicular to the transverse uhf magnetic field and parallel to the interrogation field $\mathbf{H}$ which is applied by means of an orthogonal winding. Thus, nondestructive read-out can thus be accomplished by applying a longitudinal interrogation field of magnitude $H < H_c$ while driving the transmission line at a frequency above or below f_k. Depending upon whether the detected resonance frequency f_o is larger or smaller than f_k, one can ascertain the initial state of the film. Experimentally, it has been found that the unamplified pulse outputs of the detector are typically 2 to 6 mV with 5 to 15 mW of rf driving power with interrogation pulses as narrow as 7 nsec and at a repetition rate of 7 Mc/sec. This resonance read-out technique with its potentially low access time and good read-out signal/noise ratio should be adaptable to medium-sized, semipermanent storage-type memories.

Film memories are usually subjected to quasistatic and a sequence of pulse tests.[14] Low-frequency composite characteristics of arrays of spots can be measured with a hysteresis looper in the same manner as for individual films (see Chap. 8).

[39] R. E. Matick, *J. Appl. Phys.*, **34**: 117 (1963).
[40] H. D. Toombs and T. E. Hasty, *Proc. Inst. Radio Engrs.*, **50**: 1526 (1962).

The characteristics of a spot within an array under pulse-switching conditions may be measured by means of a pulse tester. To ensure identical test conditions for all spots and to minimize the amount of test equipment required, a mechanical manipulator is used to index the array under the only set of crossed drive lines, and a sense coil used.

Three pulse tests are given to every element in each array. These are (1) the ONE amplitude test, (2) the read-disturb test and (3) the transverse disturb test.[14, 41]

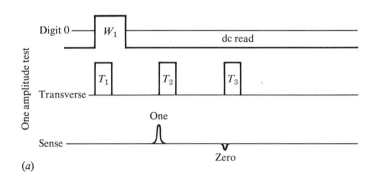

(a)

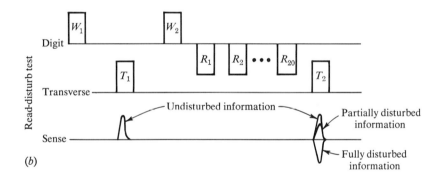

(b)

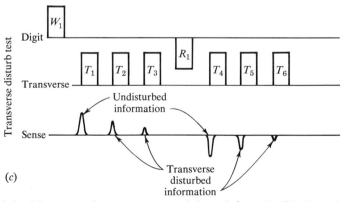

(c)

FIG. 12.6. Memory pulse test sequence (adopted from Raffel, Crowther, Anderson, and Herndon, Ref. 14, and Anderson and Crowther, Ref. 41).

41 A. H. Anderson and T. S. Crowther, *MIT Lincoln Lab. Group Rept.* #*51–11*, January, 1960.

The ONE amplitude test simulates the memory cycle[8] with the pulse sequence given in Fig. 12.6(a). This test is performed twice, the second time with read and write polarities interchanged. A difference between ONE amplitudes for the two digit polarities indicates skew of the easy axis; the ONE amplitude will be low if the transverse (read) field makes an acute angle with the ONE state direction due to skew. If both ONE amplitudes are low, the reason may be high H_k or read-disturbing. If H_k is too high, the combination of longitudinal and transverse fields will fall short of the switching threshold requirement (see Sec. 12.1 and Fig. 9.2). On the other hand, read-disturbing results if the read field is larger than the coercive force. A second pulse sequence, as shown in Fig. 12.6(b), is then used to determine whether or not read-disturbing is the cause of any low outputs. In this read-disturb test, the film is magnetically saturated along the easy axis by large write pulses W_1 and W_2. The two transverse pulses will generate identical outputs unless the read pulses are of sufficient amplitude to cause complete or partial switching. The final transverse disturb test determines how well a film will operate in the nondestructive read mode. Here, the film is again saturated along the easy axis by a large write pulse W_1. Then a number of transverse pulses follow. A film is defined as being transverse disturbed if the sensed pulse amplitude occurring during the rise time of succeeding transverse pulses is less than that obtained from the first. A saturating read pulse R is also used to repeat the transverse disturb situation for the ZERO state.

We shall not consider the details of the pulse test equipment here; a detailed description of it can be found in Ref. 41.

12·3 LOGIC ELEMENTS

Thin films may be utilized as logic devices in the form of a shift register, AND and OR or inverter element, a parametron, or a flip-flop circuit. In this section, we shall describe the operation of each of these devices briefly.

(a) Individual and Array Film Logic

AND logic could be performed using either the easy-axis or hard-axis loop of a thin film.[42] In the former case, a transverse sense loop would pick up a voltage due to magnetization changes only if both a transverse biasing field (input x) and a longitudinal switching field (input y) are applied. In other words, the output is proportional to xy. If the biasing field is zero and the switching field is less than the coercive force of the film, the state of the film clearly would not change so that the output is zero. On the other hand, if a biasing field is present, application of the switching field, however small, would cause the magnetization to rotate giving rise to an output.

For AND logic using the transverse loop, let us look at Fig. 12.7(a). The film is initially biased to the P_2 state. A bias field H_B, corresponding to logical input y, then causes a change in the state of the film. Since the change is in the steep region of the transverse loop, a transverse output voltage appears in the sense line. This voltage corresponds to a logical output of x and y. Note that an output is obtained only if H_B is less than the difference between the fields corresponding to states P_2 and P_1.

---

[42] A. Franck, G. F. Marette, and B. I. Parsegyan, *1959 Eastern Joint Computer Conf. Proc.*, p. 28.

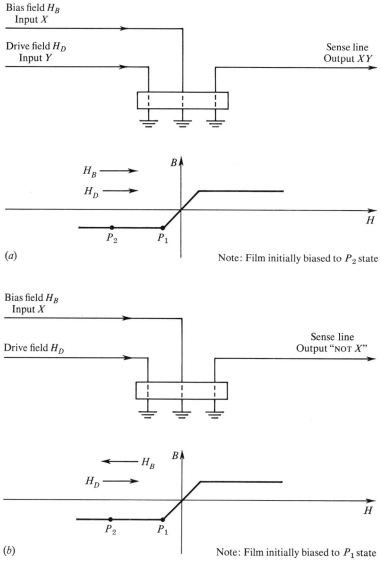

FIG. 12.7. (a) AND logic (saturable-transformer mode) and (b) inverter logic (saturable transformer mode) (after Franck, Marette, and Parsegyan, Ref. 42).

Fig. 12.7(b) shows a simple method of obtaining logical inversion, i.e., negation, using the transverse loop of a thin film. The film shown in the figure is initially biased to the P_1 state. A bias field H_B, corresponding to logical input x, biases the film to the P_2 state. Application of a drive field H_D in a direction opposite to H_B then merely biases the film back toward P_1 if it is not of sufficient strength to drive the film into the steep portion of the hysteresis loop. Consequently, no voltage is induced on the sense winding representing a NOT x logical output. If, on the other hand, the bias field H_B were absent, meaning a NOT x input, the film would remain in its original biased state at P_1. Application of a drive field H_D would then induce a voltage on the sense winding which would correspond to output x.

Functional-array logic can be illustrated by a scale factoring device whose function is to find the most significant digit in a binary word, to shift that word to the left until the most significant digit is in a position immediately to the right of the position reserved for the sign bit, and to record the number of places shifted in an auxiliary register. The details of the method are given in Ref. 42.

(b) Domain Wall Logic

A shift register in which binary information is stored and translated in and along a continuous film has been constructed.[43] These thin magnetic film shift registers are capable of storing information having a density of several hundred bits per square inch of film and of translating this amount of information at bit rates in excess of a megacycle with powers of less than 10 watts. The basic simplicity of continuous shifting systems which eliminate the usual cell-to-cell coupling networks makes such an approach rather attractive. A difference between the energy required to establish or create a particular domain configuration and that required to translate the given domain configuration a distance through the film can be made to exist. This energy difference allows these "written" domains to be moved unilaterally under the influence of periodically pumped forcing fields without these fields introducing any spurious information. Thus, a configuration may be devised in which it is possible to drive propagating electrodes hard enough to move domains, but not hard enough to create them; the domain is created by a separate writing electrode and current. Details of construction and operation of an experimental film register will not be discussed here but can be found in Ref. 43.

Propagation of a domain through the film consists of translating the walls of the domain in phase to preserve the essential configuration. Thus, a stringent requirement is placed upon the uniformity of the film. However, this is a common problem with elements whose operation depends upon rather small portions of a film.

The two opposite senses of rotation of spins in a domain wall (Néel or Bloch) as well as the bistable states of an uniaxial film, can be utilized to represent binary information.[44] The simplest utilization of domain wall coding would be in a shift register; thus methods of read-in, shifting and read-out are required. AND, OR, and complementing operations are also conceptually possible. Furthermore, logical operations, such as conditional and unconditional erase, can be performed by using the fact that when two walls of opposite sense are brought together they will destroy each other, but if of same sense they do not necessarily do so but can form a double wall which can be separated into two walls again. Thus, erasure occurs on condition that the walls have opposite sense.

In order to be useful as a storage medium, walls of known sense have to be injected into the material. This can be accomplished by reversing the magnetization of a localized region by means of a locally applied field so that walls of opposite sense appear on opposite sides of the region. Then shifting can be accomplished by applying to the material a field with a proper spatial distribution by means of a slanted double winding. The logical functions AND and OR can be performed by the sequence of operations (1) juxtaposition, (2) conditional erase, and (3) read-in; in the juxtaposition operation, data from two input strips are juxtaposed into an

[43] K. D. Broadbent, *IRE Trans. Electronic Computers*, **EC-9**: 321 (1960).
[44] D. O. Smith, *IRE Trans. Electronic Computers*, **EC-10**: 708 (1961).

output strip. Finally, complementation might be accomplished with laterally offset strips. If the correct strip dimension and film thickness are used, a Néel wall entering the wide region connecting the input and output strips should become two Néel segments in order to minimize the wall magnetostatic energy. The lower Néel segment is the complement of the upper, and hence the output will be the complement of the input.

The operations of read-in, shifting, conditional erase, and fan-out in a system of domain wall storage and logic proposed by Smith[44] have been experimentally demonstrated.[45] These operations were performed by controlling the current flowing through a narrow-spaced grid of series-connected parallel wires placed closely under a 5 to 40 mil wide, 50 to 300 Å thick Permalloy strip. The sequence of events was observed on the top side of the film using the Bitter technique.

Walls were read in singly, in pairs, or as a series, and series of walls were shifted in either direction using the slanted double-layer winding configuration. There appears to be little difference in magnitude between the field required to read in a domain and that required to shift a series of walls along the strip. Thus, it is necessary that no gaps be left in the information train for otherwise an extraneous wall would be read into such gaps during the shifting operation. It was found that the success of the conditional erase operation depends strongly on the uniformity of the wall and the film thickness. Walls must be straight and free of cross ties, breaks, or perturbation trails, since if any of these are present when two walls are brought together, the walls will break at the imperfection and erase each other regardless of sense. Thus, any large scale production of these domain wall logic elements would present a rather acute materials control problem. For films less than 100 Å thick, practically no difference was found between the fields required to erase a pair of walls of the same or opposite sense. In films from 50 to 100 Å thick, however, the field required to erase a pair of walls of the same sense is some 9 to 20 times as large as the 2 Oe field necessary to shift walls and erase pairs of walls of opposite sense. The same wire configuration used for shifting was employed without difficulty to fan out information in a Y strip. The operation of juxtaposing data from double legs of a Y strip into the single leg is more difficult since both legs must be separately controlled.

It is of interest to note that the domain wall logic of Smith utilizes the different sense of spin rotation within a wall while the scheme of Broadbent[43] uses instead domain direction coding.

(c) Parametrons and Flip-Flop Circuits

The use of phase-locked, subharmonic, parametric oscillators as logical elements for computers was first proposed by Goto[46] and Von Neumann[47] in 1954. Since then ferrite and thin-film parametrons which utilize the nonlinear inductance characteristics of ferromagnetic materials and semiconductor diode parametrons which capitalize upon the nonlinear capacitance of the diodes have been built. Ferrite core parametrons operate at low pump frequency while diode parametrons function at microwave

[45] J. M. Ballantyne, *J. Appl. Phys.*, **33**: 1067 (1962).

[46] E. Goto, The Parametron, a New Circuit Component Using Non-linear Reactors, *J. Inst. Elec. Engrs. (Japan)*, **38**: 770 (1955).

[47] J. Von Neumann, Non-linear Capacitance or Inductance Switching, Amplifying and Memory Organs, U.S. Patent No. 2, 815, 488, December 3, 1957.

frequencies. The thin-film parametrons, on the other hand, operate in the tens or hundreds of megacycle range.

Thin-film parametrons were reported by Pohm et al.[48] They have also analyzed the behavior of the parametrons by means of the Landau–Lifshitz equation of motion of the magnetization[49] and considered their application as logic devices.[50] An inductor can be made by winding a magnetic film deposited on a substrate with a pump and signal winding, as shown in Fig. 12.8(a). It is seen that the signal field h_s is applied

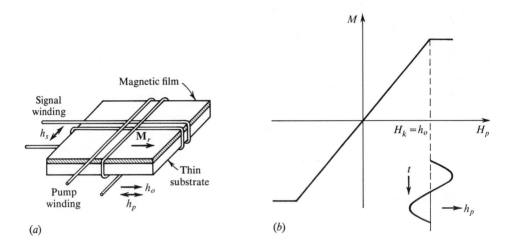

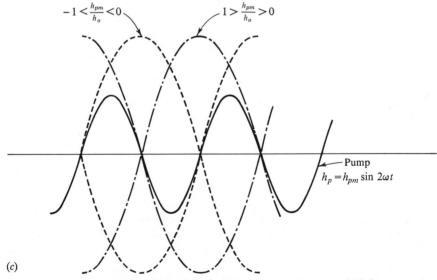

FIG. 12.8.   (a) Magnetic film inductor; (b) thin-film transverse loop; and (c) four parametron phase states (adopted from Schauer, Stewart, Pohm, and Read, Ref. 50).

[48] A. V. Pohm et al., *Proc. Natl. Electronics Conf.*, **15**: 202 (1959).
[49] A. V. Pohm et al., *J. Appl. Phys.*, **31**: 119S (1960).
[50] R. F. Schauer et al., *IRE Trans. Electronic Computers*, **EC-9**: 315 (1960).

along the easy axis while the pump field H_p is applied along the hard axis. The pump field H_p is composed of a constant component h_o and a time-varying component h_p ($<h_o$). Consider first the combined static and time-varying pump fields. For example, if $h_o = H_k$, then we see from the transverse loop of Fig. 12.8(b) that the incremental susceptibility is equal to M/H_k for one half of the pump cycle but is equal to zero for the other half. Thus, the inductor displays a time-variable nonlinear characteristic which, when connected as part of a shunt loaded tank circuit, makes operation as a phase-locked, subharmonic, parametric oscillator possible. If the parametron is tuned to one half of the pump frequency, the circuit will oscillate in either of two stable phase states 180° apart, for a particular pump field polarity and bias field (h_o) polarity. Another set, displaced 90° at the frequency of oscillation, is obtained if either the polarity of the bias field is reversed or the pump field inverted. The four possible stable phase states are as shown in Fig. 12.8(c).

The magnetic film parametron exhibits a hysteresis characteristic, with respect to the pump drive, which is a function of the frequency of oscillation ω and the magnitude of the pump field when $\omega = \omega_o$ where ω_o is the resonance frequency of the tank circuit. Thus, for ω/ω_o greater than the starting threshold for a specific pump magnitude, a certain input excitation is required for the oscillation to build up.

The most common case of parametron operation occurs when an oscillation of half the frequency of excitation is present in the parametrically excited element, and results in exponent build-up of the oscillation. The process is usually described by the equations of Mathieu and Hill:

$$\frac{d^2x}{dt^2} + \omega_o^2(1 + \Gamma \sin 2\omega t)x = 0 \qquad (12.5)$$

where x has an exponentially increasing solution when ω/ω_o lies within any of the specified intervals, known as unstable regions, that depend upon Γ. For the thin-film parametron, Γ (known as the modulus of parametric excitation) is related to the nonlinear inductance characteristic exhibited in Fig. 12.8(a). For small Γ, the intervals lie in the neighborhood of integral values 1, 2, 3, ... and only the interval about $\omega/\omega_o = 1$ is wide enough to be of practical importance. Since the oscillation phase of a parametron (0 or π) persists as long as the oscillation is maintained, it could function as a memory. Since any small input signal can control the amplitude of the exponentially growing oscillation, the parametron thus amplifies. Since the phase of the stationary states is either 0 or π regardless of the phase of the initial oscillation or input, the parametron also performs a normalizing action.

Another useful logic device is a threshold element, in which the input excitation must reach a minimum level to sustain oscillation. The magnetic film inductor, when suitably clocked, can be used as a gate to permit unilateral flow of information in a system. Proposed designs for a two-element binary adder, a binary shift counter, a shift register, and the possibility of through-state logic with parametrons have been discussed in some detail.[50] Pohm et al. have also shown that operation of film parametrons in the 100 to 500 Mc region is feasible and a way of fabrication with stripline technique is shown.[49]

A flip-flop circuit may be constructed by properly loading an easy-axis oriented loop around a film with a series R–L–C combination. A hard-direction drive field h_d rotates $\mathbf{M}$ toward the hard direction and induces a current i_s in the pickup winding, producing a rest-direction field h_s which opposes the change in flux linkages. If once the capacity is sufficiently charged by i_s and h_d is reduced, this reversed rest direction and the anisotropy field together would cause **M** to seek the rest orientation anti-parallel to the initial one. Thus, by means of successive drive-field pulses, this circuit could function as a flip-flop.

12·4 MICROWAVE AND MISCELLANEOUS APPLICATIONS

Because of the high conductivity of metallic Permalloy films and consequent eddy-current loss, no microwave applications using these films have appeared. However, an experimental V-band resonance isolator using an insulating nickel ferrite film on low-loss aluminum substrate has been tested by Wade et al.[51] The film was positioned at the plane of circular polarization in a rectangular wave guide. The maximum forward-to-reverse loss ratio obtained at 34.8 Gc/sec was 22.7 and > 10 in the frequency range 34.4 to 35.4 Gc/sec. For a nickel-zinc ferrite, the said ratio is 16 at 36.1 Gc/sec.

Variable time delay could be obtained when a magnetic film is incorporated into a strip line.[52] Under the influence of an applied pulse field **M** is deflected coherently through a small angle from the easy axis. Since this deflection gives rise to a high effective permeability (~ 1500), the time delay of the strip line is increased. Experimental results indicated that delays of 2.3 nsec should be typical. Furthermore, it has been found that the delay is decreased when an easy-axis (axial) biasing field is applied. For example, a 20 Oe biasing field decreases the delay time by 5 nsec; also, a biasing field decreases the rise time of the output pulse.

The strip line is made by depositing a silver ground plane, a uniaxial Permalloy film, a SiO insulating layer, and a silver signal conductor on a glass substrate in that order. Thus, the effective transmission line dielectric is made up of the Permalloy and SiO films.

A sensitive field magnetometer has been constructed using a magnetic film as the sensing element.[53] A cyclically varying field ($> H_k$) applied in the average hard direction causes the film to split up into domains parallel to that axis. The net flux which cuts a sensing coil, the axis of which is parallel to the domains, remains zero during such cyclic magnetization. If there is a small component of field along the anisotropy axis, however, the net flux is proportional to that field. This principle forms the bases of the magnetometer.

In the actual device, a 4 Mc/sec source drives the film along the hard axis and a modulation field is applied along the easy axis. In the absence of an ambient field along the easy axis, the diode-rectified and phase-detected signal has a frequency equal to twice that of the modulation field. If an easy-axis ambient field is present, a fundamental frequency component, proportional to the field for small fields, appears. The phase of the signal determines the direction of the field. Fields as low as 10^{-6} Oe and of frequencies from dc to 0.1 the modulation frequency have been detected in this way.

[51] W. Wade et al., J. Appl. Phys., **34**: 1219 (1963).
[52] P. Kurnreich and S. R Pollack, J. Appl. Phys., **34**: 1169 (1963).
[53] F. G. West et al., J. Appl. Phys., **34**: 1163 (1963).

APPENDIX A

INHOMOGENEOUS DEMAGNETIZING FIELD OF CYLINDERS

In Section 5.1(b) we showed that the demagnetizing field in the z direction of a cylinder magnetized perpendicular to the axis and in the z direction is given by Eq. (5.8) as

$$H_z = -M_o \int \frac{(z' - z)dx'r'dr'd\phi'\delta(r' - R)\cos\phi'}{[(x' - x)^2 + (y' - y)^2 + (z' - z)^2]^{3/2}} \tag{A.1}$$

where the geometry of the problem is illustrated in Fig. 5.2. To find H_z at the center of the film, we obtain by straightforward integration of Eq. (5.8) that

$$H_z|_{x=y=z=0} = -2\pi M_o \frac{T}{\sqrt{d^2 + T^2}} \simeq 2\pi M_o\left(\frac{T}{d}\right) \tag{A.2}$$

which corresponds to Eq. (5.9) in the text. Of course, from symmetry we see that $H_x|_{x=y=z=0}$ is also given by Eq. (A.2) if the film were saturated in the x direction. Since $H_x + H_y + H_z = -4\pi M_o$, according to the sum rule for nonellipsoidal samples discussed in Sec. 5.1(b), we find

$$H_x = -4\pi M_o\left(1 - \frac{T}{2\sqrt{d^2 + T^2}}\right) \qquad \text{at } x = y = z = 0$$

For the demagnetizing field at $y = \pm R$ and $z = 0$, we can again easily find H_z by integration of Eq. (A.1). Since the pole density is zero at these points, the integrand is well defined. Thus, we find

$$H_z|_{y=\pm R, z=0} = -4M_o\left\{x_{n+}\sqrt{1 + x_{n+}^2}\left[K\left(\sqrt{\frac{1}{1 + x_{n+}^2}}\right) - E\left(\sqrt{\frac{1}{1 + x_{n+}^2}}\right)\right]\right.$$

$$\left. - x_{n-}\sqrt{1 + x_{n-}^2}\left[K\left(\sqrt{\frac{1}{1 + x_{n-}^2}}\right) - E\left(\sqrt{\frac{1}{1 + x_{n-}^2}}\right)\right]\right\} \tag{A.3}$$

where K and E are the usual tabulated elliptic integrals. Here $x_{n+} = (x + T/2)/d$ and $x_{n-} = (x - T/2)/d$. It is seen from Eq. (A.3) that H_z clearly depends upon the thickness to diameter ratio of the film. However, numerical calculations show that H_z at $y = \pm R$ and $z = 0$ approaches a very small number compared to $4\pi M_o$ as T/d

becomes very small. By symmetry, if the film is saturated instead in the y direction, H_y at $y = 0$, and $z = \pm R$ are also given by Eq. (A.3).

Since the integrand is undefined at $y = 0$ and $z = \pm R$ due to the presence of the delta function, H_z at these points cannot be similarly evaluated. However, we may alternatively obtain its value by the sum rule if H_x at $y = 0$ and $z = \pm R$ could be found.

By an entirely analogous calculation to that shown above, we find that if the film is saturated along its normal, the associated demagnetizing field is given by[1]

$$H_z = -M_o \int \frac{dx' \delta\left(x' + \frac{T}{2}\right) r' dr' d\phi'}{(x' - x)^2 + (y' - y)^2 + (z' - z)^2} \tag{A.4}$$

An evaluation of Eq. (A.4) yields $H_x \simeq -2\pi M_o$ at $x = 0$ and $r = R$. It follows that

$$H_z|_{y=0, z=\pm R} \simeq -2\pi M_o \tag{A.5}$$

Eq. (A.5) was obtained with help of the sum rule for nonellipsoidal samples $H_x + H_y + H_z = -4\pi M_o$ discussed in Sec. 5.1(b). Again, from symmetry arguments, if the film were saturated in the y direction, $H_y \simeq -2\pi M_o$ at $y = \pm R$ and $z = 0$.

---

[1] See also J. R. Eshbach, *J. Appl. Phys.*, **34**: 1298 (1963).

APPENDIX B

NÉEL SURFACE ANISOTROPY ENERGY[1]

We have already discussed some aspects of Néel's two-atom interaction theory in Chap. 7 with regard to the origin of induced uniaxial anisotropy in thin films. Here, we shall employ his same general theory for the determination of surface anisotropy energy in thin films.

In Néel's theory the coupling energy of an atom pair can be expanded in a series of Legendre polynomials, the first term of which corresponds to the ordinary magnetic dipole-dipole coupling. Since the magnetic dipole-dipole coupling is too small to account for the observed magnetostriction, another form of dipole-dipole interaction, probably of spin-orbit coupling origin, is introduced as a parameter. To be more explicit, the energy of interaction $W(r,\phi)$ between two atoms is given by

$$W(r, \phi) = g_1(r)P_2(\cos \phi) + g_2(r)P_4(\cos \phi) + \cdots \tag{7.31}$$

where P_2, P_4, ... are Legendre polynomials. The coefficient of $P_2(\cos \phi)$, namely $g_1(r)$, is the sum of a term due to ordinary dipole-dipole coupling between atoms of moment u and other terms probably due to spin-orbit coupling. Since the spin-orbit interaction decreases more rapidly than $1/r^3$ at large distances, it is sufficient to take only nearest neighbors into account for the spin-orbit term in Eq. (7.31). Assuming that the deviation from the equilibrium radius r_o, that is, $\delta_r = r - r_o$, is very small compared to r_o itself, we find from Eq. (7.31) that

$$W = \left(\frac{-3\mu^2}{r^3} + L + M\delta r\right)\left(\cos^2 \phi - \frac{1}{3}\right) + (Q + S\delta r)\left(\cos^4 \phi - \frac{30}{35}\cos^2 \phi + \frac{3}{35}\right) \tag{7.32}$$

where L, M, Q, and S are coefficients that are dependent upon r_o.

The first term in Eq. (7.32) plays the dominant role in determining the magnetostriction of the material. However, since Becker[2] has shown that the magnetic dipole-dipole interaction accounts for only a small part of the observed magnetostriction, we can ignore the μ^2 term in Eq. (7.32) for this purpose. Utilizing experimental values of magnetostrictive constants for cubic crystals it has been found that L is of the order of 10^8 to 10^9 ergs.[1] For a cubic crystal of constant dimensions, that is, $\delta r = 0$, the mean value of $\cos^2 \phi$ is $\frac{1}{3}$ and the first term in Eq. (7.32) vanishes. We then observed that the form of the cubic anisotropy energy volume density must be determined by the mean value of $\cos^4 \phi$, which is proportional to $\sum_{i,j}' \beta_i \beta_j$ where the β's

---

[1] L. Néel, *Compt. Rend.*, **237**: 1468 (1953); *J. Phys. Radium*, **15**: 225 (1954).
[2] R. Becker, *Z. Physik*, **62**: 253 (1930).

are the direction cosines of the magnetization relative to the quatenary axes of the crystal.

The foregoing discussion is applicable to atoms at the interior but not at the surface of a crystal, whereas the interior atoms are in an environment of complete cubic symmetry; the surface atoms are in an environment of lower symmetry due to the absence of neighbors on the free space side of the crystal surface. In this case, the mean value of $P_2(\cos\phi)$ relative to its neighbors is no longer zero. Whereas the magnetic dipole-dipole term yields the well-known shape demagnetizing field, the spin-orbit term involving L gives rise to a ϕ-dependent surface anisotropy energy density E_s. According to Eq. (7.32), it is given by an expression of the form

$$E_s = K_s \cos^2\theta \qquad\qquad (B.1)$$

where K_s is the surface anisotropy energy density constant and θ is the angle between the spontaneous magnetization and the normal to the surface. The value of E_s depends upon the nature of the lattice structure and the surface orientation as enumerated in Table B.1. The results of this Table, combined with the previous estimate of L, yield a value for K_s of the order of 0.1 to 1 erg/cm^2 for a fcc structure with (111) and (100) planes parallel to the surface.

The foregoing theory can be easily extended to include solid solutions of two constituents A and B. In that case, we have to introduce component energies W_{aa}, W_{ab} and W_{bb} for the A–A, A–B, and B–B interactions, respectively. In particular, for an ideal solution with no correlation between the nature of two nearest neighbors, we find that the quantity L in Eq. (7.32) for a single constituent solution must now be replaced by a composite L, denoted by L_c given by

$$L_c = C_a^2 L_{aa} + 2C_a C_b L_{ab} + C_b^2 L_{bb} \qquad\qquad (B.2)$$

where C_a and C_b are the atomic concentrations for the two constituents A and B respectively.

TABLE B.1 Surface Anisotropy Energy Density E_s

Type of Crystal	Surface Plane	E_s
Face-centered cubic	111	$-L\cos^2\theta/\sqrt{3}r_0^2$
	100	$-L\cos^2\theta/2r_0^2$
	011	$L(\beta_2 - \beta_3)^2/4\sqrt{2}r_0^2$
Body-centered cubic	111	0
	100	0
	011	$-L\beta_2\beta_3/\sqrt{2}r_0^2$
Simple cubic	111	0
	100	$-L\cos^2\theta/2r_0^2$
	011	$L\beta_1^2/2\sqrt{2}r^2$
12 isotropically distributed neighbours		$8L\cos^2\theta/9\sqrt{3}r_0^2$

BIBLIOGRAPHY

The following is a list of references on magnetic thin films. Most of the papers dealing directly with magnetic thin films published mainly between the years 1955 and 1963 in the pertinent physics journals, both in the United States and foreign, are included. It may be recalled here that the age of magnetic thin film began in 1955 with the preparation of Permalloy films by Blois. Listed also are references published in the major engineering journals dealing with applications of thin films as well as papers presented at a number of conferences.

The references are grouped according to the topics covered in different chapters. In order that the bibliography would not be unduly long, we have endeavored to classify each paper according to its major content only. Thus, each paper would usually appear only once in the bibliography. This method of classification has the further advantage of minimizing the amount of reading required for a given subject of special interest. Of course, this is done at the expense of losing some sense of close correlation between various topics.

Papers that do not deal directly with magnetic thin films or that predate the age of magnetic thin films are sometimes referred to in the text but do not explicitly appear in the bibliography, again in the interest of keeping it to a manageable size. If the reader is interested in a particular aspect of magnetic thin film, e.g., its anisotropy, he should consult the proper chapter for discussion and further pertinent references not listed herein.

CHAPTER 1: INTRODUCTION

W. Andra *et al.*, "Ferromagnetic Thin Films I. Introduction," *Phys. Status Solids*, **2**: 99 (1962), in German.

J. B. Goodenough and D. O. Smith, "The Magnetic Properties of Thin Films," in C. A. Neugebauer *et al.*, *Structure and Properties of Thin Films*, John Wiley & Sons, Inc., New York, 1959, p. 112.

D. O. Smith, "Static and Dynamic Behavior of Thin Permalloy Films," *J. Appl. Phys.*, **28**: 264 (1958).

D. O. Smith, "Magnetic Films for Computer Memories," in F. R. Von Hippel (ed.), *Molecular Science and Molecular Engineering*, The Technology Press of MIT, Cambridge, and John Wiley & Sons, Inc., New York, 1959.

CHAPTER 2: PREPARATION OF THIN FILMS

J. C. Anderson, "Preparation and Magnetic Anisotropy of Continuous, Single Crystal Nickel Films," *1961 Trans. 8th Vacuum Symposium and 2nd Internat. Congress*, Pergamon Press, New York, 1962, p. 930.

P. Astwood and M. Prutton, "The Influence of Crucible Material upon the Magnetic Anisotropy of Evaporated Permalloy Films," *Brit. J. Appl. Phys.*, **14**: 48 (1963).

J. Bagrowski and M. Lauriente, "Electroless Ni-Co-P Films with Uniaxial Anisotropy," *J. Electrochem. Soc.*, **109**: 987 (1962).

A. Baltz, "Influence of Vacuum Conditions on Epitaxially Grown Permalloy Films," *J. Appl. Phys.*, **34**: 1575 (1963).

E. Banks *et al.*, "Formation and Study of Thin Ferrite Films," *1960 Vacuum Symposium Trans.*, Pergamon Press, New York, 1960, p. 297.

M. Beckerman and K. H. Behrndt, "The Influence of Edge Effects on Domain Structure and Coercive Force of Circular Ni-Fe Films," *IBM J. Res. Develop.*, **4**: 198 (1960).

K. H. Behrndt, "Large-area Sources and Tow-source Control," *1959 Vacuum Symposium Trans.*, Pergamon Press, New York, 1960, p. 242.

K. H. Behrndt, "The Influence of the Deposition Parameters on the Properties of Evaporated Thin Ferromagnetic Films," *1961 Trans. 8th Vacuum Symposium and 2nd Internat. Congress*, Pergamon Press, New York, 1962, p. 912.

K. H. Behrndt, "Investigation of the Coercive Forces of Nickel, Iron and Nickel–Iron Films During Evaporation," *J. Appl. Phys.*, **33**: 193 (1962).

K. H. Behrndt, "Films of Uniform Thickness Obtained from a Point Source," *1962 Trans. 9th Vacuum Symposium* (The Macmillan Company, New York, 1962), p.111.

K. H. Behrndt, "Influence of the Deposition Conditions on Growth and Structure of Evaporated Films," *Vacuum*, **13**: 337 (1963).

K. H. Behrndt and R. A. Jones, "A Comparison between the Evaporation Characteristics of a Crucible and a Ring Source," *1958 Vacuum Symposium Trans.*, Pergamon Press, New York, 1959, p. 217.

K. H. Behrndt and F. S. Maddocks, "Influence of Substrate Processing on the Magnetic Properties and Reproducibility of Evaporated Nickel–Iron Films," *J. Appl. Phys.*, **30S**: 276 (1959).

R. B. Belser, "Alloying Behavior of Thin Bimetal Films, Simultaneously or Successively Deposited," *J. Appl. Phys.*, **31**: 562 (1960).

P. Benjamin and C. Weaver, "The Adhesion of Evaporated Metal Films on Glass," *Proc. Roy. Soc.* (London), **A261**: 516 (1962).

J. A. Bennett and T. P. Flannagan, "Instruments for Recording the Resistance During the Deposition of a Thin Film," *J. Sci. Instr.*, **37**: 143 (1960).

B. I. Bertelsen, "Silicon Monoxide Undercoating for Improvement of Magnetic Film Memory Characteristics," *J. Appl. Phys.*, **33**: 2026 (1962).

H. Bethge, G. Kastner, and M. Krohn, "Cleavage Structure of NaCl Single Crystals," *Z. Naturforsch.*, **16A**: 321 (1961), in German.

M. S. Blois, Jr., "Preparation of Thin Magnetic Films and Their Properties," *J. Appl. Phys.*, **26**: 975 (1955).

M. S. Blois, Jr., "Evaporated Magnetic Materials," *Electronics*, **28**: 210, June, 1955.

E. M. Bradley, "Properties of Magnetic Films for Memory Systems," *J. Appl. Phys.*, **33**: 1051S (1964).

M. Briggs-Smith, "Visual Monitoring During Vacuum Evaporations," *Rev. Sci. Instr.*, **34**: 191 (1963).

C. J. Calbick, "Electron Microscopy of Glass and Quartz Surfaces for Thin Films," *1960 Vacuum Symposium Trans.*, Pergamon Press, New York, 1961.

S. Chikazumi, "Epitaxial Growth and Magnetic Properties of Single-Crystal Film of Iron," *J. Appl. Phys.*, **32**: 81S (1961).

E. C. Crittenden, Jr., and R. W. Hoffman, "Techniques for Production of Thin Flat Films of Metal by Vapor Condensation," *J. Phys.*, **17**: 179 (1956), in French.

E. C. Crittenden, Jr., R. W. Hoffman, and E. H. Layer, "Effects of Brillouin Zone Stratification on the Electrical Properties of Thin Films," *J. Phys.*, **17**: 220 (1956), in French.

C. E. Drumheller, "Silicon Monoxide Evaporation Technique," *1960 Vacuum Symposium Trans.*, Pergamon Press, New York, 1961.

J. Eckardt, "Investigation on Thin Nickel–Iron–Molybdenum Films," *Z. Angew. Phys.*, **14**: 189 (1962), in German.

J. H. Engelman and A. J. Hardwick, "The Relationship of Deposition Parameters to the Structure and Magnetic Properties of Evaporated Ni-Fe Thin Films," *1962 Trans. 9th Vacuum Symposium*, The Macmillan Company, New York, 1962, p. 100.

B. L. Flur and J. Riseman, "Preparation of Uniaxial Permalloy Films by Cathode Sputtering on Glass and Metal Substrates," *J. Appl. Phys.*, **35**: 344 (1964).

M. H. Francombe and A. J. Noreika, "Magnetic Anisotropy and Structure of Sputtered Permalloy Films," *Electrical and Magnetic Properties of Thin Metallic Layers, Proc. Internat. Conf. Liege*, September 4–7, 1961, p. 193.

F. R. Gleason, Jr., and L. R. Watson, "Ferrite Films Prepared by Pyrohydrolytic Deposition," *J. Appl. Phys.*, **34**: 1217 (1963).

F. R. Gleason, Jr., J. H. Greiner, and L. R. Yetter, "Gas Absorption by Vacuum Evaporated Magnetic Films," *1959 Vacuum Symposium Trans.*, Pergamon Press, New York, 1960, p. 222.

C. Gonzalez and E. Grunbaum, "The Oriented Overgrowth of Thin Cobalt Films," in S. S. Breese, Jr. (ed.), *Electron Microscopy, 5th Internat. Congress, DD*, Academic Press, New York, 1962.

D. M. Hart, "A Demountable Glass Vacuum System Using Electron Bombardment in the Vacuum Deposition of Ferromagnetic Films," *1958 Vacuum Symposium Trans.*, Pergamon Press, New York, 1959, p. 230.

O. S. Heavens, "Single Crystal of Ferromagnetic Materials," in *1962 Trans. 9th Vacuum Symposium*, The Macmillan Company, New York, 1962, p. 52.

R. J. Heritages, A. S. Younger, and I. B. Bott, "Compositional Studies of Evaporated Nickel–Iron Layers," *Brit. J. Appl. Phys.*, **14**: 439 (1963).

J. S. Hirschhorn and R. J. Maciag, "Aggregation Structure in Thin Nickel Films," *Nature*, **195**: 169 (1962).

T. Ichinokawa and Y. Yamada, "Measurement of Evaporated Film Thickness and Concentration by Electron Probe X-ray Microanalyser," *J. Phys. Soc. Japan*, **18**: 1223 (1963).

D. Kantelhardt and O. Schott, "Determination of the Mass-Thickness of Metallic Evaporation Films by Electron Scattering," *Z. Angew. Phys.*, **15**: 307 (1963), in German.

E. Kay, "Magnetic Thin Films Prepared by Sputtering," *J. Appl. Phys.*, **32**: 99S (1961).

D. T. Keating and O. F. Kammerer, "Film Thickness Determination from Substrate X-ray Reflections," *Rev. Sci. Instr.*, **29**: 34 (1958).

F. Z. Keister and R. Y. Scapple, "Thickness and Rate Monitor for Evaporated Silicon Monoxide Films," *1962 Trans. 9th Vacuum Symposium*, The Macmillan Company, New York, 1962, p. 116.

A. Kolk and H. White, "Magnetic Properties of 97 Fe-3Ni Thin Film Electroplate," *J. Electrochem. Soc.*, **110**: 98 (1963).

H. Koritke, "Lattice Constant Measurements in Thin γ-Fe and Ni Films," *Z. Naturforsch.*, **16a**: 531 (1961), in German.

N. V. Kotel'nikov, N. A. Korenev, T. D. Ermolina, "The Temperature Dependence of the Saturation Magnetization and the Magnetic Structure of Films of Nickel Produced by a Chemical Method," *Soviet Phys.—Doklady*, **143**: 908 (1962).

N. V. Kotel'nikov *et al.*, "The Magnetic Properties and Structure of Chemically Prepared Nickel Films," *Soviet Phys.—Doklady*, **I**: 896 (1963).

L. Kozlowski and S. Kubiak, "Influence of Cathode Hydrogen on the Magnetic Moment of Electrolytically Deposited Nickel Films," *Phys. Status Solidi*, **3**: K177 (1963), in German.

K. Kresin, "Rectangular Loops with Ring-Shaped Elements with Thin Ferromagnetic Layers Made by Application of Mechanical Stresses," *Monatsber. Deutschen. Akad. Wiss. Berlin*, **4**: 112 (1962), in German.

J. S. Lemke, "Effect of Substrate Cleanness on Permalloy Thin Films," *J. Appl. Phys.*, **33**: 1097S (1962).

S. J. Lins, "Thickness Determination of Thick Films with Multiple Interferometry," *1961 Trans. 8th Vacuum Symposium and 2nd Internat. Congress*, Pergamon Press, New York, 1962, p. 846.

S. J. Lins and H. S. Kukuk, "Resonance Frequency Shift Thin Film Thickness Monitor," *1960 Vacuum Symposium Trans.*, Pergamon Press, New York, 1961, p. 333.

F. S. Maddocks and K. H. Behrndt, "On a Contaminating Film Formed Prior to the Evaporation of Nickel–Iron in a Bell-Jar," *1958 Vacuum Symposium Trans.*, Pergamon Press, New York, 1959, p. 225.

D. M. Mattox and J. E. McDonald, "Interface Formation During Thin Film Deposition," *J. Appl. Phys.*, **34**: 2493 (1963).

D. B. Medved and H. Poppa, "Electron Microscope Diagnostics of Thin Film Sputtering," *J. Appl. Phys.*, **33**: 1759 (1962).

R. F. Miller, "An Anisotropic Shape Effect in Epitaxial Single Crystal Nickel Films," *Electrical and Magnetic Properties of Thin Metallic Layers, Proc. Internat. Conf. Liege*, September 4–7, 1961, p. 151.

Y. Mizushima and O. Ochi, "The Order Process in Condensed Films of Transition Metals," *Z. Naturforsch.*, **18a**: 252 (1963), in German.

D. M. Moore, "The Preparation of Magnetic Films by High Vacuum Evaporation," *Proc. Special Tech. Conf. Nonlinear Magnetics and Magnetic Amplifiers*, p. 278 (1958).

R. D. Morrison and R. R. Lachenmayer, "Thin Film Thermocouples for Substrate Temperature Measurement," *Rev. Sci. Instr.*, **34**: 106 (1963).

O. W. Muckenhirn, M. H. Monnier, and P. J. Besser, "Shape-Sensitive Uniaxially Magnetized Domains in Ni-Fe Films," *J. Appl. Phys.*, **33**: 2632 (1962).

S. Nielsen, "Clean Substrates for Evaporated Permalloy Films," *1960 Vacuum Symposium Trans.*, Pergamon Press, New York, 1961, p. 293.

A. J. Noreika and M. H. Francombe, "Factors Influencing Coercive Force in Sputtered Permalloy Films," *J. Appl. Phys.*, **33**: 1119S (1962).

P. E. Oberg, "Mechanical Rate of Deposition Monitor," *Rev. Sci. Instr.*, **34**: 1055 (1963).

B. J. Pines and R. I. Kuznetskova, "Alteration of the Submicroporosity in Electrolytic Iron Films After Annealing Under Load," *Soviet Phys.—Solid State*, **4**: 914 (1962).

A. Politycki and H. Gotthard, "Influence of Preparation Conditions on the Magnetic Properties of Electrolytically Produced Layers of Permalloy," *Z. Angew. Phys.*, **14**: 363 (1962), in German.

H. Poppa, "A Method of High-Resolution Studies of Thin-Film Growth," *1962 Trans. 9th Vacuum Symposium*, The Macmillan Company, New York, 1963.

H. J. Quin, "Immersion Substrate Heater for Vacuum Deposition of Films," *Rev. Sci. Instr.*, **32**: 1410 (1961).

J. P. Reames, "Cleaning of Slides for Vacuum Deposition," *Rev. Sci. Instr.*, **30**: 834 (1959).

L. Reiner, "Magnetic Properties of Thin Electrolytically Deposited and Evaporated Ni and Fe Films," *Z. Naturforsch.*, **12**: 550 (1957), in German.

L. Reiner, "Composition of the Magnetic Properties of Electrolytically Deposited Nickel Films from Ballistic Measurements and from the Change of Electrical Resistance in a Magnetic Field," *Z. Naturforsch.*, **12a**: 558 (1957), in German.

T. N. Rhodin and D. Walton, "Nucleation and Growth of Films," *1962 Trans. 9th Vacuum Symposium*, The Macmillan Company, New York, 1962, p. 3.

R. W. Roberts, "Absorption and Decomposition of Hydrocarbons on Clean Metal Films," *Brit. J. Appl. Phys.*, **14**: 485 (1963).

J. S. Sallo and J. M. Carr, "Instability of the Fine Particle Structure of Certain Electrodeposits," *J. Appl. Phys.*, **34**: 1309 (1963).

H. Schlotterer, "Orientation and Surface Morphology of Electrolytically Deposited Layers," S. S. Breese, Jr. (ed.), *Electron Microscopy, 5th Internat. Congress, Philadelphia, 1962*, Vol. I, Paper DD-6, Academic Press, New York, 1962.

F. Schossberger and I. Ticulka, "In Situ X-ray Diffraction Studies of Thin Film Formation," *1960 Vacuum Symposium Trans.*, Pergamon Press, New York, 1961, p. 1001.

H. Schwarz, "Method of Measuring and Controlling Evaporation Rates during the Production of Thin Films in Vacuum," *1960 Vacuum Symposium Trans.*, Pergamon Press, New York, 1960, p. 326.

H. Schwarz, "Method of Measuring and Controlling Evaporation Rates during the Production of Thin Films in Vacuum," *Rev. Sci. Instr.*, **32**: 194 (1961).

A. Segmüller, "Determination of Lattice Strain and Crystallite Size in Thin Films," *IBM J. Res. Develop.*, **6**: 464 (1961).

G. N. Shirastara and D. D. Scott, "Use of Helium in the Vacuum Deposition of Thin Films," *Brit. J. Appl. Phys.*, **12**: 255 (1961).

J. G. Simmons and D. E. Moister, "High Temperature Substrate Holder," *Rev. Sci. Instr.*, **34**: 199 (1963).

R. S. Smith, L. E. Godycki, and J. C. Lloyd, "Effects of Saccharin on the Structure and Magnetic Properties of FeNi Films," *J. Electrochem. Soc.*, **108**: 10 (1961).

W. G. Spitzer and M. Tanenbaum, "Interference Method for Measuring the Thickness of Epitaxially Grown Films," *J. Appl. Phys.*, **32**: 744 (1961).

B. J. Stern, "Thin Film Thickness Measurement Using Silver-Modified Newton's Rings," *Rev. Sci. Instr.*, **34**: 152 (1963).

R. Suhrmann, A. Hermann, and G. Wedler, "On the Rules Covering the Electronic Interaction Between Hydrogen and 3d Metal Evaporated Films," *Z. Phys. Chem.* (Frankfurt), **35**: 155 (1962), in German.

W. E. Sweeney, Jr., R. E. Seebold, and L. S. Birks, "Electron Probe Measurements of Evaporated Metal Films," *J. Appl. Phys.*, **31**: 1061 (1960).

G. Turner and E. Bauer, "The Structure of Metal Films Evaporated in an Inert Gas and Its Relation to Heterogeneous Catalysis," in S. S. Breese, Jr. (ed.), *Electron Microscopy, 5th Internat. Congress, Philadelphia, 1962*, Vol I, Paper II-9, Academic Press, New York, 1962.

J. A. Turner, J. K. Birfwistle, and G. R. Hoffman, "A Method for the Continuous Measurement of Thickness and Deposition Rate of Conducting Films During a Vacuum Evaporation," *J. Sci. Instr.*, **40**: 557 (1963).

G. J. Unterkofler and R. R. Verderber, "Preparation of Very Thin Suspended Metal Films," *Rev. Sci. Instr.*, **34**: 820 (1963).

A. van Itterbeek, G. Forrez, and W. van Itterbeek, "Investigation of the Structure of Thin Metallic Layers by Means of the Replica-Method," *Appl. Sci. Res. B* (Netherlands), **10**: 1 (1963).

R. W. Vook and F. R. L. Schoening, "X-ray Diffractometer Attachment for Direct Observation of Evaporated Thin Films," *Rev. Sci. Instr.*, **34**: 792 (1963).

W. Wade *et al.*, "Chemically Deposited Thin Ferrite Films," *J. Appl. Phys.*, **34**: 1219 (1963).

A. W. Winston, C. A. Baer, and L. R. Allen, "A Simple Film Thickness Gauge Utilizing Newton's Rings," *1959 Vacuum Symposium Trans.*, Pergamon Press, New York, 1960, p. 249.

I. W. Wolf, "The Effect of Small Quantities of Copper on the Magnetic Properties of Electrodeposited Permalloys," *Electrical and Magnetic Properties of Thin Metallic Layers, Proc. Internat. Conf. Liege*, September 4–7, 1961, p. 158.

I. W. Wolf, "Electrodeposition of Magnetic Materials," *J. Appl. Phys.*, **33**: 1152S (1962).

CHAPTER 3: DOMAIN STRUCTURES

P. C. Archibald *et al.*, "High Speed Magnetooptical Measurements on Films," *Rev. Sci. Instr.*, **31**: 653 (1960).

L. F. Bates and R. Carey, "Domain Observation on a Nickel Iron Film," *Proc. Phys. Soc.* (London), **79**: 1245 (1962).

M. Beckerman and K. H. Behrndt, "The Influence of Edge Effects on Domain Structure and Coercive Force of Circular Ni-Fe Films," *IBM J. Res. Develop.*, **4**: 198 (1960).

G. Blet, "The Study of the Structure of Epitaxial Layers," *Vide*, **18**: 293 (1963).

H. Boersch and M. Lambeck, "Faraday Observation of Domains," *Z. Physik*, **159**: 248 (1960), in German.

H. Boersch and M. Lambeck, "The Observation of Magnetic Domain Structures by Means of the Faraday-Effect," *Electrical and Magnetic Properties of Thin Metallic Layers, Internat. Conf. Liege*, September 4–7, 1961, p. 91.

H. Boersch and H. Raith, "Electron Microscope Observation of Weiss Domain in Thin Ferromagnetic Films," *Naturwiss.*, **46**: 574 (1959), in German.

H. Boersch, M. Lambeck, and H. Raith, "Investigation of Thin Iron Films with the Aid of the Faraday Effect," *Naturwiss.*, **46**: 595 (1959), in German.

H. Boersch, H. Raith, and D. Wohleben, "Electron Microscope Observations of Domains in Fe Films," *Z. Physik*, **159**: 388 (1960), in German.

H. Boersch et al., "Antiparallel Magnetic Domains as Biprism for Electron Rays," *Z. Physik*, **159**: 397 (1960), in German.

C. Boulesteix, "Influence of Surface Energy on the Size of Microcrystals in Discontinuous Thin Metal Films," *Compt. Rend.*, **256**: 1486 (1963), in French.

P. Brennan and M. Williams, "Contrast Dispersion in Magneto-Optic Apparatus for Domain Studies," *J. Appl. Phys.*, **34**: 1228 (1963).

W. S. Carter, "Magnetic Interactions in Thin Films Induced by Strip Line Fields," *Electrical and Magnetic Properties of Thin Metallic Layers, Proc. Internat. Conf. Liege*, September 4–7, 1961, p. 205.

W. W. L. Chu, J. E. Wolfe, and B. C. Wagner, "Some Observations on Evaporated Permalloy Films," *J. Appl. Phys.*, **30S**: 272S (1959).

R. L. Coren and H. J. Juretschke, "Magnetoresistance and Domain Structure in Thin Nickel Films," *Phys. Rev.*, **126**: 1378 (1962).

M. D. Coutts and H. L. Pinch, "Surface Decoration and Domains in Very Thin Magnetic Films," *J. Appl. Phys.*, **34**: 2113 (1963).

D. J. Craik and R. S. Tebble, "Magnetic Domains," *Reports on Progress in Physics*, Inst. Phys. and Physical Soc., London (1961), Vol. 24, p. 116.

W. Drechsel, "An Arrangement for Photographic Registration of Domain with Shutterspeed in the Order of 1 msec.," *Z. Physik*, **164**: 324 (1961), in German.

W. Drechsel, "On the Magnification of the Meridional Magneto-Optic Kerr Effect Through the Evaporation of Dielectric Films," *Z. Physik*, **164**: 308 (1961), in German.

C. A. Fowler, Jr., and E. M. Fryer, "Magnetic Domains in Thin Films of Ni-Fe," *Phys. Rev.*, **100**: 746 (1955).

C. A. Fowler, Jr., E. M. Fryer, and D. Treves, "Domain Structures in Iron Whiskers as Observed by the Kerr Method," *J. Appl. Phys.*, **32**: 296S (1961).

E. Fuchs, "Electron Microscope Observations of Domains," *Naturwiss.*, **47**: 392 (1960), in German.

E. Fuchs, "The Magnetization Reversal of Thin Ni-Fe Films in the Hard Direction—Pt. I. Electron Microscope Observations of the Origin of Domains," *Z. Angew. Phys.*, **8**: 157 (1961).

E. Fuchs and W. Liesk, "A Device for Magnetizing Specimens in the Electron Microscope," *Optik*, **19**: 307 (1962), in German.

C. E. Fuller, "Domain Patterns and Reversals by Wall Motion of Iron and Nickel-iron Films," *J. Phys. Radium*, **20**: 310 (1959), in French.

H. W. Fuller and M. E. Hale, "Determination of Magnetization Distribution in Thin Films Using Electron Microscope," *J. Appl. Phys.*, **31**: 238 (1960).

H. W. Fuller and M. H. Hale, "Static and Dynamic Studies of Magnetization Distribution in Thin Films by Electron Microscopy," *J. Appl. Phys.*, **31**: 308S (1960).

L. Gold, "Constraint Principle in Ferromagnetic Domain Theory," *J. Appl. Phys.*, **29**: 544 (1958).

Y. Gomi, Y. Odani, and M. Sugihara, "Domain Patterns on Thin Films of Perminvar," *J. Phys. Soc. Japan*, **15**: 533 (1960).

A. Green and M. Prutton, "Magnetic-Optic Detection of Ferromagnetic Domains Using Vertical Illumination," *J. Sci. Instr.*, **39**: 244 (1962).

C. Greiner, "Deformation of Domain Structures by Stresses," *Z. Angew. Phys.*, **13**: 134 (1961), in German.

P. J. Grundy and R. S. Tebble, "Electron Microscope Observations of Ferromagnetic Domains in Face Centered Cubic Cobalt," *Proc. Phys. Soc.*, **61**: 971 (1963).

M. E. Hale, "Magnetic Domain Configuration," *1959 Vacuum Symposium Trans.*, Pergamon Press, New York, 1959, p. 212.

J. W. Hart, "Domain Behavior in Thin Magnetic Films," *1960 Proc. Spec. Tech. Conf. Nonlinear Magnetics and Magnetic Amplifiers*, p. 15 (1960).

O. S. Heavens and R. F. Miller, "Faraday Rotation in Thin Epitaxially Grown Nickel Films," in C. A. Neugebauer, J. B. Newkirk, and D. A. Vermilyea (eds.), *Structure and Properties of Thin Films*, (1959), John Wiley & Sons, Inc., New York, 1959, Chap. V.

O. S. Heavens and R. F. Miller, "Measurement of Faraday Rotation in Single-Crystal Nickel Films," *Proc. Roy. Soc. (London)*, **266A**: 547 (1962).

W. Hellenthal, "Determination of the Orientation Distribution of the Magnetization Vectors in Evaporated Layers of Nickel and Iron from Changes in Magnetoresistance," *Z. Physik*, **153**: 359 (1958), in German.

W. Hellenthal, "The Effect of Stress on the Transverse Magnetization of Evaporated Nickel Layers," *Z. Physik*, **156**: 573 (1959), in German.

A. A. Hirsch, "Temperature Dependence of Coercivity and Domain Structure in Thin Ferromagnetic Layers," *Electrical and Magnetic Properties of Thin Metallic Layers, Proc. Internat. Conf. Liege*, September 4–7, 1961, p. 218.

R. M. Hornreich, "90° Magnetization Curling in Thin Films," *J. Appl. Phys.*, **34**: 1071 (1963).

E. E. Huber, Jr., and D. O. Smith, "Properties of Permalloy Films Having a Magnetoelastic Easy Axis Normal to the Film," *J. Appl. Phys.*, **30**: 267 (1959).

T. Ichinikawa, "Observation of Dynamic Changes of Domain Structures in Ferromagnetic Thin Films by Electron Microscope," in S. S. Breese, Jr. (ed.), *Electron Microscopy, 5th Internat. Congress, Philadelphia, 1962*, Vol. I, Paper II-8, Academic Press, New York, 1962.

J. Kaczer, "On the Domain Structure of Thin Ferromagnetic Films," *Czech. J. Phys.*, **I**: 557 (1957), in Czechoslovakian.

S. Kainuma and N. Tsuya, "Domain Patterns in Electrodeposited Nickel-Iron Thin Films," *J. Appl. Phys.*, **34**: 795 (1963).

L. V. Kirenskii, S. V. Kan, and M. K. Savchenko, "Behavior of the Domain Structure of Thin Ferromagnetic Films at Different Temperatures," *Acad. Sci. USSR, Phys. Ser.*, **26**: 310 (1963).

C. Kittel, "Theory of the Structure of Ferromagnetic Domains in Films and Small Particles," *Phys. Rev.*, **70**: 965 (1946).

C. Kittel and J. K. Galt, "Ferromagnetic Domain Theory," *Solid State Physics*, **3**: 437, Academic Press, New York, 1956.

A. J. Kolk and M. Orlovic, "Increasing the Kerr Magneto-Optic Effect in Thin Films," *J. Appl. Phys.*, **34**: 1060 (1963).

J. Kranz and W. Drechsel, "Observation of Weiss Domains in Polycrystalline Material by the Enlarged Magnetooptic Kerr Rotation," *Z. Physik*, **150**: 632 (1958), in German.

G. Krause and G. Meyer, "Optical Absorption and Polarization of Evaporated Nickel Films," *Z. Physik*, **169**: 511 (1962), in German.

K. Kuwahara and M. Goto, "Thickness Dependence of Domain Orientation in Thin Ni Films," *J. Phys. Soc. Japan*, **15**: 359 (1960).

M. Lambeck, "Optical Investigations on Ferromagnetic Layers," *Z. Angew. Phys.*, **15**: 272 (1963), in German.

E. W. Lee, D. R. Callaby, and A. C. Lynch, "The Use of the Kerr Effect for Studying the Magnetization of a Reflecting Surface," *Proc. Phys. Soc.*, **72**: 233 (1958).

M. P. Martines, "Theory of Ferromagnetic Films," *Anales Real Soc. Espan. Fís. Quím.* (Madrid), **58**(A): 27 (1962).

L. Mayer, "Observation on MuBi Films During Heating Treatment," *J. Appl. Phys.*, **31**: 346 (1960).

S. Methfessel, S. Middelhoek, and H. Thomas, "Partial Rotation in Permalloy Films," *J. Appl. Phys.*, **31**: 1959 (1961).

G. Meyer, "Optical Constants of Evaporated Iron Films," *Z. Physik*, **168**: 169 (1962), in German.

S. Middelhoek, "The Influence of the Anisotropy Variations on the Domain Behavior of Ni-Fe Films," *Proc. Internat. Conf. Liege*, September 4–7, 1961, p. 182.

S. Middelhoek, *Ferromagnetic Domains in Thin Ni-Fe Films*, Drukkerij Wed. G. Van Soest, N.V., Amsterdam, 1961.

S. Middelhoek, "Domain Walls in Thin Ni-Fe Films," *J. Appl. Phys.*, **34**: 1054 (1963).

H. Morimoto, "Electron Diffraction Study of Evaporated Films of Nickel and Cobalt," *J. Phys. Soc. Japan*, **17**: 274S (1962).

O. W. Muckenhirn, A. E. Labonte, and P. J. Besser, "Annular Uniaxially Magnetized Domains in Thin Li-Fe Films," *J. Appl. Phys.*, **31**: 304S (1960).

O. W. Muckenhirn, M. H. Monnier, and P. J. Besser, "Shape-sensitive Uniaxially Magnetized Domains in Ni-Fe Films," *J. Appl. Phys.*, **33**: 2632 (1962).

L. Néel, "On the Effects of Interaction Between Elementary Ferromagnetic Domains: Bascule and Reptation," *J. Phys. Radium*, **20**: 215 (1959), in French.

B. Passon, "An Application of the Magneto-Optical Kerr Effect for the Investigation of Fast Magnetization Processes," *Z. Angew. Phys.*, **16**: 81 (1963), in German.

M. Prutton, "Observation of Domain Structure in Magnetic Thin Films by Means of Kerr Magneto-Optic Effect," *Phil. Mag.*, **4**: 1063 (1959).

M. Prutton, "Observation of Magnetization Reversal Process In Thin Films of Ni-Fe, Using Kerr Magneto-Optic Effect," *Brit. J. Appl. Phys.*, **11**: 335 (1960).

G. Rasigni, M. Belzons, and N. Emeric, "Investigation of the Absorption of Very Thin Layers of Iron, Nickel and Cobalt as a Function of Wavelength," *Compt. Rend.*, **254**: 2325 (1962), in French.

L. Reimer *et al.*, "Electron-Optical Investigation of Domain Structure in Thin Single and Polycrystalline Nickel Films," *Z. Angew. Phys.*, **15**: 204 (1063), in German.

H. Rother, "Magnetic Properties of Ferromagnetic Films. II Theory of Domain Splitting," *Z. Physik*, **168**: 148 (1962), in German.

H. Rother, "Variations of the Direction of Magnetization, Wall Spacing and Coercive Force in Thin Films," *Z. Angew. Phys.*, **14**: 187 (1962).

S. M. Rubens and R. W. Olmen, "Domain Structure and Dispersion of the Preferred Axis in Ferromagnetic Films," *Electrical and Magnetic Properties of Thin Metallic Layers, Proc. Internat. Conf. Liege*, September 4–7, 1961, p. 111.

H. Sato and R. W. Astrue, "Checkerboard Domain Pattern of Single-Crystal Thin Iron Film," *J. Appl. Phys.*, **33**: 2956 (1962).

H. Sato, R. S. Toth, and R. W. Astrue, "Checkerboard Domain Patterns on Epitaxially Grown Single-Crystal Thin Films of Iron, Nickel and Cobalt," *J. Appl. Phys.*, **34**: 1062 (1963).

K. Shaffernicht, "Measurement of The Magnetization Distribution in Thin Films of Iron by the Deflection of Electrons," *Z. Angew. Phys.*, **15**: 275 (1963), in German.

S. Shirai and Y. Fukudor, "Structure of Thin Layers of some F.C.C. Metals Deposited on Oriented Ag Pd and Ni Films," *J. Phys. Soc. Japan*, **17**: 319S (1962).

J. Silcox, "Magnetic Domains in Thin Films of Cobalt," in S. S. Breese, Jr. (ed.), *Electron Microscopy, 5th Internat. Congress, Philadelphia, 1962*, Vol. I, Paper II-5, Academic Press, New York, 1962.

J. Silcox, "Magnetic Domain Structure in Thin Crystals of Cobalt," *Phil. Mag.*, **8**: 1395 (1963).

D. Treves, "Limitations of the Magneto-Optic Kerr Technique in the Study of Microscope Magnetic Domain Structure," *J. Appl. Phys.*, **32**: 358 (1961).

D. Unangst, "On the Magnetic Domain Structure of Thin Iron 'Single Crystal' Films," *Ann. Physik*, **7**: 280 (1961), in German.

R. H. Wade, "Transverse Magnetization in Permalloy Films," in S. S. Breese, Jr. (ed.), *Electron Microscopy, 5th Internat. Congress, Philadelphia, 1962*, Vol. I, Paper II-7, Academic Press, New York, 1962.

G. P. Weiss and D. O. Smith, "Measurement of Internal Friction in Thin Films," *Rev. Sci. Instr.*, **34**: 522 (1963).

H. J. Williams and R. C. Sherwood, "Magnetic Domain Patterns on Thin Films," *J. Appl. Phys.*, **28**: 548 (1957).

H. J. Williams and R. C. Sherwood, "Motion Pictures of Magnetic Writing on Thin Films of MnBi," *J. Appl. Phys.*, **29**: 296 (1958).

G. Wilson, "A Note on a Phenomenon Observed in Magnetic Microscope," *Brit. J. Appl. Phys.*, **14**: 523 (1963).

CHAPTER 4: DOMAIN WALLS

J. J. Becker, "Domain Boundary Configurations During Magnetization Reversals," *J. Appl. Phys.*, **30**: 387 (1959).

R. E. Behringer, "Comments on a Theory of Double Bloch Walls in Thin Films," *J. Appl. Phys.*, **29**: 1380 (1958).

R. E. Behringer and R. S. Smith, "The Influence of Demagnetization and Anisotropy Energy on Bloch Wall Thickness and Coercive Force in Thin Films," *J. Franklin Inst.*, p. 14 (July, 1961).

R. D. Burbank and R. D. Heidenreich, "Microtwinning in Epitaxial Nickel-Iron Films," *Phil. Mag.*, **5**: 373 (1960).

W. S. Carter, "Magnetic Interactions in Thin Films Induced by Strip Line Fields," *Electrical and Magnetic Properties of Thin Metallic Layers, Proc. Internat. Conf. Liege* September 4–7, 1961, p. 205.

H. Clow, "Very Low Coercive Force in Nickel-Iron Films," *Nature*, **194**: 1035.

M. S. Cohen, "Spiral and Concentric-Circle Walls Observed by Lorentz Microscopy," *J. Appl. Phys.*, **34**: 1221 (1963) .

D. J. Craik and P. M. Griffiths, "New Techniques for the Study of Bitter Figures," *Brit. J. Appl. Phys.*, **9**: 279 (1958).

H. D. Dietz and H. Thomas, "Bloch and Néel Walls in Thin Ferromagnetic Films," *Z. Physik*, **163**: 523 (1961).

E. Feldtkeller, "Bloch Lines in Thin Nickel-Iron Films," *Electrical and Magnetic Properties of Thin Metallic Layers, Proc. Internat. Conf. Liege*, September 4–7, 1961, p. 98.

E. Feldtkeller and W. Liesk, "360° Walls in Magnetic Films," *Z. Angew. Phys.*, **14**: 195 (1962), in German.

N. C. Ford, Jr., "Domain Wall Velocities in Thin Fe-Ni Films," *J. Appl. Phys.*, **31**: 300S (1960).

E. Fuchs, "Behavior of Magnetization Direction in Domain Walls of Ferromagnetic Films," *Naturwiss.*, **12**: 450 (1961).

E. Fuchs, "Magnetic Structures in Thin Ferromagnetic Films Investigated by Electron Microscope," *Z. Angew. Phys.*, **14**: 203 (1962), in German.

E. Fuchs and H. Pfisterer, "Domain Wall Motions in Thin Ferromagnetic Films," in S. S. Breese, Jr. (ed.), *Electron Microscopy, 5th Internat. Congress, Philadelphia, 1962*, Vol. I, Paper II-4, Academic Press, New York, 1962.

H. W. Fuller and L. R. Lakin, "Wall–Wall Interaction Between Thin Magnetic Films," *J. Appl. Phys.*, **34**: 1069 (1963).

H. W. Fuller and H. Rubinstein, "Observations Made on Domain Walls in Thin Films," *J. Appl. Phys.*, **30S**: 84S (1959).

H. W. Fuller and D. L. Sullivan, "Magnetostatic Interaction Between Thin Magnetic Films," *J. Appl. Phys.*, **33**: 1063S (1962).

H. W. Fuller, H. Rubinstein, and D. L. Sullivan, "Spiral Walls in Thin Magnetic Films," *J. Appl. Phys.*, **32**: 286S (1961).

J. R. Garrood, "Methods of Improving the Sensitivity of the Bitter Technique," *Proc. Phys. Soc. (London)*, **79**: 1252 (1962).

J. R. Garrood, C. W. B. Grigson, "On the Domain Walls Inclined to the Easy Axis in the Ferromagnetic Films," *J. Phys. Soc. Japan*, **17**: 614S (1962).

Y. Gomi and Y. Odani, "Chain Wall in Permalloy Thin Films," *J. Phys. Soc. Japan*, **15**: 535 (1960).

Y. Gondo, "Domain Structure in Single-Crystal Thin Films of Iron," *J. Phys. Soc. Japan*, **17**: 1129 (1962).

Y. Gondo, Z. Funatogawa, "Some Observations of the Domain Walls in Thin Films," *J. Phys. Soc. Japan*, **15**: 1126 (1960).

Y. Gondo and Z. Funatogawa, "Structure of Domain Walls in Thin Films," *J. Phys. Soc. Japan*, **17**: 621S (1962).

A. L. Houde, "Observation of Cross-Tie Domain Walls by the Faraday Effect," *J. Appl. Phys.*, **32**: 1234 (1961).

A. L. Houde, "Observation of the Fine Structure of Domains and Reversible Rotation of the Magnetization in Thin Permalloy Films by the Faraday Effect," *J. Phys. Soc. Japan*, **17**: 618S (1962).

E. E. Huber, Jr., D. O. Smith, and J. B. Goodenough, "Domain-Wall Structure in Permalloy Films," *J. Appl. Phys.*, **20**: 294 (1958).

J. Kaczer, "The Interaction Energy of Parallel Bloch Walls," *Czech. J. Phys.*, **8**: 278 (1958), in Czechoslovakian.

J. Kaczer, "On the Theory of Double Bloch Walls in Thin Films," *J. Appl. Phys.*, **29**: 569 (1958).

J. Kaczer and R. Gemperle, "The Rotation of Bloch Walls," *Czech. J. Phys.*, **B11**: 157 (1961), in Czechoslovakian.

L. V. Kirenskii and V. A. Buravikhin, "Polarities of the Domain Boundaries in Thin Ferromagnetic Films," *Dokl. Akad. Nauk SSSR*, **136**: 575 (1961), in Russian.

B. Kostyshyn *et al.*, "External Fields from Domain Walls of Cobalt Films," *J. Appl. Phys.*, **31**: 772 (1960).

L. Mayer, "Magnetic Image Contrast in Electron Mirror Microscopy," *J. Phys. Soc. Japan*, **17**: 547S (1964).

S. Methfessel, S. Middelhoek, and H. Thomas, "Domain Walls in Thin Magnetic Ni-Fe Films," *J. Appl. Phys.*, **31**: 302S (1960).

S. Methfessel, S. Middelhoek, and H. Thomas, "Domain Walls in Thin Ni-Fe Films," *IBM J. Res. Develop.*, **4**: 96 (1960).

R. M. Moon, "Internal Structure of Cross Tie Walls in Thin Permalloy Films Through High-Resolution Bitter Techniques," *J. Appl. Phys.*, **30S**: 82S (1959).

M. W. Muller and S. Dawson, "Structure of a Bloch Wall," *J. Math. Phys.*, **3**: 800 (1962).

L. Néel, "Energy of Bloch Walls in Thin Films," *Compt. Rend.*, **241**: 533 (1955), in French.

L. Néel, "A New Method for Measuring Bloch Wall Energies," *Compt. Rend.*, **254**: 2891 (1962), in French.

R. W. Olmen and E. N. Mitchell, "Slow Domain-Wall Motion in Homogeneous Vacuum-Deposited Iron-Nickel Films," *J. Appl. Phys.*, **30S**: 258S (1959).

M. Prutton, "Cross-Tie Walls in Thin Permalloy Films," *Phil. Mag.*, **5**: 625 (1960).

M. Prutton and K. D. Leaver, "On the Effective Mass of 180° Domain Walls in Magnetic Films," *Phys. Letters*, **6**: 15 (1963).

I. B. Puchalska and R. J. Spain, "Interaction Between Magnetic (Domain) Walls in Superimposed Thin Layers," *Compt. Rend.*, **254**: 2937 (1962), in French.

I. B. Puchalska and R. J. Spain, "Thin Film Switching as Observed by Electron Microscopy," in S. S. Breese, Jr. (ed.), *Electron Microscopy, 5th Internat. Congress, Philadelphia, 1962*, Vol. I, Paper II-9, Academic Press, New York, 1962.

L. Reiner, "Electro-Optical Investigation of Domain Boundaries in Thin Ferromagnetic Films," *Z. Angew. Phys.*, **13**: 143 (1961), in German.

L. Reiner, "Domain Wall Movement in Ferromagnetic Layers," *Electrical and Magnetic Properties of Thin Metallic Layers, Proc. Internat. Conf. Liege*, September 4–7, 1961, p. 123.

H. Rubinstein and R. J. Spain, "Cross Tie Walls in Thin Films," *J. Appl. Phys.*, **31**: 306S (1960).

H. Rubinstein, H. W. Fuller, and M. E. Hale, "Observation of Néel Walls in Thin Films," *J. Appl. Phys.*, **31**: 437 (1960).

H. Sato, R. S. Toth, and R. W. Astrue, "Bitter Patterns on Single-Crystal Thin Films of Iron and Nickel," *J. Appl. Phys.*, **33**: 1113S (1962).

J. Silcox, "Magnetic Domain Walls in Thin Films of Nickel and Cobalt," *Phil. Mag.*, **8**: 7 (1963).

R. J. Spain and I. B. Puchalska, "Interaction of Domain Walls in Superimposed Thin Ferromagnetic Films," in S. S. Breese, Jr. (ed.), *Electron Microscopy, 5th Internat. Congress, Philadelphia, 1962*, Vol. I, Paper II-5, Academic Press, New York, 1962.

R. H. Wade, "The Determination of Domain Wall Thickness in Ferromagnetic Films by Electron Microscopy," *Proc. Phys. Soc.*, **79**: 1237 (1962).

W. Zieteck, "Influence of a Uniform External Magnetic Field on Néel Walls," *Bull. Acad. Polon. Ser. Sci. Math. Astron. Phys.*, **11**: 27 (1963).

W. Zietek, "Quantum Theory of the Néel Wall in Thin Ferromagnetic Films," *Z. Phys.*, **171**: 487 (1963), in German.

CHAPTER 5: IMPERFECTIONS

K. H. Behrndt, "On the Coercive Force and its Connection to the Impurities in Ferromagnetic Thin Films," *Electrical and Magnetic Properties of Thin Metallic Layers, Proc. Internat. Conf. Liege*, September 4–7, 1961, p. 419.

J. Brachman, W. Kustere, and W. Metzdorf, "The Influence of Film Edge on Magnetization Reversal in Thin Permalloy Films," *Z. Angew. Phys.*, **8**: 313 (1961), in German.

W. F. Brown, Jr., "Rigorous Calculation of the Nucleation Field in a Ferromagnetic Film or Plate," *Phys. Rev.*, **124**: 1348 (1961).

H. Chang, "Fields External to Open-Structure Magnetic Devices Represented by Ellipsoid or Spheroid," *Brit. J. Appl. Phys.*, **12**: 160 (1961).

H. Chang and A. G. Milnes, "Magnetic Fields of Square-Loop Thin Films of Oblate
Spheroidal Geometry," *Inst. Radio Engr. Trans.*, **EC8**: 458 (1959).

D. M. Ellis and C. J. Bader, "Measurement of Magnetic Thin Film Rotational Properties
and Uniformity," *Rev. Sci. Instr.*, **34**: 1188 (1963).

A. A. Hirsch and N. Friedman, "Induced Magnetic Anisotropy in Thin Ferromagnetic
Films Investigated at Low Temperatures," *Physica*, **29**: 543 (1963).

K. D. Leaver and M. Prutton, "The Effect of Applied Field Inhomogeneity on the
Reversal Behavior of Thin Magnetic Films," *J. Electronics Control*, **15**: 173 (1963).

Z. Malek, "A Study of the Influence of Dislocations on Some of the Magnetic Properties
of Permalloy Alloys," *Czech. J. Phys.*, **9**: 613 (1959), in Czechoslovakian.

R. F. Soohoo, "A Microwave Magnetic Microscope," *J. Appl. Phys.*, **33**: 1276S
(1962).

E. C. Stoner and E. P. Wohlfarth, "A Mechanism of Magnetic Hysteresis in Heterogeneous Alloys," *Phil. Trans. Roy. Soc. London*, **240A**: 599 (1946–1948).

J. Trait *et al.*, "Local Variations in Uniaxial Anisotropy in Thin Films," *Czech. J. Phys.*,
10: 616 (1960), in Czechoslovakian.

G. Turner and E. Bauer, "The Structure of Metal Films Evaporated in an Inert Gas
and its Relation to Heterogeneous Catalysis," in S. S. Breese, Jr. (ed.), *Electron Microscopy,
5th Internat. Congress, Philadelphia, 1962*, Vol. I, Paper II-9, Academic Press, New York,
1962.

S. Yamaguchi, "Measurement of the Magnetic Field in a Thin Film," *J. Appl. Phys.*,
30: 1619 (1959).

CHAPTER 6: MAGNETIZATION OF THIN FILMS

W. Andra, "The Influence of Cathodic Hydrogen on the Magnetic Properties of Thin
Nickel Films," *J. Phys. Soc. Japan*, **14**: 585S (1962).

W. Andra *et al.*, "Spontaneous Magnetic Anisotropy in Polycrystalline Thin Films,"
J. Appl. Phys., **31**: 442 (1960).

T. Ayukawa, "The Effect of Surface Anisotropy on the Spontaneous Magnetization of
Ferromagnetic Thin Films," *J. Phys. Soc. Japan*, **18**: 970 (1963).

H. J. Bauer and E. Schmidtauer, "The Influence of Hydrogen on the Magnetization of
Nickel," *Naturwiss.*, **II**: 425 (1961), in German.

C. P. Bean, "Aspects of Ferromagnetism of Thin Films," in C. A. Neugebauer *et al.*
(eds.), *Structure and Properties of Thin Films*, John Wiley & Sons, Inc., New York, 1959,
Chap. V.

K. Chu and J. R. Singer, "Thin Film Magnetization Analysis," *Proc. Inst. Radio Engrs.*,
47: 1237 (1959).

A. Corciovei, "On the Ferromagnetism of Thin Films," *Czech. J. Phys.*, **10**: 568 (1960),
in Czechoslovakian.

A. Corciovei, "Magnetic Anisotropy Included in Thickness *vs* M. Calculation," *Czech.
J. Phys.*, **10**: 917 (1960), in Czechoslovakian.

A. Corciovei, "Spontaneous Magnetization of Ferromagnetic Thin Films," *Acta. Phys.
Polon.*, **24**: 91 (1963).

A. Corciovei and G. Ghika, "On the Theory of Ferromagnetic Thin Films," *Czech. J.
Phys.*, **12**: 278 (1962), in Czechoslovakian.

E. C. Crittenden, Jr., and R. W. Hoffman, "Thin Films of Ferromagnetic Materials,"
Rev. Mod. Phys., **25**: 310 (1953).

E. C. Crittenden, Jr., and R. W. Hoffman, "Ferromagnetic Properties of Thin Films of
Nickel," *J. Phys.*, **17**: 270 (1956), in French.

J. A. Davis and F. Keffer, "Effect of Surface Pinning on the Magnetization of Thin
Films," *J. Appl. Phys.*, **34**: 1135 (1963).

Z. Frait and N. Ondris, "The Spin Wave Resonance and Saturation Magnetization of Thin Cobalt Films," *Czech. J. Phys.*, **B11**: 463 (1961).

Z. Frait *et al.*, "On the Effective Magnetization and Uniaxial Anisotropy of Permalloy Films," *Czech. J. Phys.*, **13**: 279 (1963), in Czechoslovakian.

S. J. Glass and M. J. Klein, "Thin Ferromagnetic Films," *Phys. Rev.*, **109**: 288 (1958).

Y. Gondo, H. Konno, and Z. Funatogawa, "Spontaneous Magnetization in Thin Films of Ni," *J. Phys. Soc. Japan*, **16**: 2345 (1961).

G. Goureaux, "Consideration on the Curie Point of Thin Nickel Layers," *J. Phys. Soc. Japan*, **17**: 610S (1962).

W. Hellenthal, "Determination of Curie Temperatures of Thin Films by Measurement of Ferromagnetic Resistivity Changes," *Z. Naturforsch.*, **13a**: 566 (1958), in German.

W. Hellenthal, "Investigation of Long-Time Changes of Magnetization in Films," *Naturwiss.*, **47**: 371 (1960), in German.

W. Hellenthal, "Curie Temperature of Thin Ni Films," *Z. Angew. Phys.*, **8**: 147 (1961), in German.

W. Hellenthal, "On the Magnetic Properties of Thin Polycrystalline Nickel Films," *Electrical and Magnetic Properties of Thin Metallic Layers, Proc. Internat. Conf. Liege*, September 4–7, 1961, p. 258.

H. Hoffman, "Saturation Magnetization and Anisotropy Field in Thin Evaporated Fe Films," *Z. Phys.*, **165**: 261 (1961), in German.

H. Hoffman, "The Magnetic Properties of Very Thin Iron Films in Vacuum and Their Alternation in Air," *Z. Angew. Phys.*, **3**: 149 (1961), in German.

R. W. Hoffman and A. M. Eich, "Magnetization of Ni Films at Low Temperatures," *Proc. AIEE Conf. Magnetism Magnetic Mater.*, Boston (1956).

M. J. Klein and R. S. Smith, "Thin Ferromagnetic Films," *Phys. Rev.*, **81**: 378 (1951).

N. V. Kotel'nikov, N. A. Korenev, and T. D. Ermolina, "The Temperature Dependence of the Saturation Magnetization and the Magnetic Structure of Films of Nickel Produced by a Chemical Method," *Soviet Phys.—Doklady*, **143**: 908 (1962).

L. Kozlowski and S. Kubiak, "Influence of Cathode Hydrogen on the Magnetic Moment of Electrolytically Deposited Nickel Films," *Phys. Status Solidi*, **3**: K177 (1963), in German.

H. J. Kump and T. G. Greene, "Magnetization of Uniaxial Cylindrical Thin Films," *IBM J. Res. Develop.*, **7**: 130 (1963).

H. Mayer and D. Stunkel, "The Temperature Dependence of the Magnetization of Very Thin Iron Films," *Naturwiss.*, **49**: 277 (1962), in German.

H. Mayer *et al.*, "Some Applications of a Torsion Microbalance for the Investigation of Surface Phenomena and Thin Film Properties in Ultrahigh Vacuum," *Vacuum Microbalance Technique*, Vol. 3, Plenum Press, New York, 1963, p. 87.

N. Morita, "Curie Temperature of Evaporated Nickel Films," *J. Phys. Soc. Japan*, **17**: 1155 (1962).

G. Musa, "The Properties of Thin Ferromagnetic Films," *Rev. Phys. (Roumania)*, **7**: 193 (1962), in Russian.

L. Néel, "Remarks on the Theory of the Magnetic Properties of Thin Films and Fine Particles," *J. Phys. Radium*, **17**: 250 (1956), in French.

C. A. Neugebauer, "The Saturation Magnetization of Nickel Films of Thickness Less than 100Å," *Phys. Rev.*, **116**: 1441 (1959).

C. A. Neugebauer, "Study of the Saturation Magnetization and Magnetic Anisotropy of Ultra Thin Films Under Ultrahigh Vacuum Conditions," *Electrical and Magnetic Properties of Thin Metallic Layers, Proc. Internat. Conf. Liege*, September 4–7, 1961, p. 231.

C. A. Neugebauer, "Study of the Magnetization of Ultrathin Evaporated Nickel Films in a Changing Environment," *1961 Trans. 8th Vacuum Symposium 2nd Internat. Congress*, Pergamon Press, New York, 1962, p. 924.

A. Nishimura, T. Hiraoka, and K. Kuwahara, "Spontaneous Magnetization and Hall Effect in the Thin Film of Ni-Fe," *J. Sci. Hiroshima Univ.*, **A26**: 113 (1963).

T. Rappeneau, "Magnetization of Thin Ni Films," *Compt. Rend.*, **205**: 674 (1960), in French.

K. H. Rosette and R. W. Hoffman, "Spontaneous Magnetization of Iron Films," in C. A. Neugebauer *et al.* (eds.), *Structure and Properties of Thin Films*, John Wiley & Sons, Inc., New York, 1959.

K. H. Rosette and R. W. Hoffman, "Temperature Dependence of Magnetization in Thin Films," *Electrical and Magnetic Properties of Thin Metallic Layers, Proc. Internat. Conf. Liege*, September 4–7, 1961, p. 218.

H. Rother, "Magnetic Properties of Ferromagnetic Films. I. Stochastic Theory of Magnetization Fine Structure," *Z. Physik*, **168**: 42 (1962), in German.

L. Valenta, "On the Theory of the Spontaneous Magnetization of Thin Films, I and II," *Czech. J. Phys.*, **7**: 127 (1957), in Czechoslovakian.

L. Valenta, "Ferromagnetic Thin Films II. Theory of Spontaneous Magnetization," *Physica Status Solidi*, **2**: 112 (1962), in German.

A. van Itterbeek *et al.*, "Some Experimental Results on Ferromagnetic Resonance in Nickel Films," in J. Smidt (ed.), *Magnetic and Electric Resonance and Relaxation*, North-Holland Publishing Company, Amsterdam, 1963, p. 495.

E. P. Wohlfarth, "Thermal Fluctuation Effects in Thin Magnetic Films," *J. Electronics Control*, **10**: 33 (1961).

S. Yamaguchi, "Spontaneous Magnetization of a Thin Film Measured by Electron Diffraction," *Can. J. Phys.*, **36**: 1251 (1958).

S. Yamaguchi, "The Magnetism of Thin Films of Nickel," *J. Chem. Phys.*, **59**: 101 (1962), in French.

CHAPTER 7: ANISOTROPY

R. F. Adamsky, "Preferred Orientation and Ordering in Evaporated Films of Fe, Ni and Fe-Ni," *J. Appl. Phys.*, **31S**: 298S (1960).

R. G. Alexander, "Anisotropy Field Measurements on Nickel-Iron Thin Films," *J. Appl. Phys.*, **30S**: 266S (1959).

J. C. Anderson, "Magnetic Anisotropy in Single-Crystal Ni-Fe Films," *Proc. Phys. Soc.* (*London*), **78**: 25 (1961).

J. C. Anderson, "Preparation and Magnetic Anisotropy of Continuous, Single Crystal Nickel Films," *1961 Trans. 8th Vacuum Symposium 2nd Internat. Congress*, Pergamon Press, New York, 1962, p. 930.

W. Andra *et al.*, "Magnetic Field Induced Anisotropy in Thin Evaporated Permalloy Films," *Naturwiss.*, **46**: 257 (1959), in German.

P. Astwood and M. Prutton, "The Influence of Crucible Material upon the Magnetic Anisotropy of Evaporated Permalloy Films," *Brit. J. Appl. Phys.*, **14**: 48 (1963).

C. J. Bader and D. M. Ellis, "Instrument for Observation of Magnetization Vector Position in Thin Magnetic Films," *Rev. Sci. Instr.*, **33**: 1429 (1962).

J. Bagrowski and M. Lauriente, "Electroless Ni-Co-P Films with Uniaxial Anisotropy," *J. Electrochem. Soc.*, **109**: 987 (1962).

A. Baltz, "Electron Microscope Study of the Roughness of Permalloy Films Using Surface Replication," *J. Appl. Phys.*, **33**: 1115S (1962).

W. R. Beam and K. Y. Ahn, "A New Magnetic-Film Dispersion Measurement," *J. Appl. Phys.*, **34**: 1561 (1963).

T. H. Beeforth, "The Importance of Secondary Effects when Measuring Thin Film Anisotropy Field (H_K)," *J. Electronics Control*, **13**: 437 (1962).

R. R. Birss, "The Saturation Magnetostriction of Ferromagnetics," *Adv. Phys.*, **8**: 252 (1959).

J. D. Blades, "Stress Anisotropy in Nickel-Iron Thin Films," *J. Appl. Phys.*, **30S**: 260S (1959).

E. L. Boyd, "Magnetic Anisotropy in Single-Crystal Thin Films," *IBM J. Res. Develop.*, **4**: 116 (1960.)

R. W. Clapp, Jr., "Conditions Pertinent to the Occurrence of Fiber Orientation in Iron Films 1000Å Thick Deposited onto Amorphous Substrates," *J. Appl. Phys.*, **33**: 2539 (1962).

M. S. Cohen, "Anisotropy in Permalloy Films Evaporated at Grazing Incidence," *J. Appl. Phys.*, **32**: 87S (1961).

M. S. Cohen, "Anomalous Films," *J. Appl. Phys.*, **33**: 2968S (1962).

M. S. Cohen, "Influence of Anisotropy Dispersion on Magnetic Properties of Ni-Fe Films," *J. Appl. Phys.*, **34**: 1841 (1963).

M. S. Cohen, D. O. Smith, and G. P. Weiss, "Oblique Incidence Anisotropy in Evaporated Films," *J. Appl. Phys.*, **31**: 1405 (1961).

M. S. Cohen *et al.*, "Investigations into the Origin of Anisotropy in Bolique-Incidence Films," *J. Appl. Phys.*, **31**: 291S (1960); *Erratum* **32**: 1405 (1960).

R. Collette, "New Anisotropy Recorder for Ferromagnetic Thin Films," *Rev. Sci. Instr.*, **33**: 450 (1962).

A. Corciovei, "The Effect of Magnetic Anisotropy in Cobalt Ferromagnetic Thin Films," *J. Phys. Chem. Solids*, **20**: 162 (1961).

R. L. Coren, "Hall Effect Determination of Planar Stress in Ferromagnetic Films," *J. Appl. Phys.*, **33**: 1168S.

T. S. Crowther, "Angular and Magnitude Dispersion of the Anisotropy in Magnetic Films," *J. Appl. Phys.*, **34**: 580 (1963).

W. D. Doyle, "Determination of the Anisotropy in Thin Permalloy Films," *J. Appl. Phys.*, **33**: 1769 (1962).

W. D. Doyle, J. E. Rudisill, and S. Shtrikman, "Angular Dependence of Torque in Anisotropic Permalloy Films," *J. Appl. Phys.*, **31**: 1785 (1961).

W. D. Doyle, J. E. Rudisill, and S. Shtrikman, "Angular Dependence of Torque in Anisotropic Permalloy Films," *J. Phys. Soc. Japan*, **17**: 567S (1962).

E. Feldtkeller, "Field Induced and Angle of Incidence Anisotropy in Ni-Fe Films," *Z. Angew. Phys.*, **2**: 74 (1961), in German.

E. Feldtkeller, "Inverse Ni-Fe Films," *Naturwiss.*, **13**: 474 (1961), in German.

J. D. Finegan and R. W. Hoffman, "Stress Anisotropy in Evaporated Iron Films," *J. Appl. Phys.*, **30**: 597 (1959).

J. D. Finegan and R. W. Hoffman, "Stress and Stress Anisotropy in Iron Films," *1961 Trans. 8th Vacuum Symposium 2nd Internat. Congress*, Pergamon Press, New York, 1962, p. 935.

R. D. Fisher, "The Influence of Residual Stress on the Magnetic Characteristics of Electrodeposited Nickel and Cobalt," *J. Electrochem. Soc.*, **109**: 479 (1963).

R. D. Fisher and H. E. Haber, "Maximum Dispersion of the Easy Axis in Electro-deposited Thin Permalloy Films," *Appl. Phys. Letters*, **2**: 11 (1963).

P. J. Flanders, M. Prutton, and W. D. Doyle, "Relationship Between Uniaxial, Inverted and Rotatable Initial Susceptibility Permalloy Films," *J. Appl. Phys.*, **34**: 1075 (1963).

Z. Frait *et al.*, "Local Variations of Uniaxial Anisotropy in Thin Films," *Czech. J. Phys.*, **10**: 616 (1960), in Czechoslovakian.

Z. Frait, *et al.*, "On The Effective Magnetization and Uniaxial Anisotropy of Permalloy Films," *Czech. J. Phys.*, **13**: 279 (1963), in Czechoslovakian.

M. H. Francombe and A. J. Noreika, "Magnetic Anisotropy and Structure of Sputtered Permalloy Films," *Electrical and Magnetic Properties of Thin Metallic Layers, Proc. Internat. Conf. Liege*, September 4–7, 1961, p. 193.

M. H. Francombe and A. J. Noreika, "Some Properties of Uniaxial Permalloy Films Prepared by Cathode Sputtering," *J. Appl. Phys.*, **32**: 97S (1961).

J. F. Freedman, "Stress Effects on the Magnetic Properties of Evaporated Single-Crystal Nickel Films," *J. Appl. Phys.*, **33**: 1148S (1962).

J. F. Freedman, "Residual Stress in Single Crystal Nickel Films," *IBM J. Res. Develop.*, **6**: 449 (1962).

E. Fuchs and W. Zinn, "Isotropic Permalloy Films," *J. Appl. Phys.*, **34**: 2557 (1963).

H. Gartner, "Uniaxial Magnetic Anisotropy in Sputtered Thin Ni- and Fe-Films," *Z. Naturforsch.*, **16a**: 840 (1961).

H. Gartner, "The Uniaxial Magnetic Anisotropy of Thin Films of Nickel and Iron Formed by Cathode Sputtering," *Z. Angew. Phys.*, **14**: 194 (1962), in German.

H. Gartner, "Structure and Magnetic Properties of Thin Ni Layers Produced by Cathode Sputtering," *Z. Naturforsch.*, **18a**: 380 (1963), in German.

C. D. Graham, Jr., and J. M. Lommel, "Magnetic Anisotropies of Ni Films Evaporated and Measured at 10^{-8} mm Hg and Below," *J. Appl. Phys.*, **32**: 83S (1961).

C. D. Graham, Jr., and J. M. Lommel, "Effect of Pressure During Evaporation on the Magnetic Properties of Nickel Films," *J. Phys. Soc. Japan*, **17**: 570S (1962).

R. C. Hall, "Single Crystal Anisotropy and Magnetostriction Constants of Several Ferromagnetic Materials Including Alloys of NiFe, SiFe, AlFe, CoNi, and CoFe," *J. Appl. Phys.*, **30**: 816 (1959).

A. J. Hardwick, "Interrelationship of Substrate Temperature and Angle of Incidence Effects Upon Anisotropy Variations in Evaporated Nickel-Iron Thin Films," *J. Appl. Phys.*, **34**: 818 (1963).

E. K. Hatteman, "Electron Diffraction Evidence for the Existence of Microstress in Evaporated Metal Films," *J. Appl. Phys.*, **23**: 150 (1952).

R. D. Heidenreich and F. W. Reynolds, "Uniaxial Magnetic Anisotropy and Microstructure of Ferromagnetic Films," in C. A. Neugebauer *et al.* (eds.), *Structure and Properties of Thin Films*, John Wiley & Sons, Inc., New York, 1959, Chap. V.

A. A. Hirsch and N. Friedman, "Induced Magnetic Anisotropy in Thin Ferromagnetic Films Investigated at Low Temperatures," *Physica*, **29**: 543 (1963).

H. Hoffman, "Saturation Magnetization and Anisotropy Field in Thin Evaporated Fe Films," *Z. Phys.*, **165**: 261 (1961), in German.

R. W. Hoffman, R. D. Daniels, and E. C. Crittenden, Jr., "The Causes of Stress in Evaporated Metal Films," *Proc. Phys. Soc.*, **B67**: 497 (1954).

F. B. Humphrey, "Magnetic Character of Very Thin Permalloy Films," *J. Appl. Phys.*, **34**: 1067 (1963).

F. B. Humphrey and A. R. Johnston, "Sensitive Automatic Torque Balance for Thin Magnetic Films," *Rev. Sci. Instr.*, **34**: 348 (1963).

C. E. Johnson, Jr., and W. F. Brown, Jr., "Stoner-Wohlfarth Calculation on Particles with Both Magnetocrystalline and Shape Anisotropy," *J. Appl. Phys.*, **30S**: 320S (1959).

V. Kambersky and R. Gontarz, "Easy Axis Reversal in Oblique-Incidence Iron Films," *Phys. Status Solidi*, **3**: K67 (1963), in German.

V. Kambersky *et al.*, "The Dependence of the Uniaxial Magnetic Anisotropy in Evaporated Films on the Angle of Incidence," *Czech. J. Phys.*, **B11**: 171 (1961), in Czechoslovakian.

T. G. Knorr and R. W. Hoffman, "Dependence of Geometric Magnetic Anisotropy in Thin Iron Films," *Phys. Rev.*, **113**: 1039 (1959).

V. V. Kobelev, "A New Method of Measuring Anisotropy of Ferromagnetic Films," Physics of Metals and Metallography, **13**: 146 (1963).

O. S. Kolotov, T. N. Nikitina, and N. M. Solanski, "Problems of the Anisotropy Dispersion in Thin Ferromagnetic Films," *Soviet Phys.—Solid State*, **5**: 1263(1963).

C. J. Kriessman, H. S. Belson, and F. H. Edelman, "Anisotropy and Coercivity in Thin Films," *J. Appl. Phys.*, **30S**: 262S (1959).

M. Lauriente and J. Bagrowski, "Anisotropy Sources for Electrodeposited Permalloy Films," *J. Appl. Phys.*, **33**: 1109S (1962).

K. D. Leaver, "Dependence of Anisotropy Axis Dispersion on Thickness of Thin Nickel-Iron-Cobalt Films," *Nature*, **196**: 158 (1962).

S. S. Lehrer, "Rotatable Anisotropy in Negative Magnetostriction Ni-Fe Films," *J. Appl. Phys.*, **34**: 1207 (1963).

J. M. Lommel and C. D. Graham, "Rotatable Anisotropy in Composite Films," *J. Appl. Phys.*, **33**: 1160S (1962).

J. R. MacDonald, "Stress in Evaporated Ferromagnetic Films," *Phys. Rev.*, **106**: 890 (1957).

Z. Malek and W. Schuppel, "Direct Measurements of the Uniaxial Magnetic Anisotropy of Evaporated Thin Films of Fe, Ni, Permalloy and Co.," *Ann. Physik*, **6**: 252 (1960), in German.

Z. Malek and W. Schuppel, "Ferromagnetic Thin Films III. Magnetocrystalline and Induced Anisotropy," *Physica Status Solidi*, **2**: 136 (1962), in German.

Z. Malek and W. Schuppel, "Magnetic Anisotropy of Thin Films," *Monatsber. Deut. Akad. Wiss. Berlin*, **4**: 143 (1962), in German.

Z. Malek *et al.*, "Time Variation of Uniaxial Magnetic Anisotropy of Films," *Ann. Physik*, **1**: 211 (1960), in German.

T. Matcovich, E. Korostoff, and A. Schmeckerbecker, "Anisotropy Rotation in Thin Permalloy Films at Room Temperature," *J. Appl. Phys.*, **32**: 93S (1961).

S. Methfessel, A. Segmüller, and R. Sommerhalder, "Magnetic Properties of Thin Films Evaporated in Ultrahigh Vacuum," *J. Phys. Soc. Japan*, **17**: 575S (1962).

S. Middelhoek, "The Influence of the Anisotropy Variations on the Domain Behavior of Ni-Fe Films," *Electrical and Magnetic Properties of Thin Metallic Layers, Proc. Internat. Conf. Liege*, September 4–7, 1961, p. 182.

S. Middelhoek, "The Influence of Local Fluctuations of Anisotropy on the Magnetic Characteristics of Thin Ni-Fe Films," *Z. Angew. Phys.*, **13**: 151 (1961).

E. N. Mitchell, "Effects of Heat Treatment of Thin Ferromagnetic Films at Intermediate Temperature," *J. Appl. Phys.*, **29**: 286 (1958).

E. N. Mitchell and G. I. Lykken, "Magnetoelastic Behavior of Thin Ferromagnetic Thin Films as a Function of Composition," *J. Appl. Phys.*, **33**: 1170S (1962).

E. N. Mitchell, G. I. Lykken, and G. D. Babcock, "Compositional Dependence of the Magnetostriction of Thin Iron-Nickel Films," *J. Appl. Phys.*, **34**: 715 (1963).

Y. Mizushima and O. Ochi, "The Order Process in Condensed Films of Transition Metals," *Z. Naturforsch.*, **18a**: 252 (1963), in German.

A. C. Moore and A. S. Young, "Some Physical Properties of Thin Magnetic Films," *J. Appl. Phys.*, **31**: 279S (1960).

C. A. Neugebauer, "Study of the Saturation Magnetization and Magnetic Anisotropy of Ultra Thin Films Under Ultrahigh Vacuum Conditions," *Electrical and Magnetic Properties of Thin Metallic Layers, Proc. Internat. Conf. Liege*, September 4–7, 1961, p. 231.

H. J. Ogney, "Mechanical Model for Uniaxial Magnetic Anisotropy," *Rev. Sci. Instr.*, **31**: 710 (1960).

P. W. Olmen and S. M. Rubens, "Angular Dispersion and Its Relationship with Other Magnetic Parameters in Permalloy Films," *J. Appl. Phys.*, **33**: 1107S (1962).

M. Ondris and V. Kambersky, "On the Problem of the Dependence of Uniaxial Magnetic Anisotropy of Thin Films on the Angle of Deposition," *Czech. J. Phys.*, **B11**: 454 (1961).

R. V. Peacock and G. Winsor, "Measurement of Easy Direction Dispersion in Magnetic Thin Films," *Nature*, **193**: 768 (1962).

R. F. Penoyer, "Automatic Torque Balance for Magnetic Anisotropy Measurements," *Rev. Sci. Instr.*, **30**: 711 (1959).

J. R. Priest, "Apparatus for the Measurement of Stress in Vacuum Evaporated Films," *Rev. Sci. Instr.*, **32**: 1349 (1961).

R. J. Prosen, J. O. Holmen, and B. E. Gran, "Rotatable Anisotropy in Thin Permalloy Films," *J. Appl. Phys.*, **32**: 91S (1961).

R. J. Prosen et al., "Stratification in Thin Permalloy Films," *J. Appl. Phys.*, **33**: 1150S (1962).

R. J. Prosen et al., "Influence of Minor Constitutents in Ferromagnetic Films," *J. Phys. Soc. Japan*, **17**: 580S (1962).

M. Prutton, "Structure and Anisotropy in Magnetic Films," *1962 Trans. 9th Vacuum Symposium*, The Macmillan Company, New York, 1962, p. 59.

M. Prutton, "Stress and Magnetic Anisotropy in Thin Permalloy Films," *Nature*, **193**: 565 (1963).

E. W. Pugh, E. L. Boyd, and J. F. Freedman, "Angle-of-Incidence Anisotropy in Evaporated Ni-Fe Films," *IBM J. Res. Develop.*, **4**: 163 (1960).

E. W. Pugh et al., "Magnetic Anisotropy in Evaporated Iron Films," *J. Appl. Phys.*, **31**: 293S (1960).

G. Robinson, "Torque Measurements of Uniaxial Anisotropy in Thin Films of Nickel-Iron in the Composition Range 80%–100% Nickel," *Electrical and Magnetic Properties of Thin Metallic Layers, Proc. Internat. Conf. Liege*, September 4–7, 1961, p. 140.

D. S. Rodbell, "The Temperature Dependence of the Magnetocrystalline Anisotropy of Face-Centered Cubic Cobalt," *J. Phys. Soc. Japan*, Suppl. B-1, **17**: 313 (1962).

T. D. Rossing, "Resonance Linewidth and Anisotropy Variation in Thin Films," *J. Appl. Phys.*, **34**: 3692 (1963).

S. M. Rubens and R. W. Olmen, "Domain Structure and Dispersion of the Preferred Axis in Ferromagnetic Films," *Electrical and Magnetic Properties of Thin Metallic Layers, Proc. Internat. Conf. Liege*, September 4–7, 1961, p. 111.

M. K. Savchenko, N. I. Sudahov, and T. P. Izotova, "Anisotropy of Thin Ferromagnetic Films," *Bull. Acad. Sci. USSR, Phys. Ser. 26*, 314 (1962).

W. Schuppel, "Spontaneous Character of the Time-Dependent Induced Anisotropy of Ferromagnetic Thin Films," *Physica Status Solidi*, **2**: 1175 (1962), in German.

W. Schuppel and A. Malek, "Measurement of the Magnetic Anisotropy of Evaporated Thin Ni Films," *Naturwiss.*, **46**: 423 (1959), in German.

W. Schuppel et al., "Direct Measurement of Anisotropy of Thin Films," *Phys. Met. Mettal. (USSR)*, **8**: 30 (1960).

A. Segmüller, "Annealing Behavior and Temperature Dependence of the Magnetic Properties of Thin Permalloy Films," *J. Appl. Phys.*, **32**: 89S (1961).

A. Segmüller, "The Temperature Dependence of the Magnetic Properties of Thin Permalloy Films," *Z. Angew. Phys.*, **13**: 154 (1961), in German.

D. O. Smith, "Anisotropy in Permalloy Films," *J. Appl. Phys.*, **30S**: 264S (1959).

D. O. Smith, "Some Structure Sensitive Properties of Permalloy Films," in C. A. Neugebauer et al. (eds.), *Structure and Properties of Thin Films*, John Wiley & Sons, Inc., New York, 1959, Chap. V.

D. O. Smith, "Anisotropy in Ni-Fe Films," *J. Appl. Phys.*, **32**: 70S (1961).

D. O. Smith, "Positive and Negative Anisotropy in Nickel-Iron Films," *J. Phys. Soc. Japan*, **17**: 550S (1962).

D. O. Smith et al., "Anisotropy and Inversion in Permalloy Films," *J. Appl. Phys.*, **31**: 295S (1960).

R. J. Spain, "Role of Internal Stresses in Thin Ferromagnet Films," *Compt. Rend.*, **256**: 3262 (1963), in French.

O. Stemme and W. Andra, "Anisotropy Induced by a Magnetic Field in Electrodeposited Nickel Films," *Naturwiss.*, **46**: 352 (1959), in German.

S. Szezeniowski, H. Ratajczak, and R. Gontarz, "Dependence of Magnetic Properties of Thin Iron Films on the Geometry of Evaporation," *J. Phys. Soc. Japan*, **17**: 562S (1962).

M. Takahashi, "Induced Magnetic Anisotropy of Evaporated Films in a Magnetic Field," *J. Appl. Phys.*, **33**: 1101S (1962).

M. Takahashi et al., "Magnetic Anisotropy of Evaporated Films Formed in a Magnetic Field," *J. Phys. Soc. Japan*, **14**: 1459 (1959).

M. Takahashi *et al.*, "Magnetic Anisotropy of Evaporated Films," *J. Phys. Soc. Japan*, **15**: 1351 (1960).

M. Takahashi *et al.*, "Magnetic Anisotropy of Evaporated Films, I. Iron Films Formed in Magnetic Field," *J. Phys. Soc. Japan*, **16**: 1913 (1961).

M. Takahashi *et al.*, "Magnetic Anisotropy of Evaporated Films," *J. Phys. Soc. Japan*, **17**: 554S (1962).

I. Teodorescu and A. Glodeanu, "Effects of Fast-Neutron Irradiation on Nickel Thin Films," *Phys. Rev. Letters*, **4**: 231 (1960).

E. J. Torok *et al.*, "Measurement of the Easy Axis and H_K Probability Density Functions for Thin Ferromagnetic Film Using the Longitudinal Permeability Hysteresis Loop," *J. Appl. Phys.*, **33**: 3037 (1962).

J. Trait *et al.*, "Local Variations in Uniaxial Anisotropy in Thin Films," *Czech. J. Phys.*, **10**: 616 (1960), in Czechoslovakian.

S. Uchiyama, M. Masuda, and Y. Sakaki, "Measurement of Anisotropy Dispersion by Means of Ferromagnetic Resonance," *Japan J. Appl. Phys.*, **2**: 621 (1963).

Y. Uehara, "Electrodeposited Nickel-Iron Thin Films," *Japan J. Appl. Phys.*, **2**: 451 (1963).

R. R. Verderber, "Texture of Evaporated Nickel-Iron Thin Films," *J. Appl. Phys.*, **30**: 1359 (1959).

R. R. Verderber and R. M. Kortyk, "Ni-Fe Single-Crystal Films and Their Magnetic Characteristics," *J. Appl. Phys.*, **31**: 696 (1961).

G. P. Weiss and D. O. Smith, "Annealing of Oblique-Incidence Permalloy Films," *J. Appl. Phys.*, **32**: 85S (1961).

G. P. Weiss and D. O. Smith, "Isotropic Stress Measurements in Permalloy Films," *J. Appl. Phys.*, **33**: 1166S (1962).

I. W. Wolf, "The Effect of Small Quantitites of Copper on the Magnetic Properties of Electrodeposited Permalloys," *Electrical and Magnetic Properties of Thin Metallic Layers*, *Proc. Internat. Conf. Liege*, September 4–7, 1961, p. 158.

I. W. Wolf and T. S. Crowther, "Magnetoelastic Sensitivities in Evaporated and Electrodeposited Permalloy Films," *J. Appl. Phys.*, **34**: 1205 (1963).

I. Yasumori, D. Reinen, and P. W. Selwood, "Anisotropic Behavior in Superparamagnetic Systems," *J. Appl. Phys.*, **34**: 3544 (1963).

A. Yelon, J. R. Asik, and R. W. Hoffman, "Fiber Texture and Magnetic Anisotropy in Evaporated Iron Films," *J. Appl. Phys.*, **33**: 949 (1962).

CHAPTER 8 : HYSTERESIS AND EDDY CURRENTS

G. Bate and D. E. Speliotis, "Hard Magnetic Films of Co-Ni-P," *J. Appl. Phys.*, **34**: 1073 (1963).

M. Beckerman and K. H. Behrndt, "The Influence of Edge Effects on Domain Structure and Coercive Force of Circular Ni-Fe Films," *IBM J. Res. Develop.*, **4**: 198 (1960).

K. H. Behrndt, "On the Coercive Force and its Connection to the Impurities in Ferromagnetic Thin Films," *Electrical and Magnetic Properties of Thin Metallic Layers*, *Proc. Internat. Conf. Liege*, September 4–7, 1961, p. 419.

M. S. Blois, Jr., "Evaporated Magnetic Materials," *Electronics*, **28**: 210 (June, 1955).

W. W. L. Chu, J. E. Wolfe, and B. C. Wagner, "Some Observations on Evaporated Permalloy Films," *J. Appl. Phys.*, **30S**: 272S (1959).

H. Clow, "Very Low Coercive Force in Nickel-Iron Films," *Nature*, **194**: 1035.

M. S. Cohen, "Anomalous Films," *J. Appl. Phys.*, **33**: 2968S (1962).

A. Colombani and H. Daridon, "Conductivity and Perpendicular Effect of Thin Films of Cobalt," *Electrical and Magnetic Properties of Thin Metallic Layers*, *Proc. Internat. Conf. Liege*, September 4–7, 1961, p. 58.

A. Colombani and G. Goureaux, "The Hall Effect of Thin Films of Nickel—Experimental Results," in C. A. Neugebauer *et al.* (eds.), *Structure and Properties of Thin Films*, John Wiley & Sons, Inc., New York, 1959, Chap. V.

A. Colombani, B. Laniepce, and G. Goureaux, "Variation of the Electrical Conductivity of Thin Films of Nickel Under Constraint," *Compt. Rend.*, **254**: 480 (1962), in French.

R. L. Coren and H. J. Juretschke, "Magnetoresistance and Magnetic Switching in Permalloy Films," *J. Appl. Phys.*, **32**: 292S (1961).

R. L. Coren and H. J. Juretschke, "Magnetoresistance and Domain Structure in Thin Nickel Films," *Phys. Rev.*, **126**: 1378 (1962).

E. C. Crittenden, Jr., A. A. Hudimac, and R. I. Strough, "Magnetization Hysteresis Loop Tracer for Long Specimens of Extremely Small Cross Section," *Rev. Sci. Instr.*, **22**: 872 (1951).

W. D. Doyle and M. Prutton, "Anisotropy Distribution and Unidirectional Hysteresis in Thin Permalloy Films," *J. Appl. Phys.*, **34**: 1077 (1963).

W. D. Doyle, J. E. Rudisill, and S. Shtrikman, "Unidirectional Hysteresis in Thin Permalloy Films," *J. Appl. Phys.*, **33**: 1162S (1962).

E. Feldtkeller, "Inverse Ni-Fe Films," *Naturwiss.*, **13**: 474 (1961), in German.

E. Feldtkeller, "Ripple Hysteresis in Thin Magnetic Films," *J. Appl. Phys.*, **34**: 2646 (1963).

N. C. Ford, Jr., and E. W. Pugh, "Barkhausen Effects in Nickel-Iron Films," *J. Appl. Phys.*, **30S**: 270S (1959).

M. H. Francombe, J. E. Rudisill, and R. L. Coren, "Faraday Rotation and Hysteresis Properties of Ferrite Thin Films," *J. Appl. Phys.*, **34**: 1215 (1963).

G. Goureaux, "Magnetoresistance of Thin Nickel Films Consequences," *Electrical and Magnetic Properties of Thin Metallic Layers*, Proc. Internat. Conf. Liege, September 4–7, 1961, p. 77.

G. Goureaux and A. Colombani, "Magnetoresistance of Nickel Films: Perpendicular Effect," *Compt. Rend.*, **250**: 4310 (1960), in French.

T. E. Hartman, "Electrical Conduction in Discontinuous Thin Metal Films," *J. Appl. Phys.*, **34**: 943 (1963).

W. Hellenthal, "Relation of the Coercive Force to Film Thickness and Temperature of Evaporated Thin Ni Films as Measured by Magnetic-Resistivity Changes," *Z. Naturforsch.*, **14a**: 722 (1959), in German.

W. Hellenthal, "Frequency Dependence of a Coercive Force of Thin Evaporated Nickel Films as Measured in an Alternating Magnetic Field," *Z. Naturforsch.*, **14a**: 1077 (1959), in German.

A. A. Hirsch, "Temperature Dependence of Coercivity and Domain Structure in Thin Ferromagnetic Layers," *Electrical and Magnetic Properties of Thin Metallic Layers*, Proc. Internat. Conf. Liege, September 4–7, 1961, p. 128.

A. A. Hirsch and N. Friedman, "Induced Magnetic Anisotropy in Thin Ferromagnetic Films Investigated at Low Temperatures," *Physica*, **29**: 543 (1963).

V. A. Ignatchenko, N. S. Chistyakov, and V. I. Tarasenko, "Ultra-High-Frequency Power Absorption as a Result of the Magnetic Reversal of a Thin Ferromagnetic Film," *Phys. Metals Metallograph.*, **14**: 110 (1962).

V. F. Ivlev, N. G. Pak, and S. V. Kan, "Hysteresis Loops of Plane Ferromagnetic Films," *Fiz. Metallov Metallovedenie*, **14**: 938 (1962), in Russian.

H. J. Juretschke, "Galvanomagnetic and Magnetic Properties of Thin Nickel-Iron Films," in C. A. Neugebauer *et al.* (eds.), *Structure and Properties of Thin Films*, John Wiley & Sons, Inc., New York, 1959, Chap. V.

J. Kaczer, "Contributions to the Theory of Coercive Force in Thin Sheets," *Bull. Acad. Sci. USSR*, **218**: 1168 (1958).

P. D. Kim and G. M. Rodichev, "Large Barkhausen Jumps in Thin Ferromagnetic Films," *Acad. Sci. USSR, Phys. Ser.*, **26**: 305 (1963).

E. Kondorskii and M. Rosenberg, "Temperature Dependence of the Coercive Force in Thin Specimens of Nickel and Ferronickel Alloys," *Soviet Phys.—Doklady*, **3**: 595 (1958).

E. I. Kondorsky *et al.*, "The Electrical Properties of Thin Films of Nickel at Very Low Temperatures," *J. Phys. Soc. Japan*, **17**: 588S (1962).

N. V. Kotel'nikov *et al.*, "The Magnetic Properties and Structure of Chemically Prepared Nickel Films," *Soviet Phys.—Doklady*, **1**: 896 (1963).

G. Krause and G. Meyer, "Optical Absorption and Polarization of Evaporated Nickel Films," *Z. Physik*, **169**: 511 (1962), in German.

K. Kresin, "Rectangular Loops with Ring-Shaped Elements with Thin Ferromagnetic Layers Made by Application of Mechanical Stresses," *Monatsber. Deut. Akad. Wiss. Berlin*, **4**: 112 (1962), in German.

C. J. Kriessman, H. S. Belson, and F. H. Edelman, "Anisotropy and Coercivity in Thin Films," *J. Appl. Phys.*, **30S**: 262S (1959).

J. C. Lloyd and R. S. Smith, "Structure and Magnetic Properties of Permalloy Films," *J. Appl. Phys.*, **30S**: 274 (1959).

J. C. Lloyd and R. S. Smith, "Relation of Coercive Force to Structural Properties of Electroplated Films," *Can. J. Phys.*, **40**: 454 (1962).

J. R. Mayfield, "Rotational Hysteresis in Thin Films," *J. Appl. Phys.*, **30S**: 256 (1959).

J. R. Mayfield, "Measocalorimetric Technique for the study of Damping and Hysteresis in Ferromagnetic Films," *J. Appl. Phys.*, **31**: 298 (1960).

S. Methfessel, A. Segmüller, and R. Sommerhalder, "Magnetic Properties of Thin Films Evaporated in Ultrahigh Vacuum," *J. Phys. Soc. Japan*, **17**: 575S (1962).

S. Middelhoek, "Constriction of Hard Direction Hysteresis Loop in Thin Permalloy Films," *J. Appl. Phys.*, **33**: 1111S (1962).

S. Middelhoek, "Relation Between the Thickness of Thin Metallic Films and the Coercive Force for Wall Displacement," *J. Phys.*, **24**: 173 (1963).

Y. Mizushima, "Resistance Change due to Absorption," *1960 Vacuum Symposium Trans.*, Pergamon Press, New York, 1961, p. 273.

C. A. Neugebauer, "Electrical Resistivity of Ultrathin Metal Films," in *1962 Trans. of the 9th Vacuum Symposium*, The Macmillan Company, New York, 1962, p. 45.

C. A. Neugebauer and M. B. Webb, "The Mechanism of Electrical Conduction in Ultrathin Evaporated Metal Films," *Electrical and Magnetic Properties of Thin Metallic Layers, Proc. Internat. Conf. Liege*, September 4–7, 1961, p. 37.

A. Nishimura, T. Hiraoka, and K. Kuwahara, "Spontaneous Magnetization and Hall Effect in the Thin Film of Ni-Fe," *J. Sci. Hiroshima Univ.*, **A 26**: 113 (1963).

A. J. Noreika and M. H. Francombe, "Factors Influencing Coercive Force in Sputtered Permalloy Films," *J. Appl. Phys.*, **33**: 1119S (1962).

H. J. Ogney, "Hysteresis Loops of Thin Films," *Proc. Inst. Radio Engrs.*, **48**: 1165 (1960).

H. J. Ogney, "Sensitive Flux Measurement of Thin Magnetic Films," *Rev. Sci. Instr.*, **31**: 701 (1960).

R. L. Parker and A. Krinsky, "Electrical Resistance-Strain Characteristics of Thin Evaporated Metal Films," *J. Appl. Phys,*. **34**: 2700 (1963).

F. Pfeiter, "Square-Loop Permalloy Alloys," *Z. Angew. Phys.*, **13**: 177 (1961), in German.

R. J. Prosen *et al.*, "Stratification in Thin Permalloy Films," *J. Appl. Phys.*, **33**: 1150S (1962).

R. J. Prosen *et al.*, "Effect of Surface Roughness on Magnetic Properties of Films," *J. Appl. Phys.*, **34**: 1147 (1963).

Yu G. Ptushins'ki and O. A. Panchenko, "Change in the Electrical Resistance of Thin Metal Films During Absorption," *Ukrayin Fiz. Zh. (USSR)*, **I**: 1079 (1962), in Ukrainian.

I. B. Puchalska and R. J. Spain, "Observation of the Mechanisms of Magnetic Hysteresis in Thin Films," *Compt. Rend.*, **254**: 72 (1962), in French.

T. Rappeneau, "Study of the Magnetoresistance of Thin Evaporated Nickel Films," *Cahiers Phys.*, **12**: 185 (1958), in French.

W. Reincke, "Coercive Field Strength of Thin Films of Iron," *Z. Phys.*, **174**: 35 (1963), in German.

L. Reiner, "Magnetic Properties of Thin Electrolytically Deposited and Evaporated Ni and Fe Films," *Z. Naturforsch.*, **12**: 550 (1957), in German.

H. Rother, "Variations of the Direction of Magnetization, Wall Spacing and Coercive Force in Thin Films," *Z. Angew. Phys.*, **14**: 187 (1962).

H. Rother, "Magnetic Properties of Ferromagnetic Films. III. The Wave Theory of the Coercive Force," *Z. Physik*, **168**: 283 (1962), in German.

W. Ruske, "On the Magnetic Properties of Thin Electrolytically Deposited Nickel Films," *Ann. Phys.*, **7**: 274 (1958), in German.

J. S. Sallo and J. M. Carr, "Instability of the Fine Particle Structure of Certain Electrodeposits," *J. Appl. Phys.*, **34**: 1309 (1963).

F. Savornin, "Electrical and Thermoelectric Properties of Thin Cobalt Layers," *Electrical and Magnetic Properties of Thin Metallic Layers, Proc. Internat. Conf. Liege*, September 4–7, 1961, p. 69.

M. J. Schindler, "Shear Compensated Hysteresisgraph for Thin Magnetic Films," *Rev. Sci. Instr.*, **32**: 862 (1961).

A. Segmüller, "Annealing Behavior and Temperature Dependence of the Magnetic Properties of Thin Permalloy Films," *J. Appl. Phys.*, **32**: 89S (1961).

A. Segmüller, "The Temperature Dependence of the Magnetic Properties of Thin Permalloy Films," *Z. Angew. Phys.*, **13**: 154 (1961), in German.

S. Shtrikman and D. Treves, "The Coercive Force and Rotational Hysteresis of Elongated Ferromagnetic Particles," *J. Phys. Rad.*, **20**: 286 (1959), in French.

D. O. Smith, "Some Structure Sensitive Properties of Permalloy Films," in C. A. Neugebauer *et al.* (eds.), *Structure and Properties of Thin Films*, John Wiley & Sons, Inc., New York, 1959.

E. C. Stoner and E. P. Wohlfarth, "A Mechanism of Magnetic Hysteresis in Heterogeneous Alloys," *Trans. Roy. Phil. Soc.* (London), **240A**: 599 (1946–1948).

I. Teodorescu and A. Glodeanu, "Effects of Fast-Neutron Irradiation on Nickel Thin Films," *Phys. Rev. Letters*, **4**: 231 (1960).

C. O. Tiller and G. W. Clark, "Coercive Force vs. Thickness for Thin Films of Nickel-Iron," *Phys. Rev.*, **110**: 583 (1958).

Y. Uehara, "Electrodeposited Nickel-Iron Thin Films," *Japan J. Appl. Phys.*, **2**: 451 (1963).

A. van Itterbeek, A. Dupre, and G. Brandt, "Resistivity Measurement on Permalloy Films," *Appl. Sci. Res.*, **B 9**: 470 (1963).

C. Vantier, G. Bordes, and A. Colombani, "Electrical Conductivity and Hall Effect in Thin Films of Iron," *Compt. Rend.*, **255**: 906 (1962), in French.

R. R. Verderber and R. M. Kortyk, "Ni-Fe Single-Crystal Films and Their Magnetic Characteristics," *J. Appl. Phys.*, **31**: 696 (1961).

T. Wako, M. Saheki, and T. Monyama, "Anisotropic Electrical Resistance in Nickel and Iron Films Evaporated in Magnetic Field," *Japan J. Appl. Phys.*, **2**: 659 (1963).

R. S. Webley, "Thin Magnetic Films," *Nature*, **183**: 999 (1959).

F. G. West, "Magnetoresistive Measurements on Domain Rotation and Wall-Development in Ni-Fe Alloy Films," *J. Appl. Phys.*, **32**: 290S (1961).

F. G. West, "Magnetization Processes in Permalloy Films Having Dispersed Anisotropy Axes as Revealed by Dynamic Magnetoresistance Measurements," *Electrical and Magnetic Properties of Thin Metallic Layers, Proc. Internat. Conf. Liege*, September 4–7, 1961, p. 243.

F. G. West, "Rotating-Field Technique for Galvanomagnetic Measurements," *J. Appl. Phys.*, **34**: 1171 (1963).

I. W. Wolf, "The Effect of Small Quantities of Copper on the Magnetic Properties of Electrodeposited Permalloys," *Electrical and Magnetic Properties of Thin Metallic Layers, Proc. Internat. Conf. Liege*, September 4–7, 1961.

CHAPTER 9: MAGNETIZATION REVERSAL

W. Andra, "The Theory of Magnetization Reversal of Thin Films, Pt. I—Nucleation in Homogeneous Material," *Monatsber. Deut. Akad. Wiss. Berlin,* **2**: 398 (1960), in German.

W. Andra, "The Theory of Magnetization Reversal in Thin Films," *Z. Angew. Phys.,* **13**: 141 (1961), in German.

W. A. Barrett, "Measurement of Film Relaxation Time," *J. Appl. Phys.,* **34**: 1207 (1963).

L. F. Bates and R. Carey, "Domain Observation on a Nickel-Iron Film," *Proc. Phys. Soc. (London),* **79**: 1245 (1962).

L. F. Bates, D. J. Craik, and S. Rushton, "Slow Magnetization Reversal in Cobalt Films," *Proc. Phys. Soc. (London),* **80**: 768 (1962).

J. Brachman, W. Kusterer, and W. Metzdorf, "The Influence of Film Edge on Magnetization Reversal in Thin Permalloy Films," *Z. Angew. Phys.,* **8**: 313 (1961), in German.

E. M. Bradley and M. Prutton, "Magnetization Reversal by Rotation and Wall Motion in Thin Films of Nickel-Iron Alloys," *J. Electronics Control (London),* **6**: 81 (1959).

E. M. Bradley and M. Prutton, "Magnetization Reversal in Uniaxial Films Near to the Preferred Direction," *J. Appl. Phys.,* **31**: 285S (1960).

W. F. Brown, Jr., "Rigorous Calculation of the Nucleation Field in a Ferromagnetic Film or Plate," *Phys. Rev.,* **124**: 1348 (1961).

W. S. Carter, "Magnetic Interactions in Thin Films Induced by Strip Line Fields," *Electrical and Magnetic Properties of Thin Metallic Layers, Proc. Internat. Conf. Liege,* September 4–7, 1961, p. 205.

H. Chang, "Analysis of Static and Quasidynamic Behavior of Magnetostatically Coupled Thin Magnetic Films," *IBM J. Res. Develop.,* **6**: 419 (1962).

H. Chang, A. Yelon, and O. Voegeli, "Internal Field, Dispersion, Creeping and Switching Speed of Coupled Films," *J. Appl. Phys.,* **34**: 1209 (1963).

R. L. Conger, "Magnetization Reversal in Thin Films," *Phys. Rev.,* **98**: 1752 (1955).

R. L. Conger, "High Frequency Effects in Magnetic Films," *Proc. AIEE Conf. Magnetism Magnetic Mater., Boston* (1956), p. 610.

R. L. Conger, "Thin Magnetization Reversal Studies," *Proc. Special Tech. Nonlinear Magnetics Magnetic Amplifiers* (1958), p. 444.

R. L. Conger and F. C. Essig, "Resonance and Reversal Phenomena in Ferromagnetic Films," *Phys. Rev.,* **104**: 915 (1956).

R. L. Conger and F. C. Essig, "Magnetization Reversal in Thin Films at Low Fields," *J. Appl. Phys.,* **28**: 855 (1957).

R. L. Conger and G. H. Moore, "Direction Observation of High-Speed Magnetization Reversal in Films," *J. Appl. Phys.,* **34**: 1213 (1963).

J. A. Copeland and F. B. Humphrey, "Flux Reversal by Néel Wall Motion," *J. Appl. Phys.,* **34**: 1211 (1963).

R. L. Coren, "A Description of Magnetic Switching in Disperse Anisotropy Films," *J. Appl. Phys.,* **35**: 201 (1964).

R. L. Coren and H. J. Juretschke, "Magnetoresistance and Magnetic Switching in Permalloy Films," *J. Appl. Phys.,* **32**: 292S (1961).

W. Dietrich, "Incomplete Switching Processes in Thin Magnetic Films," *Z. Angew. Phys.,* **14**: 210 (1962), in German.

W. Dietrich, "Partial Switching Processes in Thin Magnetic Films," *IBM J. Res. Develop.,* **6**: 368 (1962).

W. Dietrich and W. E. Proebster, "Millimicrosecond Magnetization Reversal in Thin Magnetic Films," *J. Appl. Phys.,* **31**: 281S (1960).

W. Dietrich and W. E. Proebster, "A Study of Switching in Thin Magnetic Films," *1961 Solid State Cir. Conf.* (1961), p. 66.

W. Dietrich, W. E. Proebster, and P. Wolf, "Nanosecond Switching in Thin Magnetic Films," *IBM J. Res. Develop.*, **4**: 189 (1960).

J. S. Eggenberger, "Influence of Nearby Conductors on Thin Film Switching," *J. Appl. Phys.*, **31**: 287S (1960); *Erratum*, **32**: 752 (1960).

D. M. Ellis and C. J. Bader, "Measurement of Magnetic Thin Film Rotational Properties and Uniformity," *Rev. Sci. Instr.*, **34**: 1188 (1963).

E. Feldtkeller, "A Description of Coherent Magnetization Reversal in Thin Ferromagnetic Films," *Z. Angew. Phys.*, **12**: 257 (1960), in German.

E. Feldtkeller, "The Magnetization Reversal of Thin Ni-Fe Films in the Hard Direction, Pt. II, Hysteresis and Domain Behavior," *Z. Angew. Phys.*, **13**: 161 (1961), in German.

E. Feldtkeller, "The Field Strength for Wall Movement in Anisotropic Nickel-Iron Films," *Z. Angew. Phys.*, **15**: 206 (1963), in German.

E. Fuchs and H. Pfisterer, "Domain Wall Motions in Thin Ferromagnetic Films," in S. S. Breese, Jr. (ed.), *Electron Microscopy, 5th Internat. Congress, Philadelphia, 1962*, Vol. I, Paper II-4, Academic Press, New York, 1962.

C. E. Fuller, "Domain Patterns and Reversals by Wall Motion of Iron and Nickel-Iron Films," *J. Phys. Radium*, **20**: 310 (1959), in French.

P. R. Gillette and K. Oshima, "Magnetization Reversal by Rotation," *J. Appl. Phys.*, **29**: 529 (1958).

E. M. Gyorgy, "Rotational Model of Flux Reversal in Square Loop Soft Ferromagnetics," *J. Appl. Phys.*, **29**: 283 (1958).

E. M. Gyorgy, "Flux Reversal in Soft Ferromagnetics," *J. Appl. Phys.*, **31**: 110S (1960).

F. B. Hagedorn, "Partial Switching of Thin Permalloy Films," *J. Appl. Phys.*, **30S**: 254S (1959).

A. L. Hanzel and R. L. Conger, "Isolation of Rotational Reversal in Ferromagnetic Films," *J. Appl. Phys.*, **30**: 1932 (1959).

K. J. Harte, "Flux Reversal by Noncoherent Rotation in Magnetic Films," *J. Appl. Phys.*, **31**: 283S (1960).

K. J. Harte and D. O. Smith, "Switching Thresholds of Weakly Coupled Ferromagnetic Domains," *J. Appl. Phys.*, **34**: 442 (1963).

T. E. Hasty, T. C. Penn, and N. G. Einspruch, "Ultrasonically Induced Switching in (80% Ni–20% Fe) Ferromagnetic Films," *J. Appl. Phys.*, **34**: 1685 (1963).

A. L. Houde, "Observation of the Fine Structure of Domains and Reversible Rotation of the Magnetization in Thin Permalloy Films by the Faraday Effect," *J. Phys. Soc. Japan*, **17**: 618S (1962).

F. B. Humphrey, "Transverse Flux Change in Soft Ferromagnetics," *J. Appl. Phys.*, **29**: 284 (1958).

F. B. Humphrey and E. M. Gyorgy, "Flux Reversal in Soft Ferromagnets," *J. Appl. Phys.*, **30**: 935 (1959).

F. B. Humphrey, F. W. Reynolds, and G. R. Stillwell, "Introduction to Magnetic Thin Films," *1958 Vacuum Symposium Trans.*, Pergamon Press, New York, 1959, p. 204.

T. Ichinokawa, "Observation of Dynamic Changes of Domain Structures in Ferromagnetic Thin Films by Electron Microscope," in S. S. Breese, Jr., (ed.), *Electron Microscopy, 5th Internat. Congress, Philadelphia, 1962*, Vol. I, Paper II-8, Academic Press, New York, 1962.

V. A. Ignatchenko and Y. V. Zakharov, "Domain Structure of Thin Ferromagnetic Films," *Soviet Phys.—JETP*, **16**: 329 (1962).

V. A. Ignatchenko, N. S. Chistyakov, and V. I. Tarasenko, "Ultra-High-Frequency Power Absorption as a Result of the Magnetic Reversal of a Thin Ferromagnetic Film," *Phys. Metals Metallograph.*, **14**: 110 (1962).

V. Kambersky and R. Gontarz, "Easy Axis Reversal in Oblique-Incidence Iron Films," *Phys. Status Solidi*, **3**: K67 (1963), in German.

R. Kikuchi, "On the Minimum of Magnetization Reversal Time," *J. Appl. Phys.*, **27**: 1352 (1956).

P. D. Kim and G. M. Radichev, "Large Barkhausen Jumps in Thin Ferromagnetic Films," *Bull. Acad. Sci. USSR, Phys. Ser.*, **26**: 305 (1962).

L. V. Kirenskii, S. V. Kan, and M. K. Savchenko, "Behavior of the Domain Structure of Thin Ferromagnetic Films at Different Temperatures," *Bull. Acad. Sci. USSR, Phys. Ser.*, **26**: 310 (1963).

H. Kronmuller, "Micromagnetic Theory of Initial Susceptibility and Its Application to Magnetic Uniaxial Crystals," *Z. Angew. Phys.*, **15**: 197 (1963), in German.

M. Lambeck, "Optical Investigations on Ferromagnetic Layers," *Z. Angew. Phys.*, **15**: 272 (1963), in German.

K. D. Leaver and M. Prutton, "The Effect of Applied Field Inhomogeneity on the Reversal Behavior of Thin Magnetic Films," *J. Electronics Control*, **15**: 173 (1963).

W. Liesk, "Magnetic Structures in Thin Films Observed by Electron Microscope," *Z. Angew. Phys.*, **14**: 200 (1962), in German.

S. Methfessel, S. Middelhoek, and H. Thomas, "Nucleation Processes in Thin Permalloy Films," *J. Appl. Phys.*, **32**: 294S (1961).

W. Metzdorf, "Processes During the Quasistatic Magnetization of Thin Films," *Z. Angew. Phys.*, **14**: 412 (1962), in German.

S. Middelhoek, "Magnetization Reversal in Thin Ferromagnetic Ni-Fe Films," *Helv. Phys. Acta* (Switzerland), **33**: 619 (1960).

S. Middelhoek, "Domain Wall Creeping in Thin Permalloy Films," *IBM J. Res. Develop.*, **6**: 140 (1962).

S. Middelhoek, "Static Reversal Processes in Thin Ni-Fe Films," *IBM J. Res. Develop.*, **6**: 394 (1962).

S. Middelhoek, "Creeping of Domain Walls in Thin Ni-Fe Films," *Z. Angew. Phys.*, **14**: 191 (1962), in German.

A. C. Moore and A. S. Young, "Some Physical Properties of Thin Magnetic Films," *J. Appl. Phys.*, **31**: 279S (1960).

C. P. Olson and A. V. Pohm, "Flux Reversal in Thin Films of 82% Ni, 18% Fe," *J. Appl. Phys.*, **29**: 274 (1958).

B. Passon, "An Application of the Magneto-Optical Kerr Effect for the Investigation of Fast Magnetization Processes," *Z. Angew. Phys.*, **16**: 81 (1963), in German.

A. M. Radichev and E. N. Rumanov, "Contribution to the Theory of High-Field Switching of Thin Ferromagnetic Films," *Bull. Acad. Sci. USSR, Phys. Ser.*, **26**: 294 (1962).

V. S. Pokopenko, "Distribution of the Magnitudes of Magnetization Jumps in Cylindrical Films," *Soviet Phys.—Tech. Phys.*, **7**: 1035 (1963).

I. B. Puchalska and R. J. Spain, "Thin Film Switching as Observed by Electron Microscopy." in S. S. Breese, Jr. (ed.), *Electron Microscopy, 5th Internat. Congress, Philadelphia, 1962*, Vol. I, Paper II-9, Academic Press, New York, 1962.

L. Reimer, "Domain Wall Movement in Ferromagnetic Layers," *Electrical and Magnetic Properties of Thin Metallic Layers, Proc. Internat. Conf. Liege*, September 4–7, 1961, p. 123.

R. M. Sanders and T. D. Rossing, "Reversible Rotation in Magnetic Films," *J. Appl. Phys.*, **29**: 288 (1958).

M. K. Savchenko, N. I. Sudakov, and T. P. Izotova, "Anisotropy of Thin Ferromagnetic Films," *Bull. Acad. Sci. USSR, Phys. Ser.*, **26**: 314 (1963).

F. Schuler, "Magnetic Films Nucleation Wall Motion and Domain Morphology," *J. Appl. Phys.*, **33**: 1845 (1962).

J. F. Schwenker and T. R. Long, "Support and Extension of the Rotational Model of Thin Film Magnetization," *J. Appl. Phys.*, **33**: 1099S (1962).

J. P. Smith, "Display of Rotational Switching Characteristics of Magnetic Thin Films," *Rev. Sci. Instr.*, **33**: 1401 (1963).

D. O. Smith and K. T. Harte, "Noncoherent Switching in Permalloy Films," *J. Appl. Phys.*, **33**: 1399 (1962).

D. O. Smith and G. P. Weiss, "Steady-State and Pulse Measurements Techniques for Thin Magnetic Films in the vhf-uhf Range," *J. Appl. Phys.*, **29**: 290 (1958).

R. J. Spain, "Thin Film Switching by Non-Coherent Rotation," *J. Phys Soc. Japan*, **17**: 625S (1962).

R. J. Spain and H. Rubenstein, "Thin Film Switching in the Hard Direction by Wall Motion," *J. Appl. Phys.*, **32**: 288S (1961).

F. D. Stacey, "Thermally Activated Ferromagnetic Domain Wall Motion," *Australian J. Phys.*, **13**: 599 (1960).

J. C. Suits and E. W. Pugh, "Magneto-Optically Measured High-Speed Switching of Sandwich Thin Film Elements," *J. Appl. Phys.*, **33**: 1057S (1962).

E. Tatsumoto, K. Kuwahara, and M. Goto, "Magnetoresistance Effect in Magnetization of Permalloy Films," *J. Phys. Soc. Japan*, **15**: 1703 (1960).

E. Tatsumoto, K. Kuwahara, and M. Goto, "Magnetization Reversal in Permalloy Films," *J. Phys. Soc. Japan*, **17**: 628S (1962).

R. V. Telesnin, O. S. Kolotov, and T. N. Nikitina, "Amplitude and Time-Dependent Properties of Some Ferromagnetic Films," *Radio Eng. Electronic Phys.*, **I**: 1155 (1962).

H. Thomas, "A Theoretical Model for Partial Rotation," *J. Appl. Phys.*, **33**: 1117S (1962).

H. Trauble and A. Seeger, "The Characteristic Function of Ferromagnetic Single Crystals," *Z. Angew. Phys.*, **14**: 237 (1962), in German.

R. H. Wade, "Transverse Magnetization in Permalloy Films" in S. S. Breese, Jr. (ed.), *Electron Microscopy, 5th Internat. Congress, Philadelphia, 1962*, Vol. I, Paper II-7, Academic Press, New York, 1962.

F. G. West, "Magnetization Processes in Permalloy Films Having Dispersed Anisotropy Axes Revealed by Dynamic Magnetoresistance Measurements," *Electrical and Magnetic Properties of Thin Metallic Layers, Proc. Internat. Conf. Liege*, September 4–7, 1961, p. 243.

P. Wolf, "Free Oscillation of the Magnetization in Permalloy Films," *J. Appl. Phys.*, **32**: 95S (1961).

CHAPTER 10: FERROMAGNETIC RESONANCE

W. A. Barrett, "Measurement of Film Relaxation Time," *J. Appl. Phys.*, **34**: 1207 (1963).

R. L. Conger, "High Frequency Effects in Magnetic Films," *Proc. AIEE Conf. Magnetism Magnetic Mater.*, Boston (1956), p. 610.

R. L. Conger and F. C. Essig, "Resonance and Reversal Phenomena in Ferromagnetic Films," *Phys. Rev.*, **104**: 915 (1956).

A. Coumes, "Local Study of Thin Films by Ferromagnetic Resonance," *Arch. Sci.* (Switzerland), **14**: 206 (1961).

A. Coumes, "Superficial and Deep Layers of a Thin Metallic Film," in J. Smidt (ed.), *Magnetic and Electric Resonance and Relaxation*, North-Holland Publishing Company, Amsterdam, 1963, p. 501.

W. G. Egan and H. J. Juretschke, "Detection of Ferromagnetic Resonance," *Bull. Am. Phys. Soc.*, **3**: 194 (1958).

W. G. Egan and H. J. Juretschke, "DC Detection of Ferromagnetic Resonance in Thin Nickel Films," *J. Appl. Phys.*, **34**: 1477 (1963).

Z. Frait, "Thin Ferromagnetic Films. V. (8). Ferromagnetic Resonance," *Phys. Status Solidi*, **2**: 1417 (1962), in German.

A. L. Framkin, "Theoretical Investigation of the Permeability of Anisotropic Thin Films," *Bull. Acad. Sci. USSR Phys. Ser.*, **26**: 298 (1963).

A. L. Framkin, "Experimental Investigation of the Permeability of Anisotropic Magnetic Films at Radio Frequencies," *Bull. Acad. Sci. USSR Phys. Ser.*, **26**: 302 (1963).

T. E. Hasty, "Ferromagnetic Resonance in Thin Films with Perpendicular Fields at Radio Frequencies," *J. Appl. Phys.*, **34**: 1079 (1963).

T. E. Hasty and L. J. Boudreaux, "Ferromagnetic Resonance in Thin Magnetic Films at Radio Frequencies," *J. Appl. Phys.*, **32**: 1807 (1961).

R. J. Huber, G. S. Baker, and P. Gibb, "Damping Effects of Thin Surface Films," *J. Appl. Phys.*, **32**: 2488 (1961).

S. Iida, "The Difference Between Gilbert's and Landau-Lifshitz's Equations," *J. Phys. Chem. Solids*, **24**: 625 (1963).

H. J. Juretschke, "DC Detection of Spin Resonance in Thin Metallic Films," *J. Appl. Phys.*, **34**: 1223 (1963).

R. Kikuchi, "On the Minimum of Magnetization Reversal Time," *J. Appl. Phys.*, **27**: 1352 (1956).

R. H. Kingston and P. E. Tannenwald, "Ferromagnetic Resonance at VHF in Thin Films," *J. Appl. Phys.*, **29**: 232 (1958).

M. Kobale and W. Kung, "Influence of Base Conductivity and Surface Micro-structure on the Spin Damping Constant of Thin Magnetic Films," *Z. Angew. Phys.*, **15**: 39 (1963), in German.

M. Kuriyama, H. Yamaguchi, and S. Hosoga, "Ferromagnetic Absorption of Single Crystal Thin Films of Nickel," *J. Phys. Soc. Japan*, **16**: 701 (1961).

L. Landau and E. Lifshitz, "The Theory of the Dispersion of Magnetic Permeability in Ferromagnetic Bodies," *Phys. Z. Sowjetunion*, **8**: 153 (1935).

P. V. Lenzo, "Low Frequency Ferromagnetic Resonance Spectrometer," *Rev. Sci. Instr.*, **34**: 1374 (1963).

J. R. Mayfield, "Measocalorimetric Technique for the Study of Damping and Hysteresis in Ferromagnetic Films," *J. Appl. Phys.*, **31**: 298 (1960).

D. T. Ngo, "Measurement of Ferromagnetic Resonance of Thin Permalloy Films at Low Bias Field," *J. Appl. Phys.*, **34**: 3626 (1963).

K. M. Polivanov and A. L. Framkin, "Differential Susceptibility of Thin Magnetic Films with Uniform Rotation of Magnetization," *Phys. Metallography*, **14**: 5 (1962).

T. D. Rossing, "Resonance Linewidth and Anisotropy Variation in Thin Films," *J. Appl. Phys.*, **34**: 3692 (1963).

M. H. Seavey, Jr., and P. E. Tannenwald, "Ferromagnetic Resonance in Ultra-Thin Films," *J. Appl. Phys.*, **29**: 292 (1958).

Y. G. Seiji *et al.*, "Ferromagnetic Resonance in Single-Crystal Thin Films of Iron," *J. Appl. Phys.*, **34**: 1081 (1963).

D. O. Smith, "Magnetic Relaxation in Thin Films," *Proc. AIEE Conf. Magnetism Magnetic Mater.*, Boston (1956).

D. O. Smith and G. P. Weiss, "Steady-State and Pulse Measurement Techniques for Thin Magnetic Films in the vhf-uhf Range," *J. Appl. Phys.*, **29**: 290 (1958).

R. F. Soohoo, "Initial Susceptibility Spectra of Permalloy Films," *J. Appl. Phys.*, **31**: 218S (1960).

H. Thomas, "Paramagnetic Behavior of Thin Ferromagnetic Films Above the Curie Point," *Z. Angew. Phys.*, **15**: 201 (1963), in German.

E. J. Torok and R. A. White, "Longitudinal Permeability in Thin Permalloy Films," *J. Appl. Phys.*, **34**: 1064 (1963).

S. Uchiyama, M. Masuda, and Y. Sakaki, "Measurement of Anisotropy Dispersion by Means of Ferromagnetic Resonance," *Japan J. Appl. Phys.*, **2**: 621 (1963).

S. Usami *et al.*, "Ferromagnetic Resonance in Thin Single-Crystal Films of Iron," *Bull. Fac. Eng. Yokohama Natl. Univ.*, **12**: 97 (1963).

A. van Itterbeek, G. Forrez, and J. Witters, "Ferromagnetic Resonance in the Films of a Ni-Fe Alloy," *J. Phys. Radium*, **22**: 19 (1961), in French.

A. van Itterbeek *et al.*, "Ferromagnetic Resonance in Permalloy Films," *J. Phys. Radium*, **21**: 8 (1960), in French.

A. van Itterbeek *et al.*, "Some Experimental Results on Ferromagnetic Resonance in Nickel Films" in J. Smidt (ed.), *Magnetic and Electric Resonance and Relaxation*, North-Holland Publishing Company, Amsterdam, 1963, p. 495.

CHAPTER 11: SPIN-WAVE RESONANCE

R. Abbel, "Ferromagnetism of Thin Films," *Z. Naturforsch.*, **18a**: 371 (1963), in German.

A. I. Akhiezer, U. G. Baryakhtar, and S. V. Peletminskii, "Coherent Amplification of Spin Waves," *Phys. Letters*, **4**: 129 (1963).

D. Chen and A. H. Morrish, "Ferromagnetic Resonance in Thin Films," *J. Appl. Phys.*, **33**: 1146S (1962).

J. B. Comly, T. Penney, and R. V. Jones, "Spin-Wave Instabilities in Magnetic Thin Films," *J. Appl. Phys.*, **34**: 1145 (1963).

A. Corciovei, "Spin-Wave Theory of Ferromagnetic Thin Films," *Phys. Rev.*, **130**: 2223 (1963).

Z. Frait, "Ferromagnetic Resonance in Thin Cobalt Films," *Czech. J. Phys.*, **B11**: 360 (1961), in Czechoslovakian.

Z. Frait, "Thin Ferromagnetic Films. V. (8). Ferromagnetic Resonance," *Phys. Status Solidi*, **2**: 1417 (1962), in German.

D. Fraitova, "The Influence of Demagnetization, Anisotropy and Stress on the Resonance Condition of Spin Wave Resonance," *Czech. J. Phys.*, **B11**: 500 (1961), in Czechoslovakian.

M. I. Kaganov and Yui Lu, "Effect of the Boundary Condition for the Magnetic Moment on Spin-Wave Resonance in Metals," *Bull. Acad. Sci. USSR, Phys. Ser.*, **25**: 1388 (1962).

J. I. Kaplan, "Nonlinear Effects of Z-Directed Spin Waves in Thin Films," *J. Appl. Phys.*, **32**: 1831 (1961).

R. Kimura and H. Nosé, "Spin Wave Resonance in Ni and Its Alloy Films," *J. Phys. Soc. Japan*, **17**: 604S (1962).

C. F. Kooi, "Interaction of Phonons and Spin Waves," *Phys. Rev.*, **131**: 1070 (1963).

C. F. Kooi *et al.*, "Surface Spin Pinning in Permalloy by an Oxide Layer," *J. Phys. Soc. Japan*, **17**: 599S (1962).

S. Methfessel, S. Middelhoek, and H. Thomas, "A New Method for the Determination of the Ferromagnetic Exchange Constant," *J. Phys. Soc. Japan*, **17**: 607S (1962).

H. Nosé, "Spin Wave Resonance in Ni Films," *J. Phys. Soc. Japan*, **15**: 1714 (1960).

H. Nosé, "Exchange Integral in Ni and Its Alloy Film from Spin Wave Resonance," *J. Phys. Soc. Japan*, **16**: 2475 (1961).

M. Pomerantz, J. F. Freedman, and J. C. Suits, "Ferromagnetic Resonance in Single-Crystal Nickel Films," *J. Appl. Phys.*, **33**: 1164S (1962).

Yu G. Ptushins'ki and O. A. Panchenko, "Change in the Electrical Resistance of Thin Metal Films During Absorption," *Ukrayin Fiz. Zh. (USSR)*, **I**: 1079 (1962), in Ukrainian.

T. D. Rossing, "Spin-Wave Resonance in Thin Films at Oblique Angles," *J. Appl. Phys.*, **34**: 1133 (1963).

K. Sabban and W. Schedelbeck, "Investigation of the Homogeneity of Thin Permalloy Films by Means of Ferromagnetic Resonance," *Z. Angew. Phys.*, **15**: 213 (1963), in German.

M. H. Seavey, Jr., "Electromagnetic Theory of Spin Wave Resonance," *MIT Lincoln Lab. Tech. Rept. 239*, February 15, 1961.

R. F. Soohoo, "Surface Anisotropy Energies of Thin Magnetic Films," *J. Appl. Phys.*, **34**: 1149 (1963).

R. F. Soohoo, "General Exchange Boundary Condition and Surface Anisotropy Energy of a Ferromagnet," *Phys. Rev.*, **131**: 594 (1963).

P. E. Tannenwald, "Spin Waves in Magnetic Films" in C. A. Neugebauer *et al.* (eds.), *Structure and Properties of Thin Films*, John Wiley & Sons, Inc., New York, 1959, Chap. V.

P. E. Tannenwald, "Spin Wave Resonance in Magnetic Films," *J. Phys. Soc. Japan*, **17**: 592S (1962).

H. D. Toombs and T. E. Hasty, "A Resonance Technique for Nondestructive Read-Out of Thin Magnetic Films," *Proc. IRE*, **50**: 1526 (1962).

A. van Itterbeek and J. Witters, "Ferromagnetic Resonance in Thin Permalloy Films," *J. Phys.*, **24**: 315 (1963).

G. Vogler, "Impulse Magnetization," *Phys. Status Solidi*, **2**: 1241 (1962), in German.

P. E. Wigen, "Dynamic Pinning in Thin Film Spin-Wave Resonance," *Phys. Rev. Letters*, **9**: 206 (1962).

P. E. Wigen *et al.*, "Angular Dependence of Spin Pinning in Thin Ferromagnetic Films," *J. Appl. Phys.*, **34**: 1137 (1963).

P. Wolf, "The Excitation of Standing Spin Waves in Thin Permalloy Films by Means of Inhomogeneous Alternating Fields," *Z. Angew. Phys.*, **14**: 212 (1963), in German.

P. Wolf., "Spin Wave Resonance in Films Magnetized Parallel to the Surface," *J. Appl. Phys.*, **34**: 1139 (1963).

CHAPTER 12: APPLICATIONS

E. J. Alexander *et al.*, "A Permanent Magnet Twister Memory Element of Improved Characteristics," *J. Appl. Phys.*, **33**: 1075.

A. H. Anderson, T. S. Crowther, and J. I. Raffel, "Drive Current Margins for Magnetic Film Memories," *J. Appl. Phys.*, **34**: 1165 (1963).

J. M. Ballantyne, "Demonstration of Magnetic Domain-Wall Storage and Logic," *J. Appl. Phys.*, **33**: 1067S (1962).

W. A. Barrett, "Demagnetization of Twister Bits," *J. Appl. Phys.*, **32**: 35S (1961).

W. A. Barrett *et al.*, "A Card Changeable Permanent-Magnet-Twistor Memory of Large Capacity," *IRE Trans. Electronic Computers*, **EC-10**: 451 (1961).

D. R. Bennion, H. D. Crane, and D. C. Engelhart, "A Bibliographical Sketch of All Magnetic Logic Schemes," *IRE Trans. Electronic Computers*, **EC-10**: 203 (1961).

E. E. Bittman, "Thin Film Memories," *IRE Trans. Electronic Computers*, **EC-8**: 92 (1959).

E. E. Bittman, "Thin Magnetic Film Memories for High Speed Computers," *Electronics*, **34**: 39 (1961).

A. H. Bobeck, "A New Storage Element Suitable for Large-Sized Memory Arrays the Twistor," *Bell System Tech. J.*, **36**: 1319.

A. H. Bobeck and R. F. Fischer, "Reversible Diodeless, Twistor Shift Register," *J. Appl. Phys.*, **30S**: 43S (1959).

R. Bogusch and E. A. Fisch, "High Speed Thin Magnetic Film Memories," *Proc. Natl. Electronics Conf.*, **16**: 840 (1960).

E. M. Bradley, "A Computer Storage Matrix Using Ferromagnetic Thin Films," *Brit. Inst. Radio Engrs.*, **20**: 765 (1960).

E. M. Bradley, "Making Reproducible Magnetic-Film Memories Progressed Beyond the Laboratory Demonstration Stage," *Electronics*, **33**: 78 (1960).

E. M. Bradley, "Properties of Magnetic Films for Memory Systems," *J. Appl. Phys.*, **33**: 1051S (1964).

K. D. Broadbent, "A Vacuum Evaporated Random Access Memory," *Proc. Special Tech. Conf. Nonlinear Magnetics Magnetic Amplifiers* (1959), p. 281.

K. D. Broadbent, "A Thin Magnetic Film Shift Register," *IRE Trans. Electronic Computers*, **EC-9**: 321 (1960).

H. Chang and A. G. Milnes, "Magnetic Fields of Twistors Represented by Confocal Hollow Prolate Spheroids," *IRE Trans. Electronic Computers*, **EC-9**: 199 (1960).

H. Chang, A. Yelon, and O. Voegeli, "Internal Field, Dispersion, Creeping and Switching Speed of Coupled Films," *J. Appl. Phys.*, **34**: 1209 (1963).

R. L. Conger and J. L. Tomlinson, "Magneto-Optic Readout for Computer Memories," *J. Appl. Phys.*, **33**: 1059S (1962).

C. I. Cowan, "The Use of Thin Films for Computer Storage," *Electronic Eng.*, **33**: 642 (1961).

J. M. Doughton *et al.*, "Magnetic Film Devices Using Passive Loading," *J. Appl. Phys.*, **32**: 365 (1961).

D. A. Ellerbruch, "A New Memory Device—The Twistor," *IRE Trans. Component Parts*, **CP-6**: 42 (1959).

A. Franck, G. P. Marette, and B. I. Parsegyan, "Deposited Magnetic Films as Logic Elements," *1959 Proc. East. Joint Computer Conf.* (1959) p. 28.

V. F. Gianola, "Possibilities of All Magnetic Logic," *J. Appl. Phys.*, **32**: 27S (1961).

V. F. Gianola, "Disturb Threshold in Cylindrical Film Memory Wire," *J. Appl. Phys.* **34**: 1131 (1964).

R. L. Gray, "An Electrically Alterable Non-destructive Twistor Memory," *IRE Trans. Electronic Computers*, **EC-9**: 451 (1960).

J. W. Hart, "Patterns in Thin Films Make Fast Nondestructive Memories," *Electronics*, **34**: 126 (1961).

J. L. Haynes, "Logical Circuits Using Square-Loop Magnetic Devices, a Survey," *IRE Trans. Electronic Computers*, **EC-10**: 191 (1961).

O. S. Heavens, "Magnetic Properties of Epitaxially Grown Films," *Res. Appl. Industry*, **13**: 404 (1960).

G. R. Hoffman, J. A. Turner, and T. Kilburn, "High-Speed Digital Storage Using Cylindrical Magnetic Films," *Brit. Inst. Radio Engrs.*, **20**: 31 (1960).

L. Kleinrock, "Optical Information Handling with Thin Magnetic Films," *Proc. Natl. Electronics Conf.*, **4**: 789 (1958).

A. J. Kolk and M. Orlovic, "Increasing the Kerr Magneto-Optic Effect in Thin Films," *J. Appl. Phys.*, **34**: 1060 (1963).

A. J. Kolk and H. White, "Magnetic Properties of 97 Fe–3 Ni Thin Film Electroplate," *J. Electrochem. Soc.*, **110**: 98 (1963).

A. Kolk, L. Douglas, and G. Schrader, "Switching Properties of Multilayer Thin Film Structures," *J. Appl. Phys.*, **33**: 1061S (1962).

P. Kornreich and S. R Pollack, "Variable Delay Magnetic Strip Line," *J. Appl. Phys.*, **34**: 1169 (1963).

T. Lentz and J. Miyata, "Magneto-Optical Readout of Magnetic Recordings," *Electronics*, **34**: 36 (1961).

N. Lindgren, "Recent Progress in Magnetics," *Electronics*, **34**: 81 (1961).

A. W. Lo, "Some Thoughts on Digital Components and Circuit Techniques," *IRE Trans. Electronic Computers*, **EC-10**: 416 (1961).

T. R. Long, "Electrodeposited Memory Elements for a Nondestructive Memory," *J. Appl. Phys.*, **31**: 123 (1960).

R. E. Matick, "Thick-Film Read-Only Memory Device," *J. Appl. Phys.*, **34**: (1963).

D. A. Meier, "Millimicrosecond Magnetic Switching and Storage Element," *J. Appl. Phys.*, **30S**: 45S (1959).

D. A. Meier, "Magnetic Rod Memory," *Proc. Electronics Components Conf.* (1960) p. 122.

D. A. Meier, B. A. Kaufman, and D. W. Rork, "Megacycle Magnetic Rod Logic," *1959 IRE Wescon Conv. Rec.*, Pt. 4 (1959) p. 27.

P. Mossman and M. Williams, "Effect of Skew on the Performance of Magnetic-Film Storage Cells," *J. Appl. Phys.*, **34**: 1175 (1963).

L. J. Oakland and T. D. Rossing, "Coincident-Current Nondestructive Readout from Thin Magnetic Films," *J. Appl. Phys.*, **30S**: 54S (1959).

A. V. Pohm and E. N. Mitchell, "Magnetic Film Memories, A Survey," *IRE Trans. Electronic Computers*, **EC-9**: 308 (1960).

A. V. Pohm and S. M. Rubens, "A compact Coincident Memory," *Proc. East. Joint Computer Conf.*, December, 1956, p. 120.

A. V. Pohm et al., "High Frequency Magnetic Film Parametrons for Computer Logic," *Proc. Natl. Electronics Conf.*, **15**: 202 (1959).

A. V. Pohm et al., "Operation of Magnetic Film Parametrons in the 100 to 500 Mc-Range," *J. Appl. Phys.*, **31**: 119S (1960).

K. Preston, Jr., and Q. W. Simkins, "Twistor Buffer Store," *1959 Solid State Circuits Conf.* (1959) p. 14.

W. E. Proebster and H. J. Oguey, "High Speed Magnetic Film Logic," *1960 Solid State Cir. Conf.* (1960) p. 22.

J. I. Raffel, "Operating Characteristics of a Thin Film Memory," *J. Appl. Phys.*, **30S**: 60S (1959).

J. I. Raffel et al., "Magnetic Film Memory Design," *Proc. IRE*, **49**: 155 (1961).

J. A. Rajchman, "Computer Memories—A Survey of the State of the Art," *Proc. IRE*, **49**: 104 (1961).

J. A. Rajchman, "Magnetic Memories—Capabilities and Limitations," *J. Appl. Phys.*, **34**: 1013 (1963).

V. Rosler, "Thin Ferromagnetic Films VI. (9) Application in Static Storage Elements and in Switching Networks," *Phys. Status Solidi*, **3**: 3 (1963), in German.

H. Rubinstein, T. L. McCormack, and H. W. Fuller, "The Application of Domain Wall Motion to Storage Devices," *Solid State Circ. Conf.* (1961) p. 64.

R. M. Sanders, "Stable Oscillation Conditions for the Magnetic-Film Parametrons," *J. Appl. Phys.*, **32**: 478 (1961).

R. F. Schauer et al., "Some Applications of Magnetic Film Parametrons as Logical Devices," *IRE Trans. Electronic Computers* (1960) p. 315.

S. J. Schwartz and J. S. Sallo, "Electrodeposited Twistor and Bit Wire Components," *IRE Trans. Electronic Computors*, **EC-8**: 465 (1959).

Q. W. Simkins, "The State of the Art of Magnetic Memories," *J. Appl. Phys.*, **33**: 1020S (1962).

D. O. Smith, "Proposal for Magnetic Domain-Wall Storage and Logic," *IRE Trans. Electronic Computers*, **EC-10**: 708 (1961).

T. A. Smay and A. V. Pohm, "Design of Logic Circuits Using Thin Films and Tunnel Diodes," *Electronics*, **34**: 59 (1961).

P. E. Tannenwald, "Properties of Thin Magnetic Films for Microwave Applications," *Wescon Conv. Rec.*, Pt. 1, **3**: 134 (1959).

R. T. Thun, G. F. Caudle, and E. R. Pasciutti, "Rugged Film Resistor Thermometer for the Measurement of Surface Temperatures," *Rev. Sci. Instr.*, **31**: 446 (1960).

H. D. Toombs and T. E. Hasty, "A Resonance Technique for Nondestructive Read-out of Thin Magnetic Films," *Proc. IRE*, **50**: 1526 (1962).

F. G. West et al., "Detection of Low-Intensity Magnetic Fields by Means of Ferro-magnetic Films," *J. Appl. Phys.*, **34**: 1163 (1963).

G. Winsor, "Measurement of the Characteristics of Magnetic Thin Film Matrices," *J. Electronics Control*, **13**: 425 (1962).

INDEX

Abrahams, E., 218
Activation energy, 106
  defects, 114, 115
  ultrathin film, 155, 156
Aharoni, A., 63
Alexander, R. G., 131
Allen, L. R., 24
Alpert, D., 88
Anderson, A. H., 261
Andrus, J., 173
Angular momentum, 184, 185
  quenching of orbital, 94, 185–186
Anisotropic distribution of links due to diffusion, 98, 100
Anisotropy, cubic, 93–97; polycrystal, 94; single-crystal, 93
  dispersion, 93; effect on switched flux measurement, 167, 168; effect on switching, 66, 131; measurement of, 131
  measurement of, 128–133; by ferromagnetic resonance, 130–131; by hysteresis looper, 128; by torque magnetometer, 129–130
  perpendicular to film, changes due to copper deposition, 99; changes due to hydrogen or oxygen admission, 89, 92; origin, 89–90
  of polycrystals, 97
  residual, 33, 67, 143, 144
  uniaxial, see Uniaxial anisotropy
Anisotropy centers, 124
Anisotropy constant, 95
  composition dependence of film, 242
  for cubic lattices, 96
  magnetostriction dependence of film, 242; temperature dependence, 96
  skew, 131
  uniaxial, 40
Anisotropy dispersion wave, 97
Anisotropy energy, 93, 189, 242
  in domain calculation, 30
  thin-film, 138
  uniaxial crystal, 39
Anisotropy field, 139, 243
  compositional dependence, normal films 131–132; oblique-incidence films, 132
  measurement, by ferromagnetic resonance, 196; at radio frequencies, 221–222

  in resonance experiments, 191
  thin-film values for, 142
Anisotropy imperfection, 63–64
Anisotropy ripple, 63, 66
Anomalous films, anisotropy model, 124
  preparation, 122; and anisotropy centers, 124
Antiferromagnetic layer, 7, 79, 89–90
Artman, J. O., 200
Astrue, R. W., 55
Avogadro's number, 8

Babcock, G. D., 132
Baer, C. A., 24
Bagrowski, J., 15, 120
Ballantyne, J. M., 265
Banks, E., 17
Bauer, H. J., 87
Bean, C. C., 79, 91
Becker, J. J., 91
Becker, R., 100, 103, 175, 271
Behringer, R. E., 145
Behrndt, K. H., 7, 8, 20, 145
Belser, R. B., 155
Bethe, H. A., 200
Bilson, H. A., 97
Binary-coded decimal system, 244
Binary number system, 243–244
  use in problem solution, 244
Bitter pattern, cross-tie wall passing cavity, 68
  domain wall-imperfection interaction, 68-69
  locking, 122, 127
Bitter powder technique, 34, 247
  for domain observation, 27
  for imperfection distribution, 69
  for magnetization distribution, 34
Bittman, E. E., 249
Bloch, F., 37, 72, 143, 217
Bloch 3/2 power law, the, 71, 72
  basic assumption in, 74, 76
Bloch temperature, 81
Bloch wall, 144, 145, 146, 147, 176, 177
  approximated by ellipsoidal cylinder, 40
  in bulk materials, 27, 37
  configuration in magnetic field, 49
  at film edge, 58
  film thickness range for, 48